THE
WORLD'S AIRWAYS
and how they work

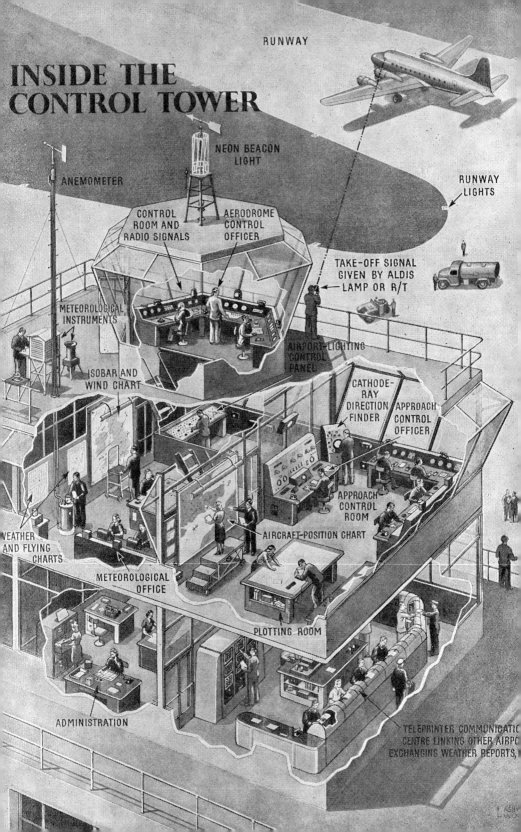

INSIDE THE CONTROL TOWER

RUNWAY

NEON BEACON LIGHT

ANEMOMETER

RUNWAY LIGHTS

CONTROL ROOM AND RADIO SIGNALS

AERODROME CONTROL OFFICER

TAKE-OFF SIGNAL GIVEN BY ALDIS LAMP OR R/T

METEOROLOGICAL INSTRUMENTS

AIRPORT-LIGHTING CONTROL PANEL

ISOBAR AND WIND CHART

CATHODE-RAY DIRECTION FINDER

APPROACH CONTROL OFFICER

APPROACH CONTROL ROOM

WEATHER AND FLYING CHARTS

AIRCRAFT-POSITION CHART

METEOROLOGICAL OFFICE

PLOTTING ROOM

ADMINISTRATION

TELEPRINTER COMMUNICATION CENTRE LINKING OTHER AIRPORTS EXCHANGING WEATHER REPORTS,

THE
WORLD'S AIRWAYS
and how they work

FOREWORD BY
SIR WILLIAM P. HILDRED, C.B., O.B.E., M.A.
Director General,
International Air Transport Association

★

EDITORIAL ADVISERS
CAPTAIN J. W. G. JAMES, O.B.E.
Flight Manager and Chief Pilot,
British European Airways Corporation
JOHN STROUD

ODHAMS PRESS LTD.  LONG ACRE, LONDON

FOREWORD

BY SIR WILLIAM P. HILDRED, C.B., O.B.E., M.A.

Director General, International Air Transport Association

Copyright by Karsh

ANY ENTERPRISE which depends upon the patronage of the public must first have its interest and its sympathy. Until a few years ago, the fact that man could fly at all was startling and compelling enough to assure sympathetic public interest in the air-transport industry.

Today, however, the public takes flight for granted. It knows that the air-line plane, properly equipped and competently piloted, will carry out its schedules on time and with ease, comfort and safety. Public thinking has therefore gone a step farther and is concentrated on the kind of service it wants at the price it can afford to pay.

Both the man in the street and the man in the air-line office have the same dreams for air transport. Both of them want the aeroplane to be the means whereby untold millions of working men and women can see the world on their holidays, whereby their children will have the whole globe for a classroom and whereby families scattered over such areas as the British Commonwealth can remain united by real bonds of personal contact. They both want to see the air a high-road over which precious and perishable cargoes, which will make the lives of everyone fuller and richer, will move without hindrance.

Yet, because the man in the street does not always know the economic, political and technical hurdles which stand between him and the fulfilment of his dream, he is often impatient with the air-lines. Air transport, therefore, needs public understanding of its problems more than ever before.

The appearance of this volume, dedicated to exploring in layman's terms the potentialities of air transport and their implications, is a service to both the air-lines and the public. Its value to the air-lines is obvious enough, but it also serves the public in a way which may not be so readily apparent. Through this book, the member of the public should be able to learn what he can do—as a direct consumer of air-line transport, as a technician or scientist, as a public official or merely as a citizen—to help realize the bright dreams of air transport.

There are many things which the air-lines are doing themselves to improve their service, both individually and through such agencies as the International Air Transport Association, but there are also many which must, in the final analysis, be done by the public.

Only an enlightened public, for example, can reduce the arbitrary political barriers to free flight everywhere, or sweep away the accumulation of border red-tape which clogs the arteries of international commerce. And in air transport, like anything else, the more light and the more understanding, the greater and faster the progress.

W. P. Hildred

Montreal, Canada.
1950.

CONTENTS

ABOVE THE SKYSCRAPERS *of Newark, N.J., flies a Convair-Liner Flagship of the American Airlines' fleet. These air-liners can carry 40 passengers at about 300 m.p.h. ; nearly 150 of them are in regular service with various air-lines throughout the world.*

CHAPTER 1

PROBLEMS OF PLANNING
THE AIR ROUTES

T HE growth of air transport has been so rapid since the end of World War II that distance has become far less important in the march of human affairs than travel time. To put it another way, distance is now measured in *hours*, not *miles*. By this unit of measurement there are no longer any "far-off lands."

The aeroplane, equally powerful as an agent for peace as for war, is often thought to owe its swift technical development to the hot-house atmosphere in which it has been reared—an atmosphere created by wars in which air supremacy was the key to victory. Today, the aeroplane is technically far in advance of the ground organization that is necessary to operate it; that is, to keep it flying regularly and punctually from anywhere to anywhere—and at reasonable cost.

The development of radio aids to navigation and landing, the creation of hundreds of airfields (many of which could later be absorbed for civil use) and new techniques of organization of control were legacies of World War II: legacies which were invaluable in bringing into being a ground organization capable of handling the great numbers of highly scientific machines which were to become the carrier vehicles of a new air-transport organization for peace.

But war must also take the blame for many of the encumbrances which have hindered the peaceful and orderly progress of civil aviation. The war put the emphasis upon the wrong things—upon power, manœuvrability, armament and defence—with the result that the air operators were left with a vast quantity of wartime aircraft types and equipment of all sorts upon their hands. New plans for a world-wide organization for the operation of air-transport services in peacetime have since had to be made. They will take a few more years to mature. However, despite this transition from war to peace conditions, air transport recovered surprisingly quickly; so well that, in 1948, the air-lines of the United Kingdom flew nearly ten times the number of passenger-miles flown in 1938. In 1948, about a million passengers travelled into or out of Great Britain in scheduled air-liners of all nations—five times as many as were carried in 1939.

Units of Travel

We are hearing more and more of the "passenger-mile"; this is a travel unit which denotes the carriage of one passenger a distance of one mile and it is a simple and fair means of comparison. One thousand passenger-miles may mean the carriage of ten passengers a distance of 100 miles, or 100 passengers ten miles. These two achievements are equal in travel value and are fairly expressed in figures by the phrase, 1,000 passenger-miles.

This is not to say, however, that to carry ten passengers 100 miles is the same thing as to carry 100 passengers ten miles. The work—and the cost—involved in handling the passengers and in ticketing alone is ten times as much in the second case. These ground costs often add up to a considerable sum and the long-stage or trunk-route operator has, therefore, a considerable advantage over the short-haul carrier in this passenger-mile comparison.

The passenger-mile, although the simplest, is not so true a commercial unit of comparison as the revenue-ton-mile; this allows for cargo and mail by weight to be included in the figures. Industry has been quick to realize the advantages of the rapid transit of goods by air—samples, news, vital machinery, medical and surgical equipment—with the result that air transport is now making a bid for new prosperity which may result from the vigorous international competition for new markets.

The operation of an air route under these conditions needs a very different kind of planning from that required in the past. Today, most (though not all) of the pioneering has been done and facilities exist at most of the world's main towns for the landing, refuelling and servicing of aircraft and for the handling of air passengers and air cargo. Although these facilities are not always adequate for the operation of a modern trunk air route, today's planners seldom have to contemplate the spending of months—perhaps years—in pioneering a new route from the ground-survey stage.

Such planning may still have to be done if it is desired to operate a service between two places not hitherto linked by air by a flight involving more than one stage; for instance, in the planning of the projected air route linking Western Australia with South Africa across the Indian Ocean there is pioneer work of an unusual kind to be done. Intermediate landing grounds,

THREE MEMBERS *of the operating crew of a Constellation are seen here: the Captain, and on his right, with arm raised, the First Officer, and the Flight Engineer. Also included in the operating crew, but not shown, are the Radio and Navigation Officers.*

LOCKHEED CONSTELLATION, *one of the most widely used types of long-range air-liner, is powered by four Cyclone motors and cruises at over 300 m.p.h. with up to 64 passengers.*

perhaps on island sites, may have to be developed or improved; ground radio stations installed; refuelling and servicing facilities organized and passenger accommodation established.

In operating a new route today, however, the primary consideration is not technical; it is economic. Is there enough traffic to make it pay? If not, can enough be created? Many commercial factors have to be studied. What is the capacity of the route as operated by surface methods? Will the advantages of the extra speed of air transport be great enough to justify the difference in fares? What is the total potential of traffic on the route, taking into account future trends in industry, tourist travel and official business? Can aircraft be spared from other, possibly more profitable, routes? Further, can the air-line afford the cost of operating with light loads while building up, if slowly, its new traffic?

In addition, international negotiations will probably be necessary with the governments of the countries in which it is desired to land, and bilateral agreements may have to be drawn up and signed before the business of operational planning can proceed.

Air, Trade, and Great Circle Routes

Because traffic is the key to the modern air route, the principal air arteries of the world tend to follow the established trade routes very closely. But, as each year goes by, the air routes are lopping more and more miles off the traditional surface routes by rail and sea. In those cases in which the difference in mileage between air and surface routes is still small, there is nevertheless an enormous saving in travel time.

For instance, the established air route from London to Sydney with long-range

9

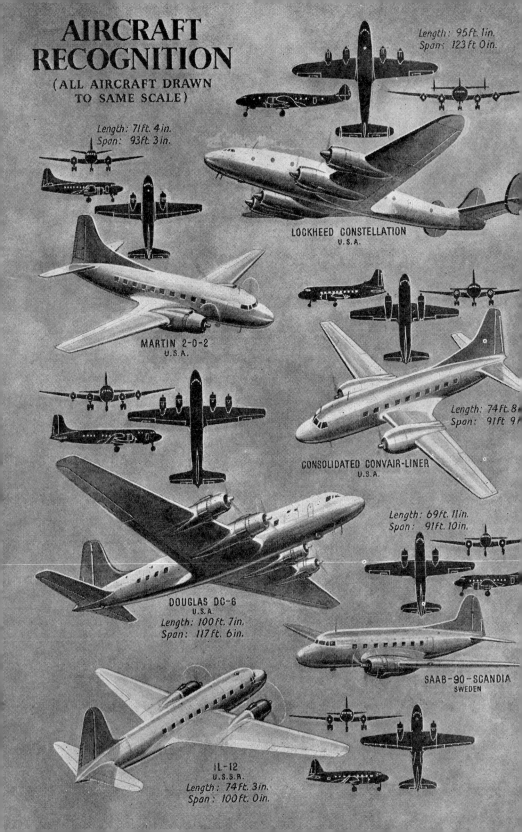

AIRCRAFT RECOGNITION

(ALL AIRCRAFT DRAWN TO SAME SCALE)

Length: 95 ft. 1 in.
Span: 123 ft. 0 in.

Length: 71 ft. 4 in.
Span: 93 ft. 3 in.

LOCKHEED CONSTELLATION
U.S.A.

MARTIN 2-0-2
U.S.A.

Length: 74 ft. 8
Span: 91 ft. 9

CONSOLIDATED CONVAIR-LINER
U.S.A.

Length: 69 ft. 11 in.
Span: 91 ft. 10 in.

DOUGLAS DC-6
U.S.A.
Length: 100 ft. 7 in.
Span: 117 ft. 6 in.

SAAB-90-SCANDIA
SWEDEN

IL-12
U.S.S.R.
Length: 74 ft. 3 in.
Span: 100 ft. 0 in.

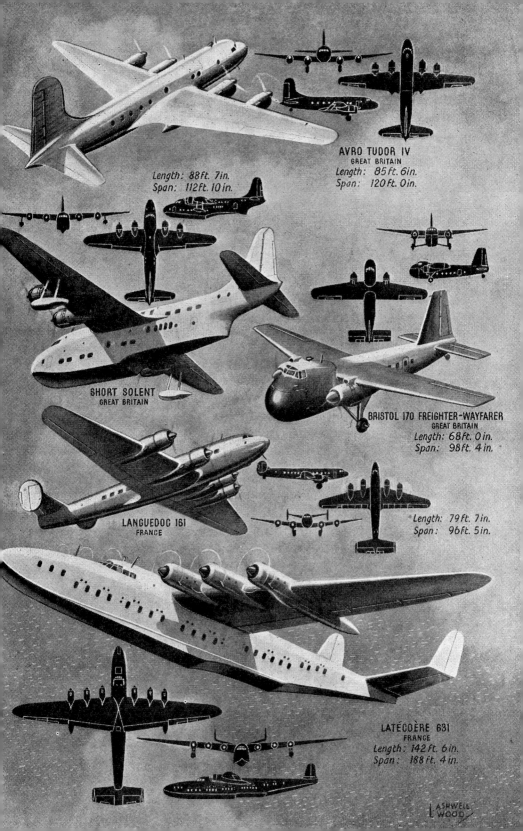

AVRO TUDOR IV
GREAT BRITAIN
Length: 85 ft. 6 in.
Span: 120 ft. 0 in.

Length: 88 ft. 7 in.
Span: 112 ft. 10 in.

SHORT SOLENT
GREAT BRITAIN

BRISTOL 170 FREIGHTER-WAYFARER
GREAT BRITAIN
Length: 68 ft. 0 in.
Span: 98 ft. 4 in.

LANGUEDOC 161
FRANCE

Length: 79 ft. 7 in.
Span: 96 ft. 5 in.

LATÉCOÈRE 631
FRANCE
Length: 142 ft. 6 in.
Span: 188 ft. 4 in.

ASHWELL WOOD

FROM SOUTHAMPTON WATER *flying-boats depart for Madeira, Egypt, Central and South Africa. The liner berthed beyond the flying-boat base is the* Queen Elizabeth.

landplanes covers 12,050 miles. The sea route via Suez covers approximately the same mileage and the route via the Cape slightly more. If the railway mileage across France is counted instead of the long sea voyage through the Bay of Biscay, the shortest surface route is several hundred miles shorter than the air route. But the saving in time amounts to anything between twenty-nine days and five and a half weeks. British Overseas Airways' and the Australian Qantas Empire Airways' Constellations do the trip regularly in four days; the fastest ships take about thirty days.

Thus, in this instance, the air route tends to follow the surface route more closely than the Great Circle. The Great Circle (or shortest direct) route from London to Sydney would pass almost over Moscow and Chungking.

The absence of sufficient traffic to re-imburse the operators for the additional costs of supplying facilities along such a route is a strong factor against its development—almost as strong as that of the international complications which there may be in trying to negotiate agreement for a foreign air-line concern to fly over some of the intervening territory.

Trade Routes of the Air

Similarly, the quickest air route between Moscow and Alaska would cross the North Pole if it were an economic possibility to operate such a route. As it is, the quickest way by air from Alaska to Moscow is via Montreal; London, Prestwick or Keflavik in Iceland; Scandinavia and either Helsinki or Berlin.

So the main traditional arteries of the world's trade remain, in general, the arteries for air transport. They lie in a broad band aslant the Equator, linking

THROUGH THE WINDOWS *of the passenger restaurant at Schiphol Airport, Amsterdam, passengers can see a selection of the Douglas and Lockheed aircraft of the K.L.M. fleet.*

London eastward to Western Europe (where the centre of gravity of the world's commercial potential may be said to lie) and thence through the Near and Middle East, to Pakistan and India, and on through Malaya and Indonesia to Australia. Westward, this band links London with North America; thence, across the Pacific, via Honolulu, with Australia and New Zealand.

Other arteries link London with South Africa, North America with South America, and Japan with India and Burma on the one flank; and with the United States (via Honolulu or the Aleutians) on the other.

The air routes follow this broad pattern created by the powerful flow of world trade. They do not fan out romantically along radii of the Great Circle. On the other hand, there is ample evidence that the aeroplane is now beginning to change the world's trade-route pattern. For example, Northwest Airlines' route to Japan is a Great Circle route and is substantially shorter than the traditional route across the central Pacific. Again, although Cape Town and Durban have been the traditional seaports of South Africa, her international airport and the terminal for the main landplane or flying-boat air routes is at Johannesburg.

Thus the pattern is already changing. The air routes are tending to create new centres of commerce, new inland ports (such as Kano in Nigeria) and new towns in hitherto backward areas. Now, trade is beginning to follow a new flag—the ensign of civil air transport.

Problems of the Past

It would be a mistake to write of the problems of planning an air route today without first referring back very briefly to

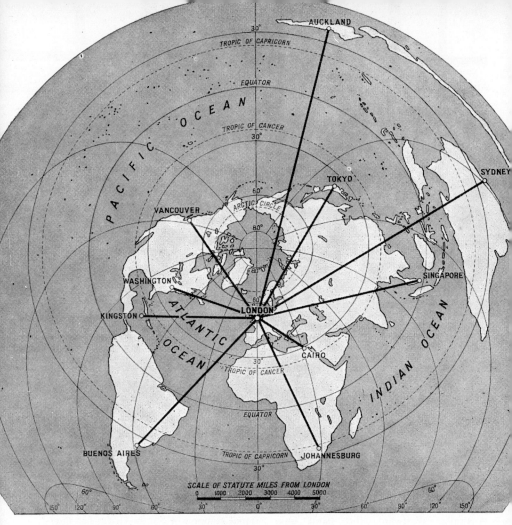

GREAT CIRCLE *world map, based on London. It shows the shortest and most direct routes, which are seldom practicable, between London and various centres of trade and commerce. It should be compared with the more usual type of map on page 16.*

the earlier problems of that important era between the two World Wars. For it was then that the great trunk routes of the air were pioneered and the solid foundations laid for the global network of air-route facilities that now exists.

The first tentative flights from the United Kingdom into Europe after the armistice that ended World War I were short-stage hops with converted war aircraft and a small payload. Favourable weather and good visibility were desirable. Fuel and maintenance had to be available, but on nothing like the scale of today. Air Traffic Control as it affects large numbers of aircraft operating in a relatively confined area was a headache to come; radio aids were virtually non-existent. The principal obstacles to more rapid progress were due more to international political obstructions caused partly by lack of faith in, and partly by fear of, the air as a medium for transport.

14

These obstructions were, indeed, formidable.

Small wonder that, in 1926, Imperial Airways set up a new base in Cairo and began to plan air routes eastward and southward from there. Political difficulties delayed progress even in the Middle East; the present route along the Persian Gulf, instead of a shorter one across Persia, is the fruit of the failure of negotiations with the Persian Government which took place in the middle 'twenties.

Pioneer Flights

By this time, however, important things had happened. In 1919, Ross and Keith Smith had flown from London to Sydney in very short hops (Hounslow—Lyons—Pisa — Rome — Taranto — Crete — Cairo —Damascus — Ramadi — Basra — Bandar Abbas — Karachi — Delhi — Allahabad — Calcutta — Akyab — Rangoon — Bangkok — Singora — Singapore — Kalidjati — Sourabaya — Bima — Timor — Darwin — and a chain of newly cleared landing-grounds across Australia — Newcastle Waters — Cloncurry — Charleville — to Sydney). Out of this magnificent flight had sprung the Australian air-line Q.A.N.T.A.S. (Queensland and Northern Territory Aerial Services) in 1920.

In 1919, too, the R.A.F. had begun the larger, harder task of putting down air-fields along the five-thousand miles of desert, swamp, jungle and mountain that separated Cairo from the Cape of Good Hope.

Many of these airfields were literally hand-made, torn out of thick forest, levelled out of the hills, built from the mud of the swamps by hordes of African labour. Torrential rain, roving herds of elephant and buffalo, fast-growing tropical vegetation, termites that built hills twenty and thirty feet high—all these hazards of nature delayed, but did not prevent, the completion of the task. Twenty-seven of these landing grounds had been created out of the African wilderness within ten years to link Cairo to the Cape by air. Van Ryneveldt and Brand in 1920, and Alan Cobham

PASSENGERS RELAX *in the forward compartment of a S.A.S. DC-6 air-liner. The pressurized cabins of this aircraft carry* 48 *passengers by day or* 26 *by night.*

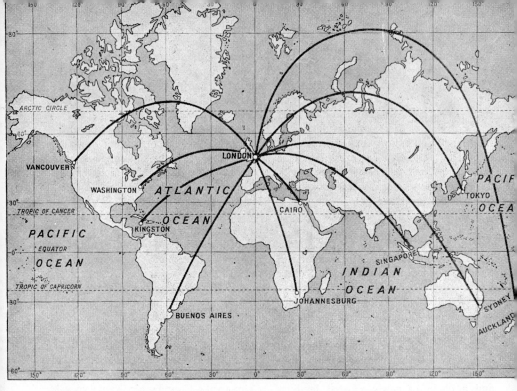

THIS MAP DEMONSTRATES *how the appearance and mileage of a route can be distorted by the projection of the map. The routes are exactly the same as those shown on page 14. On this projection, however, only the mileages at the Equator are correct.*

nearly six years later, got safely through, but not until 1929 did the British Air Ministry and Imperial Airways survey the route with a view to the possible operation of a regular air service along it.

North Atlantic Airway

The third great trunk route to be pioneered between the wars was the North Atlantic—today one of the busiest airways in the world. The intermittent Atlantic crossings, by Alcock and Brown in 1919, A. C. Read in the same year, Lindbergh in 1927, Amelia Earhart in 1932, Mollison in 1932, and many others, had opened up the somewhat remote possibility of a passenger service. But not until 1936 did four nations —Great Britain, the U.S.A., Canada and Eire—agree to share the expense and labour of providing the necessary meteorological

services, navigation aids, air bases and other facilities required. Specially modified flying-boats with additional fuel range were devised both by Britain and America. Many experiments were made to overcome the fuel problems and the war eventually crystallized them into a regular North Atlantic service—strangely enough, flown by landplanes.

The principal problems that had to be solved in planning an air route prior to World War II fell into four groups: aircraft, weather, airfields and fuel stocks. To some extent, the limitations of the aircraft of the period lessened the range of the problems, though it may not have diminished their numbers. For example, as the aircraft of the period were limited to hops of a few hundred miles, less dead weight in fuel and other equipment had to be carried.

16

THESE AFRICANS, *natives of Kampala, Uganda, are more interested in the camera than the B.O.A.C. Speedbird Solent-class flying-boat, arriving at Port Bell, Lake Victoria. The Solent, most recent of the Short series of flying-boats, weighs 33 tons.*

17

Aircraft, weather, airfields and fuel are still dominating factors in modern air-route planning; but the problems of each are quite different from those that confronted the air-line pioneers.

Problems of the Present

The added problems of air-traffic control, radio navigation, instrument-landing systems, international negotiation, and air-line economics have more recently become increasingly important.

So complex and so infinitely varied have all these problems become that it is difficult to say exactly who it is who does the planning for a modern air route or air service. Perhaps the latter term is the better one, for air routes are no longer a matter of preparing a long chain of landing grounds, supplying them with essentials and then taking off on a comparatively uncomfortable adventure at a comparatively slow speed with comparative uncertainty as to time of arrival.

Reliability and Regularity—two of the

LYING AT ANCHOR in *Augusta Harbour, Sicily, a B.O.A.C. Hythe-class flying-boat points its nose towards the tower of Avolos.*

three R's of modern air transport (the third being Revenue)—are rapidly being developed to the point when fogs, strikes and the need to wait your turn to land are alone likely to cause serious delay.

Who, then, is responsible for the planning of an air route?

There are two kinds of planning to be done: government planning and air-line planning. Both deal with operational and technical problems. The government, in addition to these, must deal with the international aspects of all proposed new routes, whilst the air-line must study more specifically their commercial and economic aspects. But at all levels there is the closest consultation and co-operation between the planners of the government departments and the civil-aviation authorities, and the planners of the air-line or air-lines which will fly the proposed new routes.

Selection of Aircraft

It is difficult to decide which group of factors confronts the air planners with their *first* problem. The type of route, and the reasons for wanting air services along it, decide which consideration predominates in the early discussions. The first essential, however, in any transport problem is to have a vehicle which is really suitable for carrying the traffic on the route on which it is to operate. This means that the operator must examine very carefully the traffic characteristics of the route. Is speed or comfort to be the main aim of the operator? Are low costs and low fares of overriding importance? Is a greater frequency of small-capacity planes more desirable than large-capacity planes that will fly the route less often? Would a flying-boat do the job better and more economically than a land-plane?

The type of aeroplane selected nowadays depends therefore on many commercial, as well as many operational factors. The amount of business has to be assessed with great care. What flow of traffic is there

AIRSPEED AMBASSADOR. *This British aeroplane is one of the few modern air-liners to have the wings set high. It is also perhaps one of the most graceful in flight.*

along the new route that is being planned? Is it steady throughout the year—and does it flow in both directions? Or is it seasonal and largely one-way?

An export drive, for example, tends to create an unequal balance on some routes which means higher costs to the exporter unless a market for incoming goods can be created that will be big enough to cover the operating costs of the homeward flight. This may mean the creation of new business or it may mean the attraction of business away from other forms of transport, such as ships, trains and road haulage, by instituting cheap rates on routes where traffic is largely one-way. Generally it is a mixture of both, with the accent very strongly on the creation of new business.

The commercial planners, with the aid of that important modern science of market research, eventually ascertain the kind of service which is required on the new route.

They can then decide whether they require aircraft with sleeping accommodation in the form either of bunks or adjustable seats, or whether they prefer aircraft which will fly mainly by day and allow passengers to spend the nights *en route* on the ground. They can, in other words, decide whether a fast or slow service is wanted and what proportion of the payload is likely to consist of passengers, what proportion will be cargo and what proportion mail.

Aircraft Types

The operational planners now know exactly what their task is and can decide whether suitable aircraft are available or whether modifications are required. One of the big problems of the British air-lines in the post-war years has been to obtain the right sort of aeroplane for each particular type of air-line job. In the attempt to do so, a multiplicity of types has appeared on the

HIGH FACTOR OF SAFETY *is guaranteed by the four D.H. Gipsy Queen engines of the Handley Page–Miles Marathon, a medium-range passenger- or freight-carrying air-liner. There is also a version of this aeroplane powered by two propeller-turbine engines.*

routes, none of them really designed for the job they may be doing. Gradually new designs are appearing especially created to do the work of the operator of civil air transport. Gradually the number of types will be reduced to five or six instead of the dozen or so which were flying the routes immediately after the war. The main types required are long-range (normally, for technical reasons, multi-engined and big in build), medium-range (general-purpose), short-range large-capacity, and short-range small-capacity, all capable of undergoing modification for freight carrying.

Size and Cost

In general, the most economical aircraft to operate are the larger ones, and the most economical route is that with the shorter hops. From this, one would expect that the most economical aircraft in operation would be the large, short-range type. But, in fact, this is not so, because the short-haul routes require a high frequency with smaller aircraft rather than a less-frequent service with big aircraft. All this means that the operating costs per mile of the two types are approximately equal.

One reason for the delay in obtaining these standard types has been the length of time (five to seven years) which must elapse before a new transport aircraft appears on the air routes after it has reached the drawing-board period of its construction.

Another reason is the great gap in civil-aircraft design and construction caused by World War II. In America this gap was smaller, if indeed it ever existed, because of the fact that long-range air transport had a high priority throughout her war effort; recovery has thus appeared to be quicker than in some parts of the world. American transport aircraft have, for a time, swept the field to such an extent that, in 1948, out of 3,646 aircraft estimated to be flying on the world's routes, excluding the U.S.S.R., 78 per cent were American-built; and of these, 1,655 were Douglas DC-3s or Dakotas converted for civil use.

The principal points to be considered in selecting aircraft for civil air-line work are fuel range—that is, how far the aircraft will fly in still air with minimum fuel load, allowing for adequate reserve fuel, and how far with the maximum load of fuel; volumetric capacity — for capacity by weight is not at all the same thing as capacity by volume; and availability of suitable navigational approach and landing aids, and runway facilities upon the main and alternative airfields along the selected route.

Special climatic considerations must also be considered. Wind, for example, can have a very great effect on fuel range. On the North Atlantic run, for instance, an eastward-bound air-liner can normally fly several hours longer, and perhaps even a few hundred miles farther, than the same air-liner with the same amount of fuel can fly on the westward flight. Local weather and seasonal phenomena, such as the monsoons of the Far East and the "haboobs" or "siroccos" of the Middle East, also affect not only flight plans but choice of aircraft.

So, too, extremes of temperature have to be considered: on some routes the same aircraft may experience arctic cold and tropical heat during the same flight.

Resultant Types

Modern air-liners must, therefore, be designed to meet varying groups of requirements. The results are difficult to classify, but the main types fall very broadly into three groups. First, there are the shorter-range types with a capacity of up to 10,000 lb. of cargo or 10 to 40 passengers, and an all-up weight of between 8,000 and 50,000 lb. Good examples

MADE IN MONTREAL, the Canadair Four carries between 40 and 55 passengers at a cruising speed of 300 m.p.h. The engines are Rolls-Royce Merlins, each of 1,760 h.p. The Canadair is Canada's first really large-scale production for the world's air-lines.

AIRSPEED AMBASSADOR

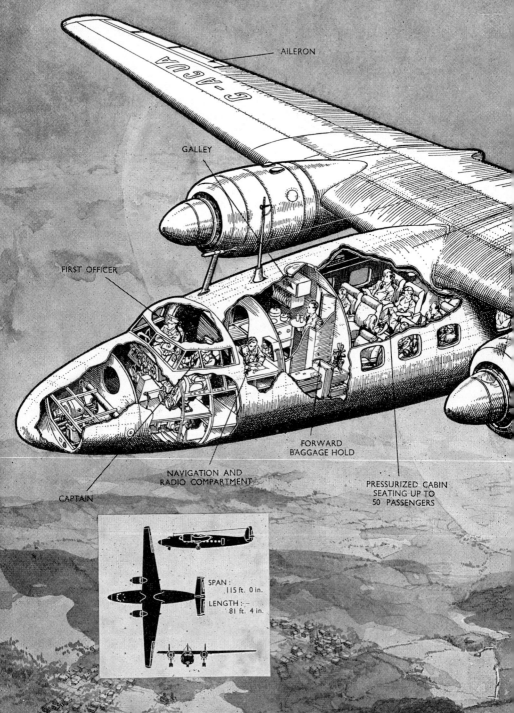

AILERON

GALLEY

FIRST OFFICER

CAPTAIN

NAVIGATION AND
RADIO COMPARTMENT

FORWARD
BAGGAGE HOLD

PRESSURIZED CABIN
SEATING UP TO
50 PASSENGERS

SPAN :
115 ft. 0 in.

LENGTH :—
81 ft. 4 in.

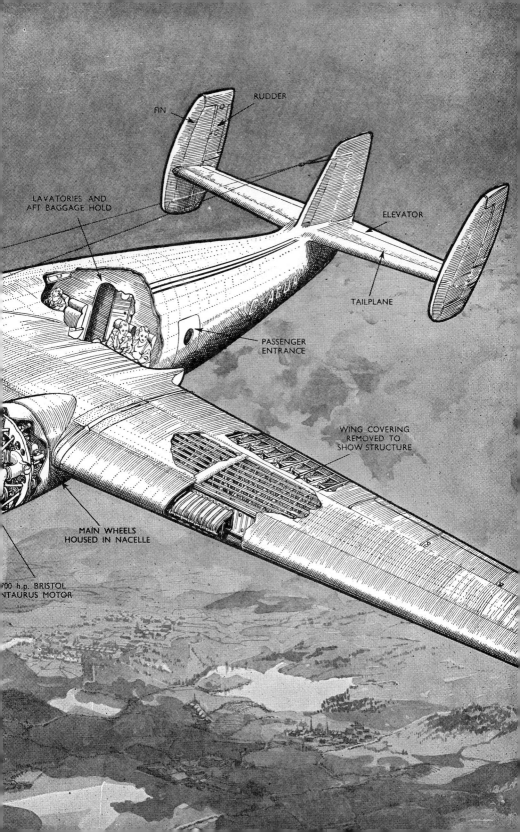

FIN

RUDDER

LAVATORIES AND
AFT BAGGAGE HOLD

ELEVATOR

TAILPLANE

PASSENGER
ENTRANCE

WING COVERING
REMOVED TO
SHOW STRUCTURE

MAIN WHEELS
HOUSED IN NACELLE

700 h.p. BRISTOL
NTAURUS MOTOR

FLYING OVER OSLO. *This photograph of a Norwegian DC-3 shows what is perhaps the most familiar civil air-liner. The DC-3 was known as the Dakota during World War II.*

of aircraft in this class are the British de Havilland Drover and Dove, Vickers-Armstrongs Viking and Viscount, Handley Page Marathon, Percival Prince, and the Airspeed Ambassador; and the American Douglas DC-3, Convair-Liner and Martin 2-0-2. The newest of these (such as the Ambassador and the Convair-Liner) are pressurized and can fly at altitudes of 20,000 to 30,000 ft. without discomfort to passengers or crew, or the wearing of oxygen masks.

The second group consists of the long-range class of four-engined air-liners and includes the conversions from military transports such as the Avro York (perhaps the last of the basic military types to fly on the civil air routes) and the newer types such as the Canadair Four, Handley Page Hermes, Douglas DC-4 and DC-6, Lockheed Constellation and Boeing Stratocruiser. This group also includes the famous Short series of flying-boats, most recent of which is the 35-ton Solent.

The capacity of aircraft of this weight (50,000–150,000 lb.) varies from a maximum payload of 10,000 lb. to one of over 25,000 lb., with a seating capacity of 30 to 60 and more. Some of the largest are de-

signed to take over one-hundred passengers on shorter flights. Fuel capacity may be anything between 2,000 and 10,000 gallons.

Multi-engined Aircraft

In a third group (yet to be tried on the air routes) are those multi-engined types such as the Bristol 167 (Brabazon) and the Saunders-Roe Princess (SR.45). Both of these are in the 100- to 140-ton class for weight and the 300- to 350-m.p.h. class for speed. The former is a landplane and the latter a flying-boat. Each is planned to carry round about a hundred passengers on long-range flights. The former will have eight power-units, the latter ten. If these both prove successful in flight and commercially suitable for operation on the routes, a new era in air-transport operations may be heralded. But there are many problems to be solved, not the least being the suitability of available airfields. Has the large flying-boat an advantage here over the large landplane? Only the future can answer this very vexed question.

If the first group of problems for the air-route planner concerns the selection and acquisition of the right aircraft, the second in importance must concern the airports at

PROPELLER-TURBINE *engines drive the advanced Armstrong-Whitworth Apollo through the air at high speed. Passengers feel little vibration and travel in near-silence.*

which the selected aircraft have to land.

As aircraft grow larger, runways must become not only longer but stronger. The impact of some 100 tons descending on any one spot of ground is considerable, however perfect the landing may be. Large aircraft are heavy and require a long take-off; the Boeing Strato-cruiser, fully loaded, needs 6,250 ft. to take the air and climb to a height of 50 ft. The Constellation needs about 4,250 ft. to do the same thing at sea-level, and the Brabazon may need very much more than either of these unless new techniques for assisted take-off can be successfully applied. At heights above

sea-level the take-off run becomes longer. At 5,000 ft. it may be half as long again.

This raises the runway problem as a barrier to aircraft development on a basis of size.

It is obvious that it may well be that the

SEATS *become berths in the "sleeper" Constellation. Each berth is 42 in. wide and has a window mirror, tray, clothes hangers and power-point close at hand.*

FIRST TRANSPORT-TYPE *aeroplane in the world to be powered by pure jet engines, the Vickers-Armstrongs Nene-Viking is a Viking airframe slightly modified to take two Rolls-Royce Nene engines, each capable of a static thrust of 5,000 lb.*

natural and economic limitations to the size of the world's airports will automatically limit the size of the land aircraft that fly the routes. Flying-boats, however, may not suffer so much from these limitations because the problem of finding water aerodromes with a long enough run of sheltered water is not quite as great as the sum total of the problems of building and equipping suitable aerodromes for landplanes, even though the flying-boat needs nearly twice the length of run as the landplane. By international standards, Class A land aerodromes must have a minimum runway length of 8,400 ft., whilst the Class A seaplane base must have 15,000 ft.

It must be remembered, in this con-

nexion, that one important reason why the great majority of the world's air-liners are landplanes is that World War II supplied the air-line operators with hundreds of ready-made airfields all over the globe. Although many of these were not suitable for civil air operation without the expenditure of much work and money, they were generally in the right places; it was found cheaper to develop the most suitable of them than to create new flying-boat bases in anything like adequate numbers.

Land and Sea Aerodromes

A first-class airport, such as Idlewild at New York, Kingsford-Smith Airport at Sydney, or London Airport may cost between twenty and thirty million pounds.

26

The flying-boat base is much less expensive because, for one thing, nature looks after the problem of strength; the sea is strong enough to take the heaviest flying-boat. The runways of a top-grade land aerodrome (Class A of the international standard classification) must have a bearing capacity of at least 100,000 lb., and this may imply 12 in. of concrete on top of a firm foundation. A channel depth of 15 ft. of water would have the same bearing capacity as a Class A runway.

Airport Facilities and their Problems

But runways are only one of the facilities that an airport must provide. The aeroplane has one essential difference from the surface vehicle: it cannot stop *en route*. It must be landed before it runs out of fuel. This fact alone means that a highly organized system of air-traffic control has had to be developed whereby aircraft can be systematically stacked (maintained at differ-

ent levels) in the sky and brought down, both in turn and in safety, with a minimum of delay.

Air-traffic control is still a young science and must develop to a far greater degree before it will be practicable to operate jet-propelled aircraft economically on the routes, for jet air-liners cannot cruise round each airport along their route awaiting their turn to land, or the value of the time saved in flight will be lost while waiting to land. Jet aircraft have a very high fuel consumption per hour which their high speed converts into a reasonable consumption per mile. Stacking, however, can be measured only by time, and the jet machine is thus at a great disadvantage if it has to await its turn to land.

Radio communications (described in Chapter 8) are the eyes and ears of the air-traffic controller. These may be of many different kinds, and one of the great problems of international and also of

LONDON AIRPORT, *Britain's largest, is shown under construction. When finished, there will be nine runways, two of them over* 3,000 *yd. in length. Every possible aid to safe flying will be installed to safeguard the* 4,000 *passengers who may be handled at peak hours.*

commonwealth air conferences in recent years has been that of standardizing them. This is gradually being done.

The first necessity is a system of ground-to-air communication enabling the location of each aircraft to be checked as it passes out of one region into another and finally into the control zone in which it is required to land. When the network of V.H.F. stations is complete it will give coverage over the whole of the United Kingdom, and this will save British European Airways many thousands of pounds a year.

Second, a system of landing by instruments (G.C.A. or Ground Controlled Approach is among those best known, although the only instrument needed in the aircraft for this is the ordinary radio set) is now a near necessity on every modern airport. Supporting these two groups of

AIRWAYS TERMINAL is the starting point for many air travellers in London. Here tickets are bought and all other arrangements made for the trip to Johannesburg illustrated in the following pages.

radio equipment are two others: aids to approach, and aids to navigation and direction-finding.

Finally there are the weather-information services, whereby information is either broadcast by radio at routine times, or channelled through the Meteorological Office organization to the airport briefing rooms, there to be passed on to the pilots when flight plans are being prepared.

Telecommunications

All these services must rely for their efficiency upon a number of very intricate radio instruments.

Also indispensable to each airport is first-class telecommunication with other airports and air terminals, so that information may pass quickly from one to the other about the movements of each aircraft as it lands and takes off. This means an efficient combination of landlines (tele-printer and cable) and radio.

Other airport facilities about which the planners must have full information, and which may have to be arranged or supplied if they are not adequate for the proposed air service, include lighting and night-flying facilities; hangar space or "hard standings"; maintenance and engineering equipment of the right kind for the type of aircraft being operated; petrol and oil stocks and refuelling facilities; accommodation for passengers, aircrew and station staff; catering facilities; and Customs facilities.

It is clear, then, that the choice of route is very largely governed by the location of the most suitable airports for the aircraft which are to be used.

Even if the planner has found aerodromes of suitable size situated where he wants them, all equipped to deal with his aeroplanes, he has still to assure himself that there are no awkward obstructions to low-flying which might make one type of aircraft less desirable than another; that the distance from the town is not too great

28

AT REST ON THE NILE. *For many years the Nile has served as a chain of airports for British flying-boats serving Africa. Here, a B.O.A.C. Solent is shown moored.*

for passenger convenience; that surface transport can be provided without long delays and high cost; and, should visibility be very bad, that there are alternative landing grounds conveniently situated.

The political problems that confront the planners of air routes today are very much more numerous and complex than those of the between-war years, because they involve much more than the mere passage over foreign territory of a somewhat infrequent flying machine of limited capacity and capable of no very hostile actions.

The modern flying machine is a vehicle of immense power. It is a frequent visitor. It can remain airborne throughout the night or day and it may be carrying half a hundred people, not all of whom will always be unable or unwilling to look for information of possible future military value. Even more important, it is a vehicle for trade, and trade is the modern nation's life blood. Air routes are arteries which could be used to drain away business that might do damage to a country's economic future. Thus, in an age when bilateralism has almost completely superseded the nineteenth-century ideal of free trade, governments must give high priority to the consideration of requests to operate air services to or from their territory, because these requests may help the foreign competitor by opening up to him new avenues of trade.

Each country quite naturally feels that the first consideration in all such negotiations must be to safeguard not only its own economic security, but also its own military security. The present tendency, however, is for narrow bilateral agreements to give way to multilateral agreements with increasing standardization of privileges, which offer greater scope to all concerned.

Political Problem

When the main Imperial Airways route was being opened between Egypt and India in 1926, a major obstacle to its progress was the uncertain attitude of the Persian Government; for after signing a provisional agreement which allowed Imperial Airways to make stops within its territory, there was a sudden change of mind just as the route was ready to be opened. As a result, passengers for India had to be transferred at Basra into ships to finish the journey by sea.

Two years more of tentative negotiations introduced new difficulties: first, one aeroplane a week was permitted to fly along the southern coast of Persia; then it was decided that this route must be changed

BERTH 50, SOUTHAMPTON, *as passengers go aboard a B.O.A.C. Solent flying-boat en route for Johannesburg. The overall time for the journey is four days.*

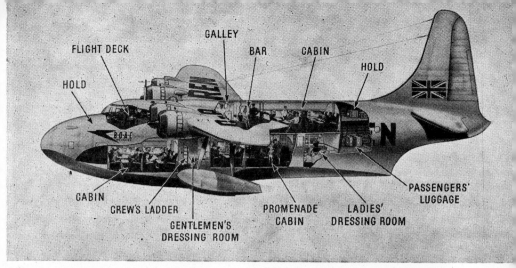

FLIGHT DECK · GALLEY · BAR · CABIN · HOLD · HOLD · CABIN · CREW'S LADDER · GENTLEMEN'S DRESSING ROOM · PROMENADE CABIN · LADIES' DRESSING ROOM · PASSENGERS' LUGGAGE

INSIDE THE SOLENT *is a small luxury hotel, with its own bar and buffet, five cabins, a promenade and dressing rooms. Thirty passengers are carried on day trips, but on a long trip such as this, twenty-four are on board. The Solent cruises at 213 m.p.h. and is powered by four Bristol Hercules engines. The span is 113 ft. The range of the Solent is over 2,000 miles.*

and must pass across the centre of Persia. This would have meant crossing many miles of mountainous country where both refuelling stops and emergency landings would have been equally impossible and the supply of petrol would have been both uncertain and expensive. In the end it was decided to by-pass Persia altogether and use the Arabian coast along the southern side of the Persian Gulf. From October, 1932, this desolate track has been developed by the provision of landing facilities of all kinds and has acquired operational and strategic importance in present-day Middle East air affairs.

International Air Conferences

This kind of political problem no longer arises. Civil aviation is now recognized as an international business in which all nations, if they value not only their prosperity but their survival, must take the keenest interest.

Although there had been several earlier international conferences on the subject, it was in December, 1944, at the invitation of the United States of America, that the representatives of 54 nations assembled at Chicago to discuss on a global scale the many and various problems of international co-operation in air matters.

P.I.C.A.O. and I.C.A.O.

The conference drew up three important documents. One of these set up the Provisional International Civil Aviation Organization (P.I.C.A.O.) which became effective in June, 1945, and made some provision for the regulation of international civil aviation. The second was the International Air Service Transit Agreement. The third, which was known as the Chicago Convention, came into force in April, 1947, and converted P.I.C.A.O. into a permanent body. By the end of 1947, 46 states had ratified this convention and become members of I.C.A.O. By the middle of 1949 this number had risen to 52. The chief task of I.C.A.O. is the development of international rules to control and regulate civil air operations in the interest of safety and order in the air.

Closely connected with these problems is the work of negotiating air-transport agree-

LIGHT REFRESHMENTS *are served in the upper-deck cabin of the flying-boat by the stewardess. Passengers can stretch their legs in the promenade on the lower deck.*

ments with those many countries over which the air routes now operate.

The Chicago Convention recommended a standard form of bilateral agreement on air-transport matters between any two of its member states, and included an annexe dealing with those controversial points which had to remain, for the time being, the subject of separate inter-state negotiation. This document dealt with such matters as the ownership of air-lines operating on agreed routes, the mutual recognition of certificates of airworthiness, and the prevention of financial discrimination in such things as, for example, airport fees; while the annexe dealt with the problems of the

exchange of traffic rights, the Fifth Freedom, and the control of fares. This form of agreement has since been amplified and modified in later important discussions (notably between the United States of America and the United Kingdom at Bermuda, in 1946) upon such matters as the granting of full and reciprocal traffic rights on specified routes.

Five Freedoms of the Air

To appreciate the significance of these developments it is important to understand the Five Freedoms of the Air. They are:
(1) The right to fly over a country without landing.

(2) The right to make non-traffic stops for such things as refuelling and repairs.

(3) The right to take traffic out of the home country into any other country.

(4) The right to bring traffic from any other country into the home country.

(5) The right to carry intermediate traffic either originating in, or destined for, countries other than the one to which the air-line belongs.

The United States and Britain were at variance over the restrictions to be placed on this fifth freedom. The U.S.A. felt that all five freedoms should be freely exchanged on a multilateral basis without any limitations at all. The United Kingdom, however, felt that, to avoid cut-throat competition, and to achieve the ideal of order in the air, it was necessary in the present stage of air transport to have some means of regulating internationally such things as fares, capacity allowed on each route, and so on. By the very important Bermuda Agreement of 1946 general principles were agreed for bilateral negotiations between the United States and Great Britain on matters in the Chicago annexe. It is hoped that these bilateral agreements might eventually lead to multilateral agreements between member states of I.C.A.O. But this will depend on the wider settlement, on a generally acceptable basis, of the important issue of fifth-freedom traffic.

There are about seventy bilateral agreements on air-transport matters in force at the time of writing, in at least twenty of which Great Britain is concerned.

The appointment of Civil Air Attachés since the end of World War II has helped considerably in the delicate business of reaching amicable solutions to political problems which might otherwise become barriers as formidable as those confronting Imperial Airways in the Middle East between 1926 and 1932.

Under this heading of political problems something should be said of the machinery for handling negotiations on civil aviation in the British Commonwealth and in the Colonies.

The Commonwealth Air Transport Council (C.A.T.C.) was set up in 1944 in Montreal. By 1947, Canada, Australia, New Zealand, South Africa, Southern Rhodesia, India, Pakistan, Ceylon, Newfoundland and the United Kingdom were members. Membership was also given to the Colonial Empire through an additional seat held by a representative of the Colonial Office.

Responsibility for civil aviation in the British Colonies rests with the Colonial Office. Colonial conferences are held periodically to discuss civil aviation affairs affecting the Colonies. The Ministry of Civil Aviation has only an advisory role in Colonial air matters.

There are also a number of regional conferences which are ancillary to the main body of C.A.T.C. The first two of these to be established have been the Southern Africa Air Transport Council and the South Pacific Air Transport Council.

MEALS *are prepared in the galley, which is positioned just behind the stewardess in the picture on the facing page.*

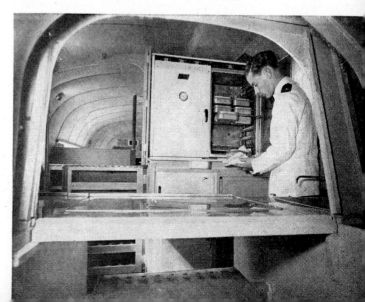

OVER THE PYRAMIDS! *Later, we alight on the Nile at Luxor for an overnight stop. This photograph was taken by an air-survey camera, which simultaneously records the readings of the instruments at the top of the picture. The clock and altimeter are at the left and right, and an exposure counter and spirit-levels are grouped in the centre.*

Through the agency of these consultative bodies, it may be said that there is little nowadays in Commonwealth or Colonial air affairs that is allowed to develop into anything which is likely to become a "political problem."

The Problem of Air-traffic Control

Controlling the growing mass of air traffic poses problems which did not exist in anything like the same magnitude before World War II. They were born, many of them, in wartime as a result of the steep rise in number of aircraft movements on the principal operational airfields. "Flying control" became a more highly specialized job requiring a greater knowledge of radio facilities and the organization of new procedures for handling air traffic reasonably safely and as expeditiously as possible.

As air-line operations came into their own, safety, punctuality and regularity became top priorities and the greater accuracy made possible by ever-developing radio equipment called for improved methods of controlling air traffic to avoid congestion and to cut down delays.

The Director of Long-Term Planning at the British Ministry of Civil Aviation said, in a memorable paper read to the Royal Aeronautical Society, that world air-traffic control was costing millions of pounds a year and losing many millions more because the traffic was increasing faster than the control could develop. Congestion and the consequent delay in bringing aircraft down safely had become the major problem that had to be solved before air transport could become not only fast enough, but cheap enough, to pay its way in the world. It would be impossible to operate the turbine aircraft of the future until the most urgent of these problems had first been solved. Most hopeful was the development of automatic landing by instruments to the point where it could be used safely in all circumstances. The aircrew and the ground scanners would then have only to watch and supervise landings.

At the beginning of 1948 the Ministry of Civil Aviation introduced a far-sighted system for the control of air traffic which was flexible and capable of absorbing a rapidly expanding volume of traffic.

The air space over the United Kingdom was divided into five great irregular areas known as Flight Information Regions: within each of these an Air Traffic Control Centre was created, responsible for providing a flight-information service by maintaining radio contact with all aircraft flying through the Region. The course of each aircraft is plotted and the search and rescue organizations can be alerted whenever a distress call is received.

Control Zones

Within these five Regions are Control Zones centred over each airport or group of airports at which large civil aircraft normally land. The Metropolitan Control Zone, for example, covers an irregular area roughly 25 miles in radius from the centre of London and includes London's airports.

B.O.A.C. SPEEDBIRD FLAG and the Egyptian green and white crescent fly over Gordon's Tree Marine Airport at Khartoum.

35

VICTORIA FALLS, *as seen from the air. We alight close to the falls and a night stop is made to give us time to examine this wonder of nature by daylight on the following morning.*

When weather conditions fall below a prescribed minimum state of safety (and in other operational circumstances decided by the Zone Air Traffic Controller) only those aircraft equipped with the requisite radio-communication channels and wishing to land within the Zone may enter it.

They must proceed according to the instructions passed from Control as to the height and point at which they may enter the Zone. They are then operating under what are known as Instrument Flight Rules as distinct from Visual Flight Rules which would allow them to fly in "by eye."

Approach Control carries out its task of guiding aircraft into and out of the circuit by using radio-communication and homing aids.

Aerodrome Control is the third phase of the system, and is responsible for guiding the aircraft on to the runway and thence to its place on the tarmac. When weather conditions are bad and Instrument Flight Rules are therefore in operation, Approach Control retains control of the aircraft until it lands and then hands over to Aerodrome

Control for taxi-ing and dispersal instructions. Both Approach and Aerodrome Control are located in the same control tower. The Air Traffic Control Officer at Aerodrome Control may also be assisted by a Runway Controller who has a mobile control caravan (easily distinguishable by its large black and white check marking) positioned at the down-wind end of the runway in use at the time.

Air Corridors

In the United States, a system of air corridors is being developed along which all radio navigation aids and weather information facilities are available. Certain of these skyways, as they are popularly called—such as the Wright Way between Los Angeles and Washington—have been planned especially for the use of private fliers. It is proposed to adapt this system of air corridors for use in the United Kingdom.

A little has already been said about the problem of weather. How soon, if ever, will air transport be independent of the effects of wind and weather?

That might well depend upon what is meant by "independent." Twenty years ago, when a head-wind reached a certain (and not uncommon) intensity, aircraft operating short-range air routes were grounded because they could not carry enough fuel to make headway against it. Today this is most unusual, and there are very few instances of even long-distance ocean flights being thus delayed.

Wind Effect

In 1928 a 60-m.p.h. head-wind meant that the 210-mile flight from London to Paris would take seven instead of two-and-a-half hours, so that the three-engined Argosy biplane then in use could not fly, as its flying time without refuelling had a top limit of three-and-a-half hours. But the same wind today adds only 23 minutes to the flying time. In another 20 years, if speeds of 700 m.p.h. should become common, the effect of such a head-wind on the aircraft's progress will be negligible.

Wind, therefore, influences the choice of aircraft and the choice of route and may sometimes cause the captain to change his flight plan; but it no longer grounds the air-liner. Even in the teeth of the persistent North Atlantic head-winds, fuel ranges are now great enough normally to allow · diversions or changes in altitude, and power units are powerful enough to permit the aircraft to fly the straightest course regardless of wind if this should be found necessary for commercial reasons.

Icing and Thunderstorms

Icing is not the problem that it used to be even a few years ago, for not only are there many effective types of de-icing equipment, but weather forecasts have become more accurate and icing clouds can frequently be avoided.

Thunderstorms, lightning and static discharge are still major problems, not so much because of the danger of being struck by lightning as because of the turbulence

MOORED ON THE EQUATOR. *The Solent seen at anchor at Kampala is floating on the surface of Lake Victoria, which is several thousands of feet above sea-level.*

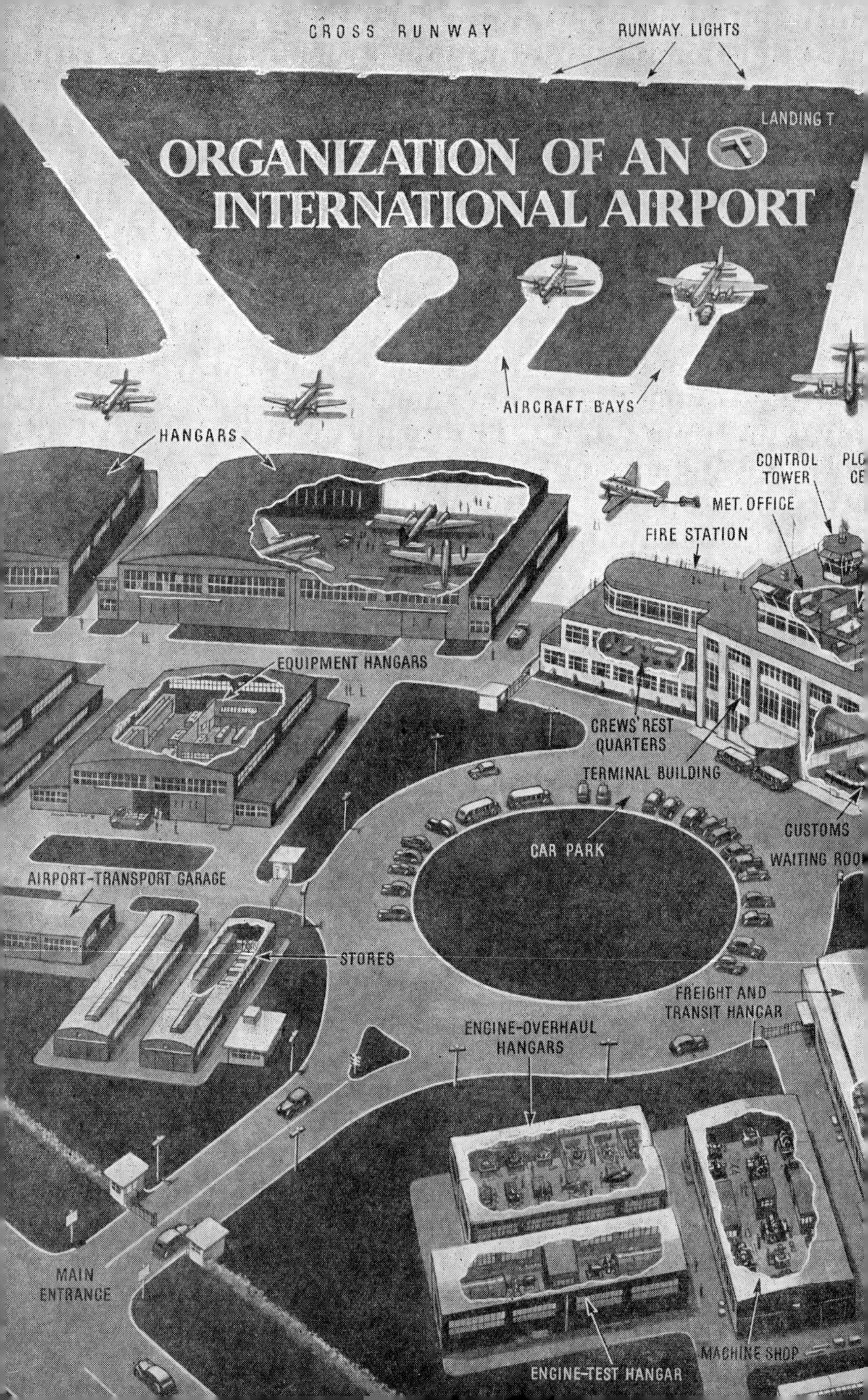

ORGANIZATION OF AN INTERNATIONAL AIRPORT

CROSS RUNWAY

RUNWAY LIGHTS

LANDING T

AIRCRAFT BAYS

HANGARS

CONTROL TOWER

PL○○
CE

MET. OFFICE

FIRE STATION

EQUIPMENT HANGARS

CREWS' REST QUARTERS

TERMINAL BUILDING

CUSTOMS

WAITING ROO○

AIRPORT-TRANSPORT GARAGE

CAR PARK

STORES

FREIGHT AND TRANSIT HANGAR

ENGINE-OVERHAUL HANGARS

MAIN ENTRANCE

ENGINE-TEST HANGAR

MACHINE SHOP

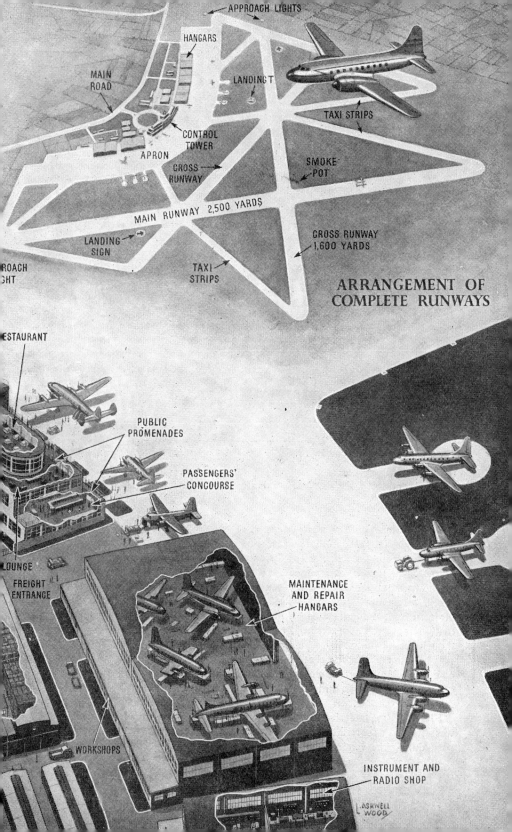

APPROACH LIGHTS

HANGARS

MAIN ROAD

LANDING T

CONTROL TOWER

APRON

CROSS RUNWAY

SMOKE POT

TAXI STRIPS

MAIN RUNWAY 2,500 YARDS

LANDING SIGN

CROSS RUNWAY 1,600 YARDS

ROACH GHT

TAXI STRIPS

ARRANGEMENT OF COMPLETE RUNWAYS

ESTAURANT

PUBLIC PROMENADES

PASSENGERS' CONCOURSE

LOUNGE

FREIGHT ENTRANCE

MAINTENANCE AND REPAIR HANGARS

WORKSHOPS

INSTRUMENT AND RADIO SHOP

L. ASHWELL WOOD

APERITIFS *to celebrate the approaching end of our flight are served by the stewardess. The Vaal River is now below us.*

of the air and the probable unserviceability of many tropical landing grounds after very heavy rain.

Fog remains a difficult problem because of the delays it causes in landing. Fog forecasts are not yet reliable. The forecast, however, is not to be compared with what is known as an "actual"—a fog warning based on definite information. Perfection of instrument-landing systems will eventually remove fog as a technical problem, though possibly not as a psychological one. It is only the densest fog that cannot now be coped with. The most effective method of dealing with fog is still diversion to a fog-free aerodrome.

FIDO (Fog, Intensive, Dispersal Of) was invented as a result of the imperative need during the war to find a means of dissipating fog on operational aerodromes. It is based on a system of petrol burning which disperses the fog by the heat of blazing low-grade fuel from a series of special burners arranged along the sides of the runway. The wartime equipment cleared fog—very expensively—to a height of 100 ft. The modified equipment now in use on selected airfields needs only to disperse it to a height of 30–50 ft., as radar can bring the aircraft accurately to within this height. This system is not, however, in very general use.

Meteorological Stations

The fact that the weather offers fewer problems to the air-route planners today than it did a few years ago is a tribute to the progress made in scientific weather research and in the provision of a vast system of weather stations, internationally co-ordinated, which are constantly collecting, collating and distributing weather information for the use of all who need it whether for air transport or other purposes.

These stations are normally maintained by the governments of the countries concerned. Observations are made at regular intervals, sometimes hourly and sometimes at longer intervals, and reports are passed quickly (by radio or by landline) to collecting centres which re-transmit them to all meteorological offices.

The observer stations are of two types: one makes surface observations of factors such as atmospheric pressure, temperature, humidity, wind, visibility, rainfall and cloud formations; the other obtains rather similar observations in the upper air up to heights of more than 20 miles. Most of the British observer stations are combined with forecasting units and are located at airfields.

Important exceptions, however, are the two ocean weather stations which Great Britain maintains in the North Atlantic, west of Ireland and south of Iceland. To man these two stations, four weather ships have to be maintained; these make both types of observation and also provide navigational aid to aircraft in flight.

Eleven nations using North Atlantic air routes have agreed to co-operate in setting up and maintaining a total of nine such ocean stations. Two vessels are needed for each station so that proper relief can be organized. The vessels are generally ex-naval corvettes and are painted yellow to make them instantly recognizable.

Maintenance

Very much a major problem in the planning of the modern air routes is that of maintenance.

One of the first requirements of any form of transport is safety. Assuming that the equipment is the best available for the job and that all the normal precautions are taken against possible emergencies (such as the provision of an adequate supply of reserve fuel, which is worked out to a standard scale based on the quantity required to reach any of the alternative landing grounds selected for the route, whatever the weather), the best guarantee of air safety, and hence of confidence, is a first-rate system of servicing and maintenance—combined, of course, with the very high standard of aircrew training which exists today.

Maintenance is invariably placed first in their list of priorities by all the major air-lines. Indeed, it has been estimated that four to five shillings out of every pound spent by the air-line represents maintenance costs in some form or another.

The modern air-liner is a highly complex vehicle which may contain over 100,000 individual components. Before it can fly

MARKING THE END of our journey is the Vaalbank Dam—the largest in South Africa. Arriving at noon, we have lunch and then go by coach to Johannesburg. Our Solent flying-boat has, in the last four days, carried us a distance of well over 6,000 miles.

with passengers it must have a Certificate of Airworthiness which has to be renewed, after a complete overhaul, each year. This is awarded, in the United Kingdom, only after the most stringent tests by the Air Registration Board (the body to which the British Government has delegated the responsibility, among other things, for the registration of aircraft and the licensing of aircraft engineers). Thereafter the aircraft's performance is the constant concern of the air-line. B.O.A.C., for example, has a Development Flight whose job it is to discover modifications which will improve the air-liner's performance in any or all of the different conditions in which it may have to operate.

Operational aircraft must be inspected every 24–30 hours and their daily safety certificate signed by a fully qualified, licensed aircraft-maintenance engineer.

Routine Inspections

In addition to this primary check, there are specific inspections to be carried out after flights involving periods of flying time which vary from 10 or 20 to about 400 hours. These routine checks may number up to as many as six, according to the type of aircraft and the particular route on which the air-liner is flying. Each check may involve the inspection of as many as 150 different items. It is normally carried out at a base and is in the nature of a minor overhaul. All of them are in addition to the progressive series of overhauls required before the annual Certificate of Airworthiness can be renewed.

In the course of these checks, any individual accessory may have reached the end of its allotted life and have to be removed for a major overhaul, in which case a new or reconditioned part must be tested and fitted in its place.

Hence the need for both trained men and adequate repair and maintenance facilities in the right places along the routes. Very often it has not been possible to secure suitably equipped maintenance bases at a terminal and many hours of "dead" flying time have been necessary in consequence. Gradually this expensive drain on air-line finances is being reduced, as new accommodation becomes available. It is, however, a slow process and constitutes an important problem for the planners to consider, when new routes are being suggested and new aircraft ordered. For each new aircraft requires specialized equipment and specially trained maintenance engineers.

A notable instance of the maintenance problem in British air-line operation has been the Constellation service across the North Atlantic between London and New

NEW YORK'S LA GUARDIA AIRPORT. *The air-liners shown here were, a few hours later, separated by hundreds of miles and were heading for Europe, the Middle West and Canada.*

NOTHING IS MORE VITAL *to safe air transport than efficient and comprehensive maintenance. This B.O.A.C. Lancastrian is being serviced at the Kallang Airport, Singapore.*

York. La Guardia (one of New York's main airports) had no maintenance facilities available to B.O.A.C. Constellations, which therefore had to fly after each flight to the Line Base at Dorval Airport, Montreal, and back again. These flights of some 350 miles were "dead" from the revenue point of view as they could not be made with passengers aboard owing to agreements which forbid air-liners of a foreign air-line to pick up traffic between Canada and the United States.

What all this means in terms of revenue will be better appreciated if it is realized that, when a time-table is prepared for the North Atlantic, it can allow for only eight hours out of 24, on the average, for revenue flying, that is, during only one-third of the aircraft's life can it earn revenue. Another third of its life is spent at the base on maintenance and overhaul, tests and training. The remaining third is "turn-around" time and includes time spent at stops (sometimes overnight) and also some of the time spent on dead flying. Other dead flying time must come out of the earning period. So the aircraft's utilization—the key to air-line economics—

is seriously reduced on routes which are not equipped with convenient maintenance facilities.

It is estimated that £1,000,000 in dollars is to be saved each year by the Corporation's removal of its maintenance facilities at Dorval to the great Bristol base at Filton. This base had been fully developed and equipped at considerable expense to cater for the Brabazon, which the Bristol Aeroplane Company was then building as part of the Ministry of Supply's civil-aircraft development programme.

Training of Personnel

This leads to another problem for the air-route planner and for the air-line operator—technical and operational training. Like maintenance and air-traffic control, this is a problem which has grown formidably as a result of the very rapid expansion of air-line operations since World War II.

The problem has not been made easier by the fact that the technical and aeronautical progress has been too quick for the ground organization which has not been able to keep pace with it. Forecasts as to future developments have been impossible and attempts at such forecasts have been—and are still—bound to prove misleading.

Nor is it a simple matter of transferring personnel from the Services to the civil air-lines. Much conversion training is necessary before the experienced R.A.F. pilot can fly on the air routes and before the experienced R.A.F. ground engineer can qualify as a ground engineer in one of the specialized jobs in the civil air-lines.

Saturation point was quickly reached in both operational and technical posts in the civil air world when the war ended, and thereafter there were limited opportunities for the experienced ex-Service flier or technician. There have been, however, vacancies at the *bottom* of the ladder—as there must always be—in each of a number of skilled careers. The number of these vacancies fluctuates, but it is governed by the normal wastage of probably 7 or 8 per cent in each trade. It is also affected by reductions and expansions due to the rather fluid state of civil aviation as a whole.

Training of pilots and navigators, radio operators and engineers is a problem both for the Government and for the air-lines. It has no immediate bearing on the planning of an air route except in so far as enough trained crews and technical ground staff must be available to fly whatever aircraft is selected, along the chosen route, without weakening other lines elsewhere.

Specialized Training

It takes years to produce these men, and route requirements for the years to come must therefore be carefully assessed, bearing in mind the number of the right kind of trained operational and technical personnel it will be possible to call upon at a given time.

There is thus a clear distinction to be drawn between initial training to qualify a man or woman for the particular licence which may be necessary, and the special-

YEARS OF TRAINING *are needed to produce an air-line pilot, and as new or re-designed equipment is constantly being brought into service, training never really ends. This photograph shows a pupil at a British school being instructed in cockpit drill.*

ized training (including conversion from one type of equipment to another) which is necessary before the trained and qualified man or woman has the experience to be of use to the air-line. Most of the former and much of the latter is in the hands of a number of excellent private training establishments.

The scope of the training courses for which the air-line must cater can be gauged from items in recent annual reports by B.O.A.C. and B.E.A.

In 1947–48, B.O.A.C. conducted 302 conversion courses, in which 463 aircrew (152 pilots, 109 navigators, 97 radio officers and 105 engineer officers) received training; 78 first officers received "command" courses, 24 being promoted from co-pilot to captain.

In the same year, B.E.A. spent over £600,000 on flying training alone. This included :

1. (*a*) Basic training (that is, the training to B.E.A. basic standards of pilots recruited from R.A.F. and other outside sources);

(*b*) conversion training (the training required to enable a pilot to fly a type of aircraft not previously flown by him on B.E.A. operations), and

(*c*) training to obtain supplementary qualifications (e.g., second-class navigator's licence).

2. Refresher training.

Training is a problem which has been variously solved by different air-lines and by different countries. The tendency is either towards the establishment of a great central training base, or to a more de-centralized programme of Line training.

Training in the U.S.A.

A good example of the former is the American Airlines' training centre at Ardmore, a former U.S. Army airfield near Oklahoma. It has the advantage of being ideally situated, away from the network of

MAKING PASSENGERS COMFORTABLE *is a science. There is a right and a wrong way, even, of helping a person into his coat. Here, future stewards and stewardesses learn the right way whilst undergoing training at the B.O.A.C. Catering Training School.*

civil air routes. Staff are trained under contract for a number of other air-lines. Although pilot training receives primary consideration, there are also courses for stewards and stewardesses, mechanics and engineers and traffic staff.

The British air-lines provide a good example of training on a Line basis. This system, however, tends to limit the degree of flexibility which is always desirable and it is probable that future years will see the re-establishment of some form of centralized training such as existed at Aldermaston (Reading) in 1946–47 when the demand was greater than it has been since, or of a combination of both systems in the interests of maximum economy.

The Economics of Air Transport

All these problems and their solution make air-route planning in its broader sense a very complex occupation, and they explain why civil air transport must be expensive even when there is maximum efficiency at all levels both on the side of the government and on the side of the operator.

It may be interesting to conclude this chapter with a summary of some of the main points in the economics of modern air transport.

Air transport is both an industry and a public service. As an industry it could, perhaps, be run purely on business lines by business people. It would then probably pay, but might not develop its vast potential to the greatest advantage of the nation.

It has also very important political, military, cultural and economic aspects which are not necessarily commercial. Because of these, some form of financial guarantee by the State must be accepted by the public, even after direct subsidies or subsidies in the form of high air-mail payments (as is the custom in the United States) have ceased to be necessary.

LUXURIOUS MEALS, *prepared in all-electric pantries, are served on K.L.M.'s DC-6 air-liners. Maintenance of a high standard of catering is of great importance in "selling" air travel.*

BIGGEST IN THE WORLD *is the Brabazon air-liner. Such giants offer the advantages of long-range, non-stop flight in great comfort. On the other hand, first costs are enormous and there are few aerodromes in the world able to withstand the Brabazon's weight.*

Four things must happen before the air routes as a whole are likely to pay for themselves: first, the development of new technique for controlling air traffic and their standardization along all international routes so that there will be no congestion and no delay; second, the end of the period of experiment in basic aeronautical design. When maximum reliability and the best possible performance have been achieved, operators will be able to decide on their basic types. The time taken to construct new machines may then be reduced from five, six or seven years to one or two. With ships, trains and automobiles the basic types have been known for some time and changes and improvements are seldom fundamental. With aircraft, it is not yet known what the basic type will finally look like.

Third, an adequate network of Class A airports must be established all over the world; and a solution to the maintenance problem must be found. This will become simpler as aircraft types become standardized; many types mean many hundreds of highly technical components needing special stores of spare parts, special equipment, and special training for those who have to handle it.

Last, aircraft development must tend towards greater speed at lower cost by reducing drag and by reducing fuel consumption. Aero-engine development will depend upon the commercial prospects of propeller-turbines and jet engines. The piston engine is thought by many to have reached its peak performance.

Future Aircraft Types

Aircraft types will tend to develop within three main classifications: the helicopter with ten or more seats, for very short flights (say up to 200 miles) and for taxi services between the airports and houses; the short-haul, fixed-wing aircraft for flights over 200 miles (aircraft cannot compete with surface transport over shorter distances, unless there are geographical barriers to be overcome); and the medium- and long-range fixed-wing aircraft developing in two directions: (*a*) size and (*b*) all-wing or all-fuselage designs. Turbo-props and, later, jets will give speeds higher than 500 m.p.h.

FLIGHT REFUELLING *may make long-range flight possible for medium-sized aircraft. Here, an Avro Lancaster is seen refuelling a jet-propelled Gloster Meteor.*

at altitudes up to 50,000 ft. where fuel consumption will be small and weather influence negligible.

The next point concerns costs. These are a combination of fixed annual expenses, hourly cruising expenses, and airport fees. They are influenced by heavy overhead expenses at stations and bases dispersed over the whole of the routes by the number of hours flown during the year (that is, the utilization of the aircraft), and by the length of the stages. A number of stops on long-range routes are made primarily for refuelling and are non-commercial.

Lastly, ground costs are a factor the size of which is not always appreciated. They are shared between the air-lines and the government. They cannot decrease suddenly. For example, because airports cannot become much larger, new aircraft will have to take advantage of methods of assisted take-off, and of devices such as multi-wheel undercarriages for reducing the impact of landing. This may add both to production and to ground costs. The cost of specialized radio equipment is also extremely high and unlikely to decrease.

These are all factors of great weight in considering overall problems involved in the planning and operating of the modern air route. To reduce the whole of this planning problem to its simplest terms, it may be defined as the business of selecting the right aircraft for the route required to be flown, and of creating enough payload for the route to be flown at a profit as frequently as possible, regularly, punctually and, of course, safely.

When the problems have been solved and the air-lines can operate economically, fares and freight rates will drop sufficiently to compare favourably not only with first-class and luxury-class surface transport, but with second-class and tourist-travel facilities. This has, in fact, already happened in the case of certain air-line fares.

CHAPTER 2

AIR-LINES
AROUND THE WORLD

THROUGHOUT the world, air communication has developed along, broadly speaking, similar lines. Local requirements, facilities and resources have obviously had to be catered for, but standards of service and safety of operation are almost uniform.

Fares and traffic matters are mainly agreed through the air-lines' own organization, I.A.T.A. (International Air Transport Association), while international problems of safety and aircraft requirements are worked out by I.C.A.O. (International Civil Aviation Organization). Both of these bodies at present have their headquarters in Montreal. Air transport is well developed on all continents and within most countries, while many of the larger countries operate international services linking them with their neighbours and, in a fairly large number of instances, with other countries which are separated by hundreds or even thousands of miles.

British Air-lines

The scheduled British air services are operated by, or on behalf of, two state-owned corporations. The British European Airways Corporation is responsible for operating all scheduled air services within Britain, and all scheduled British air services between Britain and the European countries. The other concern, British Overseas Airways Corporation, is entrusted with the operation of all British scheduled services between Britain and all overseas points outside Europe.

The reason for the repeated use of the word scheduled in this context is that the British Civil Aviation Act is built around this word—for no other British operator is allowed to operate scheduled air services within or from Britain, except by agreement with, or under charter to, B.E.A. or B.O.A.C., although charter or non-scheduled passenger-carrying is permissible.

Internal Services

Within the British Isles, where surface travel is well developed, the most successful routes must be those on which a water crossing or some other geographical barrier is involved. This rather naturally brings about certain spheres of operation such as the English cross-Channel services to the Channel Islands, by which both Guernsey and Jersey are linked to London and Southampton, and Alderney to Guernsey and Southampton. During the summer these islands are also connected to France by British services; the Irish Sea crossing has attracted British air-line operators for many years, and Belfast is thus served from London, Liverpool, Manchester and the Isle of Man.

Scotland offers much scope for air-lines.

where many routes are mostly concentrated on the Western Isles and the Orkneys and Shetlands. The main air-line base is at Renfrew, the airport for Glasgow; from there, Douglas DC-3 and de Havilland Dragon Rapide aircraft fly out over the mountains, lochs and islands to Belfast, Campbeltown on Kintyre, Islay, Tiree, Barra, Benbecula and Stornoway. From Inverness and Aberdeen, services fly north to Wick, the Orkneys and Shetlands, while the southern and northern spheres are themselves linked. Also Edinburgh and Glasgow have direct services to London.

Air Ambulances

Scotland offers the finest scenery in Britain to the air traveller. Leaving Glasgow in the early morning and climbing above the Clyde and its shipping, on over the mountains and lochs until, about forty-five minutes later, the sea and the numerous islands of the Hebrides stretch away around one, leaves a permanent and beautiful picture in the mind. And on approaching the runways stretching across such islands as Tiree, the brilliant blues and greens of the sea, together with the whites and golds

of the beaches, offer spectacles of colour seldom surpassed.

It is over these areas that the air ambulance has done such good work; operating north from Inverness and north-west and west from Renfrew, well over a thousand cases have been brought in from these islands in the past fifteen years. It is not uncommon for an islander to be in a Glasgow hospital within three or four hours of his doctor's call for an aeroplane, whereas the surface journey would often entail two days' travel even if a boat called on the desired day and the patient could stand up to such a journey.

In the south-west of the British Isles, a service operated by Dragon Rapides connects Land's End with Scilly, and in this area, too, many ambulance flights have been made.

Although the number of ambulance cases may seem large, it is obvious that there are not enough to justify a specialized ambulance service. Special stretchers have, therefore, been designed with which the Rapide can instantly be converted into an ambulance aeroplane.

Certain routes in Britain which British European Airways does not desire to

AT JERSEY AIRPORT, *passengers go aboard a Bristol Wayfarer. This type of aeroplane is also built as a freighter; it has double nose doors to facilitate loading.*

REMOTE PLACES *are well served by aircraft such as the de Havilland Dragon Rapide, which not only carries mail but has also acted as an emergency ambulance. This Rapide (above) is flying over St. Mary's in the Scilly Isles. Below, a B.E.A. Sikorsky helicopter is seen picking up mail. These machines have figured in many dramatic stories of rescue.*

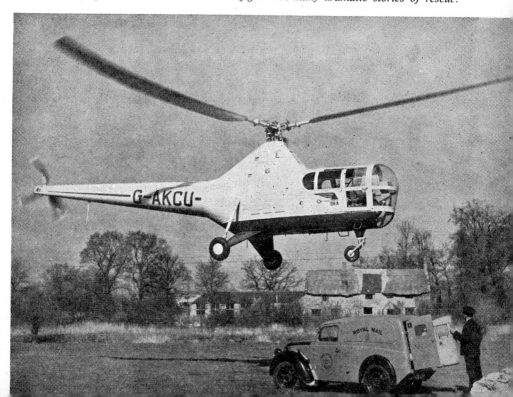

operate have been handed over to private charter companies who work as associates of the Corporation under a licensing system. Many of these services are seasonal, catering largely for summer-holiday traffic. These routes mainly converge on the Channel Islands and the Isle of Man.

On the British services to the continent of Europe, B.E.A. operates, in the main, with 27-seat Vickers-Armstrongs Viking airliners, which cruise at about 200 m.p.h.; these were the first new British air-liners to go into service after the war. These services, working from the Corporation's headquarters and main base at Northolt Airport, a few miles west of London, fly regularly to France, Spain, Portugal, Belgium, Holland, Switzerland, Denmark,

FLIGHT *to Amsterdam starts at Kensington Air Station, where the baggage is weighed.*

Norway, Sweden, Germany, Czechoslovakia, Austria, Malta, Italy, Greece and Turkey.

An associated company, Cyprus Airways, offers connexions with some of these services to points in the south-east Mediterranean, including Israel. Another associate, Gibraltar Airways, links Gibraltar with Tangier.

In most cases of international air travel, reciprocal rights exist and over most of the B.E.A. continental routes it will be found that the national air-lines of the European countries served are also operated to and from London. In addition, K.L.M. (Holland) operates to Manchester, Swissair to Glasgow, and Air France to Birmingham, Manchester, Glasgow and Belfast.

The British Overseas Airways Corporation is the successor to Imperial Airways, the company which planned, surveyed and pioneered the British trunk air routes to Central, South and West Africa, India, Australia, Hong Kong and across the North Atlantic.

B.O.A.C.'s main routes are those across the North Atlantic; to and through Africa; and along the Persian Gulf to India, the Far East and Australia.

North Atlantic Services

The present B.O.A.C. North Atlantic services between Britain and both the U.S.A. and Canada have developed from the joint Imperial Airways and Pan American Airways trials begun in 1937, and the vast experience gained during the war in the operation of the North Atlantic Return Ferry which was started to carry westward the crews engaged in ferrying new aircraft from the United States and Canada to Britain.

Making written statements about aircraft used on a particular route is always dangerous owing to frequent changes. But at the time of writing B.O.A.C. is using a fleet of Lockheed Constellation air-liners on its North Atlantic services; on the New

52

NEXT STAGE *of the journey is by coach to Northolt Airport. The Smith family is seen disembarking and (below) undergoing a luggage check by Customs officials.*

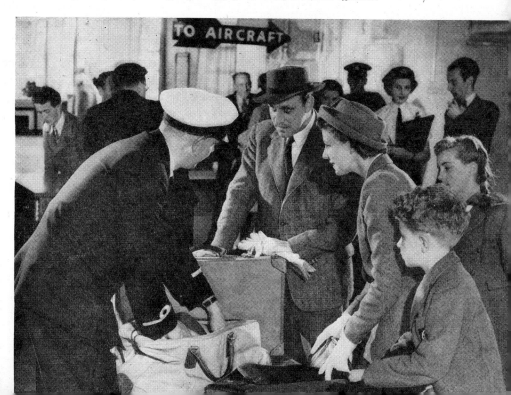

York route, however, the Boeing Strato-cruiser's range and speed enable it to fly non-stop from New York to London in normal conditions in 12 hours.

B.O.A.C.'s landplane services from Britain all depart from London Airport. The Corporation's North Atlantic Con-stellation services to Montreal normally call at Prestwick in Ayrshire, in south-west Scotland, and at Gander in Newfoundland before making the flight along the St. Lawrence and over the city of Montreal to land at the Dorval Airport. The New York services normally call at Shannon in Eire and again at Gander. Goose, in Labrador, can be used as an alternative to Gander on North Atlantic services. In bad weather or extremely high winds, Keflavik, in Iceland, is sometimes used.

Although faster, longer-range aircraft eliminate the need for some of these stops over the North Atlantic routes, these air-ports will almost certainly continue to play an important part in bad weather, if not as points of scheduled call.

British Flying-boats

Another Constellation service flown by B.O.A.C. in the Americas is that between New York and the lovely islands of Ber-muda. Britain has long been one of the foremost operators of passenger flying-boats (at one period, all the British trunk air routes were flown by marine aircraft), so it is not surprising that B.O.A.C. still main-tains a number of flying-boat routes.

These routes operate from Berth 50 in the Southampton Docks, just across Southampton Water from B.O.A.C.'s main flying-boat base at Hythe. Although the present programme of the Corporation calls for the withdrawal of flying-boats in 1950 or soon after, one type is in service, built by Short Brothers: this is the Solent,

IN ANOTHER ROOM, *the Smiths' passports are checked by the Immigration Officer. This formality completed, the family collect their personal luggage and head for the tarmac.*

a deep-hulled, four-motor, high-wing monoplane with fixed wing-tip floats.

Solent flying-boats operate two of the Corporation's Africa routes. These routes follow the same course for about 4,000 miles before dividing. The main route is from Southampton across France and the Mediterranean to Augusta in Sicily, then to Alexandria in Egypt and up the Nile, calling at Luxor and Khartoum, after which a call is made on Victoria Nyanza, where the routes separate. The lesser route branches east to Dar-es-Salaam, on the Tanganyika coast of the Indian Ocean, while the other continues south to a point just above the Victoria Falls and terminates at Vaaldam, near Johannesburg. The Solents complete the journey of approximately 6,500 miles from Southampton to Vaaldam in just over four days.

Until recently, the Corporation operated another flying-boat route with Plymouths, following the Africa route to Egypt and then branching eastward to the Persian Gulf, Pakistan, India, Burma, Thailand, Hong Kong, China and Japan, where the Far East route terminates at Tokyo. The route is now being flown by Canadair Four Argonaut-class air-liners.

Sydney by B.O.A.C.

The main England–Australia route of B.O.A.C., long worked by flying-boats, is now flown by Constellations via Rome, Cairo, Karachi, Calcutta, Singapore and Darwin, to end at Sydney. This route is operated in parallel and in collaboration with Qantas Empire Airways, the company which, in 1934, was formed out of the old Qantas company for the purpose of completing the through England–Australia route, when Imperial Airways flew to Singapore and the Australian company took over there for the eastern end of the

FOR THE YOUNGEST SMITH, *the flight to Amsterdam really begins when he sees their air-liner awaiting them. The receptionist checks in the passengers as they go aboard.*

journey. It was for the operation of the Singapore–Brisbane sector that the D.H.86 was designed.

Although B.O.A.C. does not operate a round-the-world route, the Corporation, in collaboration with other air-lines, offers round-the-world travel over more than 1,000 alternative routes. These round-the-world flights can be made from Europe east via Australasia, or across the Atlantic, America and the Pacific Ocean to Australasia and return via the east.

Landplane Services

Other B.O.A.C. landplane services include routes from England to India, Ceylon, Malaya, East and West Africa and the Near East, as well as certain local services between Egypt and the Sudan, Eritrea, Ethiopia and East Africa.

The British Overseas Airways Corporation is modernizing its fleet of landplanes,

so it is not possible to forecast in detail what its future landplane routes will be, although its network must remain much as it is now in order to serve the areas of trade. The new fleet includes Boeing Stratocruisers built in the U.S.A., Canadair Fours built in Montreal, and Handley Page Hermes built in Britain. The Lockheed Constellation will remain in service for some time and, during the early 1950s, the jet-propelled de Havilland Comet, Bristol 175 and, possibly, the Bristol 167 Brabazon will take their place on the Corporation's routes.

A number of freight services are also operated by B.O.A.C. with Avro Lancastrian monoplanes; it is possible that a freight version of the Avro Tudor, the Trader, may replace the existing types.

A third British air-line corporation, The British South American Airways Corporation, had been responsible for the opera-

MORNING COFFEE *is served by the steward as the air-liner starts its journey to Amsterdam. The cabin is soundproofed and air-conditioned, and each passenger has a table.*

SMITH FAMILY'S *air-liner is the Vickers-Armstrongs Viking, a twin-engined, medium-range machine which cruises at about* 200 *m.p.h. It carries* 24–27 *passengers in comfort.*

tion of British scheduled services to South America and the West Indies. The plans of this Corporation were mainly based on the operation of a fleet of Avro Tudor air-liners. Unfortunately, two of these aircraft were lost without trace; after this, the Tudor was permanently withdrawn from passenger service, leaving B.S.A.A. without aircraft and with little chance of obtaining new equipment without delay and, almost certainly, expenditure of dollars.

As a result of these calamities, the British Government decided to merge the British South American Airways Corporation with B.O.A.C. This means that B.O.A.C. has added to its already vast route mileage the old B.S.A.A. routes to South America and the Caribbean.

A number of large 140-ton Saunders-Roe Princess-class flying-boats was being built for B.S.A.A., and it now seems likely that these will be operated by B.O.A.C. Each of these flying-boats will be powered by ten gas-turbines driving propellers.

European Lines

Most European countries operate air-lines, which are in most cases a main national concern. Of the others, some are state-owned, some private and others part private, part state.

As a result of Soviet influence, it cannot be said that the amount of international transport is uniform throughout the continent, although western European air-lines do operate in and out of eastern Europe, and eastern European air-lines do fly to western countries.

However, no foreign air-lines are allowed to operate into the Soviet Union, although Soviet services operate into eastern and north-eastern Europe.

Working from the west of Europe towards the east, we find that in Portugal and

NEARING AMSTERDAM, *the captain of the aeroplane shows Mr. and Mrs. Smith the route they are following. The young Smiths are seeing another country for the first time.*

Spain there are local and international services. In Portugal these are run by a number of companies, the principal of which is T.A.P. (Transportes Aereos Portugueses) using Douglas DC-3 and DC-4 aircraft. The Spanish concern, Iberia, also uses a number of DC-3 and DC-4, as well as some Junkers Ju-52 aircraft. These air-liners give a splash of colour to the airports they visit, the Portuguese liners having the red and green Portuguese flag painted on their tails, while the Spanish aircraft boldly display the yellow and red colours of Spain. In the Azores, a local company, S.A.T.A., flies a fleet of 8-11 passenger de Havilland Doves.

In referring previously to services from England across the Irish Sea, no mention was made of any service to Dublin. The reason for this is that Aer Lingus, the Irish air-line, has the operating rights for all

regional services between Eire and Britain. There is a financial arrangement whereby Britain shares both profits and losses.

Aer Lingus DC-3s bear large green shamrocks on their noses and operate services from Dublin to Shannon, London, and other cities in Britain, as well as to Amsterdam, Brussels and Paris.

French Air Fleets

France has always had a large network of air services and, by most standards, big fleets of passenger aircraft. Air France is the national air-line operating throughout Europe. The fleet of Air France, easily distinguished by the company's blue, winged-seahorse symbol, includes Lockheed Constellation, Douglas DC-3 and DC-4, and a large number of French-designed 33-seat, four-motor Languedoc aircraft. This company, which naturally operates many services around and across the western Mediterranean, now has a number of new French air-liners on order.

Belgium's air-lines are mainly the responsibility of Sabena, with its main base at Melsbroek Airport, close to Brussels. Sabena flies Douglas DC-3, DC-4, DC-6 air-liners and Convair-Liners on its main routes, and also has some de Havilland Doves in service in the Belgian Congo.

Switzerland has an efficient air-line in its Swissair company, which flies DC-3s, DC-4s and Convair-Liners. Setting out from among the Alps to call at many countries, including England and Scotland, the Swiss air-liners are easily identified by the large, gay red and white Swiss flag painted across the tops of their fins and rudders.

Germany is not allowed to operate any aircraft, although a number of foreign companies fly into some of the principal cities, and British European Airways is operating a number of routes in the north and west of the country.

Italy does not come under the same restrictions as Germany. The chief air-lines are Alitalia, which is partly owned by British European Airways, and Ali-Flotte Riunite, which incorporates a number of companies. A number of DC-3s is used by the Italian companies, although Italian Savoia Marchetti S.M.95 four-motor and Fiat G.12L and G.212 three-motor monoplanes are in service. The Italian companies operate local services as well as lines north into Europe and south across the Mediterranean.

In Greece, TAE and Hellenic Airlines both operate domestic services with DC-3s, while Hellenic Airlines also runs services from Athens to London, Prestwick and Egypt.

One of the best known European air-lines is K.L.M., the Royal Dutch Airline, which operates from Amsterdam a fleet of Flying Dutchman Constellations, DC-6s

WITH AMSTERDAM BELOW, *the Smiths' journey is almost ended. Schiphol, where they land, is a few miles away. In* 1 *hour and* 30 *minutes the Smiths have travelled* 230 *miles.*

Some of the Main
EUROPEAN
AIR ROUTES

(British Services shown by heavy lines)

NOT ALL AIR-LINERS *carry passengers. This Douglas Skymaster Flying Dutchman of the K.L.M. freight service awaits its cargo at Amsterdam's famous Schiphol Airport.*

and Convair-Liners, each with the red, white and blue national colours on its rudder. The Constellations have Dutch geographical names, the DC-6s are named after the Dutch Royal family, and the Convairs have names of famous Dutch painters on their noses and display reproductions of their paintings in the cabins.

Joint Operation

Scandinavian Airlines System consists of Danish, Norwegian and Swedish Air Lines working together over all their routes, following a successful experiment made by these companies over the North and South Atlantic air routes from Scandinavia. Each of the air-liners has a Viking name, and bears a blue and red Viking longship, which is painted along the full length of the fuselage.

S.A.S., the letters by which this concern is known, gives a very high standard of service, not the least interesting part of which is the excellent Scandinavian food that is regularly served in its aircraft.

The Norwegian section of S.A.S. has what is probably the most beautiful air route in the world. Operated with British-built Short Sandringham 37-seat flying-boats, this route extends north from Oslo over the mountains and fjords, to Tromsö, within the Arctic Circle. Floatplanes continue this service north to Kirkenes. Owing to darkness and bad weather in the winter, this route can be flown for only part of the year.

A seasonal route is operated by the Danish section of S.A.S. between Copenhagen and Greenland by way of Prestwick and Iceland. The airport used in Greenland is Bluie West 1, among the fjords at the south-west corner of the country.

From Helsinki, in Finland, Aero O/Y flies routes into Finland's centre and north along the Gulf of Bothnia. These routes traverse the giant forests and hundreds of lakes of this magnificent northern countryside; Aero O/Y's other routes fly west over many wooded islands to Stockholm and also south to Copenhagen and Amsterdam.

SWITZERLAND'S SWISSAIR *air-liners are all distinguished by the red and white flag on the tail. This Convair-Liner, on course for England, flies above the Alps.*

Many of the European air-lines have a long history, and it is interesting to remember that Britain, France, Denmark and Holland have had civil air-lines for 30 years, while both Sweden and Finland have a quarter of a century's experience of airline operation—much of it under extreme conditions, with bad weather, snow-covered airports and frozen seaplane bases.

Eastern European Lines

Looking to eastern Europe, the Polish, Czechoslovak, Hungarian, Rumanian, Bulgarian, and Jugoslav air-lines all operate quite extensive systems, Czechoslovak Air-lines flying its O.K. Liners to Britain, and Polish Air Lines operating to Brussels, Paris and Stockholm. These companies mostly use either the DC-3, or the Soviet-built version of this aeroplane, which is called the LI-2. The Czech and Polish air-lines are also using the modern 28–32 seat, Soviet-designed IL-12 two-motor monoplane.

In the extreme south-east of Europe, the Turkish State Airline flies a fleet of DC-3s, each bearing the red and white Turkish crescent. Going to the other extreme of Europe—Iceland—we find two companies —Flugfélag Islands and Loftleidir. These operate internal services, and also fly from Reykjavik to Prestwick, Copenhagen, London and Oslo. The Flugfélag Islands DC-4, DC-3, and other, smaller aircraft, are named after Icelandic ponies such as Gullfaxi (Golden Horse). One of the Loftleidir DC-4s is called Hekla, after that famous Icelandic volcano.

In addition to the European services operated by these continental companies, many of them operate long trunk air routes, such as K.L.M.'s services to Indonesia and Netherlands West Indies; Air France's services to Indo-China and Madagascar; and the Belgian services to the Congo. Apart from these, however, the following companies operate North and/or South Atlantic

SMÖRGÅSBORD *is one of the attractions which tempt travellers to go by Scandinavian Airlines System's Flying Vikings. Below, an S.A.S. DC-6 receives air-conditioning service.*

SEATING CAPACITY CONTRAST *is shown here by the interior of a Constellation (above) and a de Havilland Dove. The former, a four-engined American air-liner, normally carries 40–44 passengers. The Dove, a British machine powered by two relatively small engines, seats 8 or 11 according to the requirements of the air-line operator.*

PASSENGERS BOARD *the Sandringham flying-boat at Fornebu, near Oslo. This seaplane base is an intermediate stop on the route connecting Stavanger and Tromsö.*

services: Air France, Sabena, K.L.M., Iberia, Alitalia, S.A.S. and Swissair.

Air-lines of the U.S.S.R.

The Soviet air-lines are operated, both within the U.S.S.R. and internationally, by Aeroflot. Certain Arctic routes are flown by the Arctic Aviation Service.

The principal Soviet international services are from Moscow to Berlin over two routes, one via Kaliningrad (Königsberg), the other via Minsk; to Warsaw, Prague, Vienna, Budapest, Belgrade, Tirana, Bucharest, Sofia, Helsinki, Teheran and Kabul. In the east, Aeroflot also operates an international service from Vladivostok to Dairen, Peiping, Tientsin and Shanghai.

Within the U.S.S.R., Aeroflot operates a vast network of services with a great concentration in the west, radiating mainly

LILLEHAMMER *is one of the few aerodromes where you can ski on to the tarmac! Here, young skiers watch passengers boarding a Norwegian Air Lines DC-3 air-liner.*

from Moscow. Services from Moscow to the north serve points such as Leningrad, Murmansk and Archangel.

Soviet air-lines are flown chiefly by IL-12s; the larger four-motor IL-18s are used on some long-distance services and smaller Yak-16s are believed to be employed on feeder lines.

The main trunk routes fly out east from Moscow through Sverdlovsk, Omsk, Novo-Sibirsk, Krasnoyarsk, Irkutsk and Chita, to Khabarovsk and Vladivostok. Another route branches north-east from Krasnoyarsk to serve Kirensk, Olekminsk and Yakutsk.

The 4,750-mile flight between Moscow and Vladivostok makes this the longest domestic service in the world. The fare for the journey is approximately equivalent to £68.

The Near East

The Near East, and Egypt in particular, must always be an area well served by air transport, as it is a junction for services from Europe and the U.S.A. to India, the Far East and Africa. As previously told, several of B.O.A.C.'s main trunk routes serve this area, and, in addition, the air-lines of many other countries operate to and through the Near East.

Many of the Near East countries operate their own air-lines. In Egypt, Misrair flies both local services and others to neighbouring countries. Another Egyptian company, S.A.I.D.E., flying Italian-built air-liners, runs services between Egypt, Greece and Italy.

Sudan Airways has a fleet of de Havilland Doves working a network based on Khartoum.

Jordan, Saudi Arabia, Israel, the Lebanon and Syria all have their own air-lines; while from Iraq, the Viking air-liners of Iraqi Airways fly to Egypt, Turkey, Israel, Cyprus, Greece, Italy, France and Britain. The Doves flown by this company maintain services from Baghdad to Basra, Koweit, Damascus and Beirut.

In Iran the Iranian Airways Company operates DC-3s locally and to India, Iraq and Egypt; while during the summer, Dragon Rapides of the Iranian State Air-line fly between Teheran and Baghdad.

India, Pakistan and Ceylon

India's own air-lines began to operate in the early 1930s, and the two most important companies now in being had their beginnings at that period. One of these two companies, Air-India, developed out of the

66

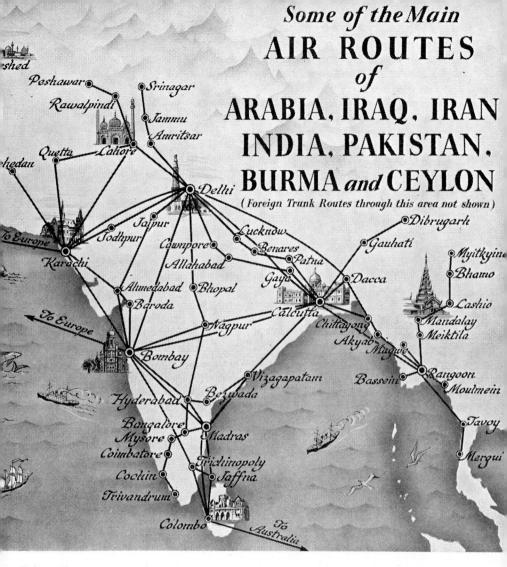

Some of the Main
AIR ROUTES
of
ARABIA, IRAQ, IRAN
INDIA, PAKISTAN,
BURMA *and* CEYLON
(Foreign Trunk Routes through this area not shown)

aviation department of Tata Sons, which began mail services in 1932. Today, Air-India operates services with Vikings and DC-3s from Bombay to Karachi in Pakistan, to Delhi, Calcutta, Hyderabad and other points in south India; and to Colombo in Ceylon.

The other big company, Indian National Airways, flies the same types of aircraft on services from Delhi to Calcutta, Lahore and Karachi, as well as a service between Calcutta and Rangoon. The Vikings of Indian National Airways are named after the great Indian rivers, such as the Ganges and the Jumna.

In June, 1948, India began its first long-distance international air route when the Air-India International (Air-India and the Government of India) Lockheed Constellation, Malabar Princess, arrived in London to inaugurate the Bombay–Cairo–Geneva–London service; this service is operated in each direction in only one day's elapsed time—one day from Bombay to London.

Indian Overseas Airlines operates its Star Line service between Bombay and Calcutta via Nagpur. The other Indian air-lines are Airways (India), Ltd., Air Services of India, Bharat Airways, Deccan Airways and Dalmia Jain Airways. Pakistan operates services with a fleet of DC-3s and 40-seat Convair-Liners. All inland mails in India to and from towns served by scheduled air-lines are carried by air without surcharge.

Ceylon's air-line, Air-Ceylon, in addition to flying local services, is collaborating with Australian National Airways. Their gaily-painted DC-4s fly between Ceylon and both England and Australia.

The Far East

The Far East countries have developed their air transport considerably since the war. In Burma, Union of Burma Airways is operating internal routes from Rangoon to such places as the famous Lashio, Myitkyina and Mandalay.

Thailand has two air-line companies, both with headquarters in that beautiful city of temples—Bangkok. These air-lines serve Hong Kong, Penang, Calcutta, Singapore and Saigon, as well as operating services to many towns within Thailand. There is also a Siamese twice-monthly trans-Pacific service from Bangkok to Los Angeles.

In Indo-China, Société Indochinoise de Transports Aériens uses British aircraft on services from Saigon to Hanoi and Tourane, as well as on other local services.

Having its headquarters at Singapore, Malayan Airways flies over jungles and rubber plantations to Penang, Bangkok and points in Malaya; across the south of the Gulf of Siam to Saigon, and over the Java Sea to Batavia.

China has been operating air-lines for twenty years. The China National Aviation Corporation's fleet of DC-3, DC-4 and Curtiss Commando transport aircraft operates a wide network of routes in China as well as flying across the Pacific to San Francisco. The Central Air Transport Corporation, which has recently added Convair-Liners to its fleet, operates from Hong Kong to Kumming and Chungking.

An associate of B.O.A.C., Hong Kong Airways flies from the Kai Tak airport, at the foot of the mountains at Hong Kong, to Canton and Shanghai. The noses of the company's DC-3s bear a red dragon crest, while the name of the company appears

AIR HOSTESSES of a Chinese DC-4 sit at their stations with seat belts fastened as their air-liner lands. China has been operating air-lines for 20 years.

CHINESE NEWSPAPER BOYS *set forth for the city of Canton with newspapers delivered by air. The Hong Kong Airways' DC-3 which brought the papers bears a red dragon crest.*

above the windows along the fuselage, in English on one side and in Chinese on the other.

There is also a Soviet-Chinese company called Hamiata, which flies LI-2s on a weekly service from Alma Ata in the U.S.S.R. to Hami.

A number of air-lines exists in the Philippines, among which is the Philippine Air Lines. This company, in addition to working local services, has two main trunk routes, one across the Pacific to San Francisco and another to Europe with calls at Madrid, London and Amsterdam. Douglas DC-4 and DC-6 air-liners operate the trunk routes.

African Routes

The air routes of Africa can be divided into two main groups: those of the continent which, for the most part, operate in regions; and the main trunk routes through Africa from Europe and America.

Mention has already been made of the B.O.A.C. services down the easterly route, which has been, for two decades, the normal British-operated route.

B.O.A.C. also operates a route between London and West Africa, terminating at Accra on the Gold Coast and routed via Tripoli, Kano and Lagos.

Before World War II, France and Belgium developed routes through Africa over a westerly course; it is this westerly route which now appears likely to become the main through-Africa route.

Since the war, Swissair has introduced a service of DC-4s from Geneva, through Tunis, Kano and Leopoldville to Johannesburg; Sabena has reopened its route, flying from Brussels to Johannesburg via Tripoli, Kano and Leopoldville with DC-6 aircraft. Sabena uses DC-4s on other services to Leopoldville and Elizabethville in the Belgian Congo. K.L.M. flies DC-6s from Amsterdam to Johannesburg over

SPLENDIDLY ROBED AFRICANS *look on at Kumasi Airport, on the Gold Coast. De Havilland Doves operating the W.A.A.C. service link together the whole Guinea coast.*

this route, with calls at Tunis, Kano and Leopoldville. Air France flies to West Africa and the Middle Congo. This company also operates a service from Paris to Tripoli, Khartoum, Nairobi, Dar es Salaam, Madagascar, Reunion and Mauritius.

Pan American World Airways' Constellation Clippers also serve Africa, flying from New York to Santa Maria in the Azores, Dakar in Senegal, Accra, Leopoldville and Johannesburg.

Operating in association with B.O.A.C., South African Airways flies the eastern route with DC-4s from Johannesburg to London, calling at Nairobi, Khartoum and Tripoli. These DC-4s, with South African Airways' blue springbok symbol on their noses and the blue, white and orange flag of the Union on their tails, also operate a trans-Africa service between Johannesburg and Cairo; this route has the same calls at Nairobi and Khartoum.

Yet another through-Africa service is provided by Central African Airways with Vikings, over a route, flown monthly, with frequent stops from Salisbury, in Southern Rhodesia, to London.

African Airways Corporations

Much of the internal air traffic of British Africa is carried by three corporations : these are the West African Airways Corporation, a public corporation owned by the Governments of Nigeria, the Gold Coast, Sierra Leone and Gambia ; the East African Airways Corporation, owned and operated by the Governments of Kenya, Uganda, Tanganyika and Zanzibar; and the Central African Airways Corporation, formed by the Southern Rhodesian Government in co-operation with the administrations of Northern Rhodesia and Nyasaland.

Bearing the names of personalities in the modern history of British colonial government, and with a winged green elephant painted on their noses, the fleet of de Havilland Doves operated by West African Airways flies a network of routes within

70

Some of the main
AIR ROUTES
in and through
AFRICA

to Europe

to Europe

to Europe

to Damascus

Europe

to Basra

Casablanca

Algiers

Tunis

Tripoli

Alexandria

Cairo

Villa Cisneros

Luxor

Jedda

Dakar

Sokoto

Katsina

Wadi Halfa

Port Sudan

Asmara

Aden
to India

Bathurst

Bamako

Kaduna

Kano

Khartoum

Freetown

Tamale

Ilorin

Maiduguri

Yola

Malakal

Jibuti

Robertsfield

Kumasi

Benin City

Jos

Addis Ababa

Monrovia

Accra

Lagos

Enugu

Bangui

Gore

Takoradi

Douala

Libenge

Lisala

Juba

Kampala

Mogadishu

Libreville

Coquilhatville

Stanleyville

Irumu

Nairobi

Brazzaville

Inongo

Kindu

Usumbura

Mombasa

Pointe Noire

Leopoldville

Tanga

Matadi

Zanzibar

Kabalo

Tabora

Dar es Salaam

Loanda

Kabulbourg

Manono

Lindi

Lobito

Elizabethville

Ndola

Mozambique

Benguella

Victoria Falls

Salisbury

Mosamedes

Bulawayo

Beira

Quelimane

Windhoek

Tamatave

Johannesburg

Lourenço
Marques

Keetmanshoop

Kimberley

Durban

Victoria West

Bloemfontein

Beaufort West

East London

Cape Town

George

Port Elizabeth

to Mauritius

to Reunion

N

W

E

S

ways, which began work in 1929.

Central African Airways' routes radiate mainly from Salisbury, in Southern Rhodesia. Apart from serving the Rhodesias, they extend to points in the Belgian Congo, Kenya, Tanganyika, Bechuanaland, Portuguese East Africa and the Union of South Africa. Bristol Freighter aircraft and Vikings and Doves are used.

In South Africa, the network of air routes is operated by South African Airways—a department of the South African Railways and Harbours Administration. Flying DC-3, DC-4, Viking, Lodestar and Dove air-liners, South African Airways flies routes linking Johannesburg, Durban, East London, Port Elizabeth, Kimberley, Bloemfontein, Cape Town and points in South West Africa including the terminal at Windhoek. The trunk routes of this air-line have already been mentioned.

Many other companies are operating scheduled air services in Africa, including Deta in Portuguese East Africa, Ethiopian Airlines and DTA in Angola; a number of French companies also operate in North Africa.

Nigeria, and also links Nigeria, the Gold Coast, the Ivory Coast, Liberia, Sierra Leone, Gambia and Senegal. The corporation's longest route is 2,230 miles from Dakar, in Senegal, to Tiko on the east Nigerian border. Flying in and out of some quite small aerodromes in extremes of weather, this air-line is playing an important part in colonial development.

One most important service introduced by West African Airways is the carriage of all mail, to and from all places served by the corporation in Nigeria and the Gold Coast, for a flat rate of one penny. The aim is same-day delivery for the whole of Nigeria.

East African Airways links points in Uganda, Kenya, Tanganyika and the Belgian Congo. This corporation can claim twenty years' operating experience going back to its predecessor, Wilson Air-

Australia and New Zealand

Australian air transport began in 1920, when Queensland and Northern Territory Aerial Services Ltd. (commonly known by the initials Q.A.N.T.A.S.) was registered.

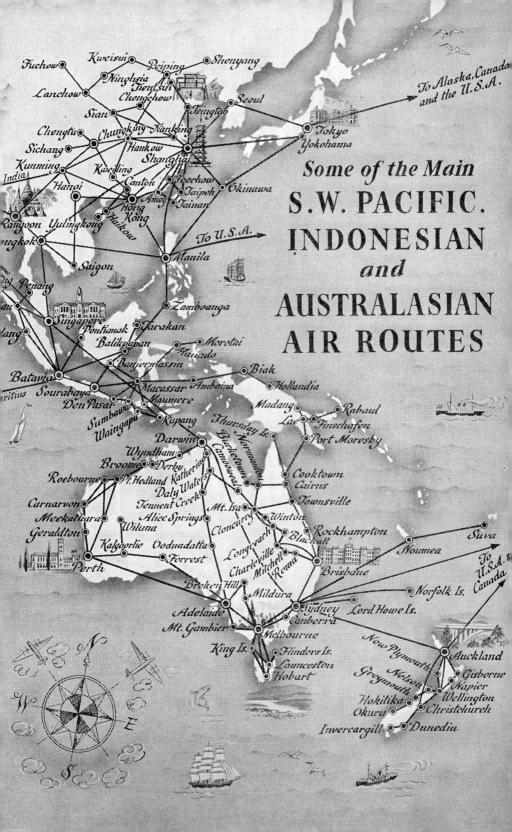

Some of the Main
S.W. PACIFIC
INDONESIAN
and
AUSTRALASIAN
AIR ROUTES

Gradually opening up the remote townships of Queensland and the Northern Territory, this company grew into the large Qantas Empire Airways organization which now operates a fleet of Constellations, in parallel with and in collaboration with B.O.A.C., over the Sydney–London route —a distance of 12,000 miles covered in only 47¾ hours of flying. Qantas Empire Airways also operates a service from Sydney, through Brisbane and along the coast, to Port Moresby and Lae in New Guinea and to Rabaul in New Britain; this area will be remembered for the wonderful supply work undertaken by Q.E.A. during the fighting in these islands. Q.E.A. also flies flying-boats from Sydney to Lord Howe Island, Noumea and Fiji. Another service links Sydney with Norfolk Island.

For many years Q.A.N.T.A.S., and later Q.E.A., operated services within Queensland to such points as Cloncurry, Charleville, Longreach and many other small places. During 1949, however, these routes were taken away from Q.E.A. and given to the government-created Trans-Australia Airlines; this organization operates a fleet comprised of DC-4s and DC-3s as well as Convair-Liners.

Australian Routes

TAA also flies many routes in and from New South Wales; among the most interesting are the trunk routes from Melbourne through Adelaide to Perth—1,821 miles flown in ten hours—and the route which runs northerly across the centre of Australia from Adelaide to Darwin via Alice Springs.

A third large Australian operator is Australian National Airways, a company which, like Qantas, has a long history of air-line operation. ANA, with a fleet of DC-3 and DC-4 aircraft, runs services from Sydney to Adelaide direct, from Sydney to Adelaide via Canberra and Mildura, from Sydney to Melbourne, from Perth to Adelaide and Melbourne, between Melbourne and Cairns via Sydney and Brisbane, from Cairns to Thursday Island and between Melbourne and Hobart and Launceston in Tasmania. Australian National Airways is also working, in collaboration with Air-Ceylon, on services from Australia to

AT VARIOUS STAGES *on the flight across the Atlantic, the chief steward of this* B.O.A.C. *Constellation "briefs" the passengers. The briefing consists of information on the aeroplane's position and approximate time of arrival.*

PASSENGERS' LUGGAGE *is hauled ashore at Mechanics' Bay, Auckland. The flying-boat, just arrived from Fiji, is a Sunderland of the New Zealand National Airways Corporation. It bears the Maori name "Mataatua." The Short flying-boats, with a fine World War II record behind them, are still giving excellent service in Australia and New Zealand on routes such as that between Sydney and Auckland—a distance of 1,342 miles.*

AT ESSENDEN, *passengers and sightseers watch as an Australian National Airways'*
Douglas DC-4 is loaded. ANA services include a flight from Australia to Ceylon.

Ceylon and from Ceylon to London, a distance of 5,430 miles.

Linking Australia and New Zealand are the British-built Short flying-boats of Tasman Empire Airways, which fly the 1,342 miles between Sydney and Auckland. For a number of years these flying-boats have provided the only means of passenger transport between Australia and New Zealand, and they have built up a fine reputation for comfort and reliability.

All air services in New Zealand are the responsibility of the New Zealand National Airways Corporation, which has a mixed fleet including DC-3s, Lodestars, Dragon Rapides and Sunderland flying-boats.

New Zealand Air-lines

Flying over magnificent scenery, with mountain peaks, glaciers and sea coasts, the National Airways Corporation links the main towns of both North and South Island; while DC-3s fly from Auckland to such places as Norfolk Island, Fiji, Samoa, and Rarotonga Island. Sunderlands fly

daily between Auckland and Fiji. All New Zealand's air-liners bear such fascinating Maori names of birds as: Kotuku, meaning white heron; Kotari, kingfisher; Tawaka, grey duck; and Puweto, spotted crane.

Linking Australia and New Zealand with the United States and Canada is the joint Australian–New Zealand–British airline, B.C.P.A. (British Commonwealth Pacific Airlines). This line has contributed a great achievement to British Commonwealth air transport by operating a route across the Pacific from Sydney and Auckland to San Francisco and Vancouver, via Fiji, Canton Island and Honolulu.

The route involves long over-water stages, with refuelling stops on very small islands. The sector mileages are: Auckland–Fiji, 1,317; Fiji–Canton Island, 1,272; Canton Island–Honolulu, 1,911; and Honolulu–San Francisco, 2,428. The total mileage from Sydney to Vancouver is 8,383. This route is operated with sleeper DC-6s. Pan American World Airways also flies this route. A third operator between

IDLEWILD IS TO REPLACE *La Guardia* (*which will handle domestic traffic*) *as New York's international airport. This view shows the temporary terminal buildings and parking area.*

North America and Australasia came into the picture in 1949, when Canadian Pacific Air Lines introduced its Canadair Four Empress-class air-liners on this route.

Air-lines in the Americas

To describe the extent of United States air transport, to list all of its maze of air routes—or even all its air-transport operators—is an impossibility in the space available. It is, therefore, probably best to mention the main companies together with their spheres of operation. These companies are described here in alphabetical order and not in order of importance.

American Airlines System includes American Airlines, operating a large network of services within the U.S.A. (known as domestic services) and American Overseas Airlines, which operates from the U.S.A. to Europe. American Airlines flies its fleet of 75 Convair-Liners and 50 DC-6s—

all known as Flagships—on many routes in the eastern States and also on transcontinental routes linking the eastern seaboard with the Middle West and California. Other services extend south to Mexico City. The A.O.A. routes from the U.S.A. across the North Atlantic serve Ireland, England, Holland, Germany, Norway, Sweden, Denmark and Finland. The A.O.A. services are worked by Boeing Stratocruisers and Constellations.

Braniff International Airways links Chicago, Kansas City, Denver, Amarillo, Memphis, Tulsa, Dallas, Houston, San Antonio and Brownsville. Additionally, Braniff flies international routes from Chicago to Havana; Panama City; Guayaquil in Ecuador; and Lima in Peru.

Capital Airlines use DC-3 and DC-4 Capitaliners on routes in the eastern States. Some of the towns served are Washington, New York, Norfolk, Atlanta, New Orleans, Memphis, Knoxville, Pitts-

IN OPERATION *on the routes of the New Zealand National Airways Corporation, the medium-range Lockheed Lodestar air-liner is here seen at Palmerston North Airport.*

burgh, Cleveland, Detroit, Chicago and the twin cities of Minneapolis and St. Paul. A popular innovation of Capital Airlines is its Nighthawk Aircoach between New York, Pittsburgh and Chicago, bringing fares on this service down practically to railway level.

Chicago and Southern Air Lines link Chicago, Detroit and Kansas City with the southern States and Havana, Kingston, Curaçao and Caracas. The named Chicago and Southern services include the *Lone Star*, linking Chicago, St. Louis, Memphis and Houston; the *Havana Limited*, flying daily from Chicago to Havana; the *Chicago Limited*, flying Havana, New Orleans, Memphis, Chicago; the *Daylight*, which is a daily service over the Houston–Memphis–St. Louis–Chicago route. Other named services are the *North Star*, the *Caribbean Comet*, the *Traveller*, the *Commuter* and the *Executive*.

First U.S. Foreign Air-mail

Colonial Airlines has been flying between New York and Montreal for over twenty years, having obtained the foreign air-mail contract for the first U.S. air-mail between the U.S.A. and Canada. Currently, Colonial links New York and Washington with Montreal and Ottawa. DC-4 Skycruisers of this company fly to Bermuda.

Continental Air Lines routes are confined to Colorado, Kansas, Missouri, Oklahoma, New Mexico and Texas.

Delta Air Lines' DC-3, DC-4 and DC-6 air-liners operate mainly in the southern States; but their routes extend west to Fort Worth, south to Miami and north to Chicago. This is another U.S. company with over twenty years' experience.

Eastern Air Lines flies its "Great Silver Fleet" of Constellations, DC-4s and DC-3s on over 10,000 route miles, extending over the western, southern and midwestern States. E.A.L. operates a number of fast non-stop services, including the 1,200-mile Chicago–Miami Constellation route flown in four hours.

Mid-Continent Airlines of Kansas City flies a fleet of DC-3s over mid-continent routes as far as Minot in North Dakota, and south to Houston in Texas and New Orleans in Louisiana.

The Routes of the Buccaneers are operated by DC-4 and DC-6 aircraft of National Airlines, whose territory follows the coast from Miami to New York and also crosses the Gulf of Mexico to New Orleans. Other

Some of the Main
NORTH AMERICAN
AIR ROUTES

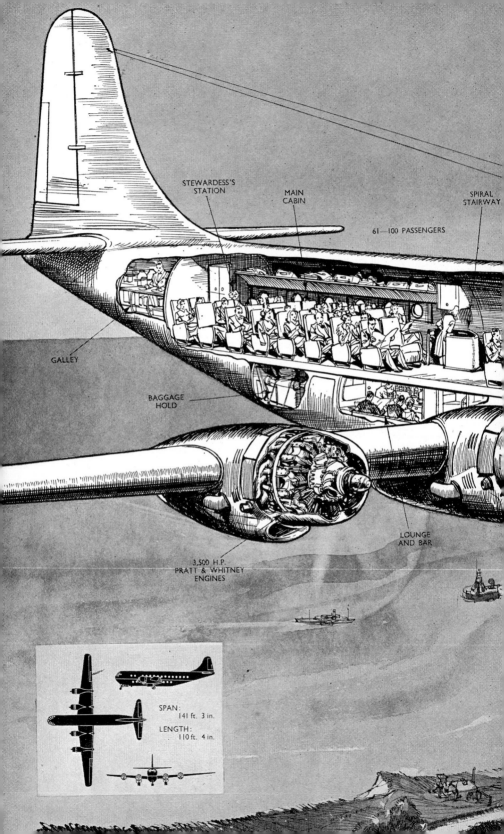

STEWARDESS'S STATION

MAIN CABIN

SPIRAL STAIRWAY

61—100 PASSENGERS

GALLEY

BAGGAGE HOLD

LOUNGE AND BAR

3,500 H.P. PRATT & WHITNEY ENGINES

SPAN: 141 ft. 3 in.

LENGTH: 110 ft. 4 in.

BOEING STRATOCRUISER

THS

LADIES'
DRESSING ROOM

MEN'S DRESSING ROOM
(PORT SIDE)

CREW OF FIVE

CONTROL
CABIN

CARGO
HOLD

FLIGHT ENGINEER'S
CONTROL PANEL

services link Tampa and Miami with Havana.

Northeast Airlines operates mainly in the New England area. Northwest Airlines operates a transcontinental system from New York and Washington through Minneapolis-St. Paul to Seattle-Tacoma and Portland. This company also operates a main trunk line from Minneapolis-St. Paul across Canada via Edmonton to Anchorage in Alaska and across the Pacific to Tokyo, Shanghai, Okinawa and Manila. Another Northwest route is from Seattle-Tacoma and Portland to Honolulu. Northwest flies a fleet of gaily painted red-and-blue Martin 2-0-2s on its short-haul routes and Boeing Stratocruisers on its trunk routes.

Pan American World Airways, already referred to, is not allowed to operate domestic routes, but extends a world-wide network of Flying Clipper services from the U.S.A., east across the Atlantic, to Europe, Africa, India and the Far East; and from the U.S.A. across the Pacific to the Orient and to Australasia.

Pan American Airways also has a round the-world flight. This flight is routed eastbound: New York–Boston–Gander–Shannon–London–Brussels–Istanbul–Damascus–Karachi–Delhi–Calcutta–Bangkok–Hong Kong–Shanghai–Manila–Tokyo–Guam–Wake–Midway–Honolulu–Los Angeles–San Francisco. The westbound flight leaves from the west coast and follows the same route in the reverse order, terminating at New York.

T.W.A. (Trans World Airline), the company originally responsible for the production of the Constellation, has a U.S. transcontinental network, and also runs services from the U.S.A. across the North Atlantic to Ireland, France, Switzerland, Italy, Portugal, Spain, North Africa, Greece, Egypt, Iraq, Arabia and India.

United Air Lines flies its Mainliner fleet right across the States, up the western seaboard and between San Francisco and Honolulu. UAL has interests in LAMSA, a company operating services in Mexico.

Western Air Lines, using mainly Convair '49ers, operates services up the west coast

LOWER-DECK LOUNGE, *equipped with a steward's station and snack bar, is an unusual feature of the Boeing Stratocruiser. A circular stairway leads to the upper deck.*

DOUBLE-BUBBLE FUSELAGE *of the Stratocruiser contains two decks and seats up to 80 passengers. A speed of 340 m.p.h. makes it one of the fastest piston-engined air-liners.*

from San Diego to Seattle-Tacoma, and an inland route from Los Angeles, through Salt Lake City, to Edmonton in Canada.

Additionally, there are many domestic feeder lines, including such lines as Southwest Airways, which operates what almost amounts to bus services over short distances in California at very low fares with the minimum of service and luxury.

Canada and Alaska

In Canada quite a number of air-lines are operating; but the two main operators are the Canadian National Railways' offshoot, Trans-Canada Air Lines, and the Canadian Pacific Railways' Canadian Pacific Air Lines.

Trans-Canada Air Lines has main trunk routes extending from Montreal across the country to Vancouver, eastward from Montreal across the North Atlantic to Prestwick and London, and southward from Montreal and Ottawa to Bermuda. Another line runs from Ottawa to Jamaica and Port of Spain.

The air-liners used by TCA are Canadair Four North Star Skyliners on main routes, and DC-3s on subsidiary routes. Each has a large maple leaf painted on its nose.

Canadian Pacific Air Lines has a network in the west running from the Vancouver and Edmonton areas north to Whitehorse, Fairbanks, Aklavik and Coppermine. Some further services are operated from the Winnipeg area and others go north and east from Montreal and Quebec. Apart from these services in Canada, C.P.A. flies Canadair Fours across the Pacific to the Orient and Australasia.

A number of air-line operators work

FROM A BALCONY *at Prestwick Airport, an eastern terminal for transatlantic flights, visitors watch a Trans-Canada Air Lines Canadair Four Skyliner arriving from Montreal.*

SOUTH AMERICAN FLAVOUR *is given to the airport at Montevideo by this arch, through which is seen a DC-4 air-liner of the Scandinavian Airlines System.*

regular services in Alaska over and amid some magnificent scenery. Two of the most important of these companies are Alaska Airlines and Alaska Coastal Airlines.

Mexico, Central and South America

Mexico has a number of air transport companies, including Compania Mexicana de Aviacion and LAMSA, already mentioned. Another Mexican company is Aerovias Guest, which is operating a service from Mexico City across the North Atlantic to Lisbon and Madrid, via Miami, Bermuda and the Azores.

The air-line companies and their services in Central and South America are far too numerous to describe in detail. The Argentine and Brazil each have a great many routes and many companies operating. All the other South and Central American countries have extensive networks.

In the Argentine, Flota Aerea Mercante Argentina (FAMA), Aeroposta, ZONDA and ALFA are of the greatest importance. FAMA, in addition to operating local services, has trunk routes to London and New York. ALFA is yet another operator of British flying-boats, having a number of Short Sandringhams flying from Buenos Aires to Montevideo and other points in the River Plate area.

In Uruguay, CAUSA also operates some Short flying-boats; these are Sunderlands converted for passenger carrying.

Brazil has a large number of air-line operators, including Panair do Brasil— which, in addition to flying many DC-3 and Catalina services in South America, also flies Constellations between Rio de Janeiro and London.

Many of the South and Central American routes are operated with DC-3s, but new equipment is being introduced. In Venezuela and Chile the Martin 2-0-2 has gone into service; in the Argentine, Convair-Liners have been bought; and in Venezuela, LAV is flying some Constellations. In the British West Indies, British West Indian Airways has a fleet of Vikings.

No survey, however brief, of Latin American air transport would be anywhere near complete without mention of Pan American-Grace Airways (PANAGRA), which is a combination of Pan American Airways and the Grace shipping line. Panagra operates many services within this area, including the named El Interamericano, which flies between Miami and Buenos Aires over the west-coast route along by the Andes. Calls are made at Balboa, Lima and Santiago.

This survey of the world's air-lines of necessity leaves many blanks, but although numerous air-line companies and routes have been omitted, a general picture of the immense amount of air transport throughout the world has been attempted.

Air-liners in Use

Air routes over most parts of the world are operated by more or less similar types of aircraft which vary in size and performance according to the sectors operated,

PANAIR DO BRASIL *offers its passengers a view of the Guanabara Bay, Rio de Janeiro, from the vantage point of a DC-3 air-liner. The famous Sugar Loaf is well in evidence.*

Some of the Main
SOUTH AMERICAN
AIR ROUTES

TROPICAL PALMS *fringe the airport buildings at San Diego. Western Air Lines Convair-Liners such as this have an integral, hydraulically operated stairway under the tail.*

traffic requirements, airports available, stage lengths and other factors.

At any one time, three main classes of aircraft are in use: first, standard types in production or in general service; second, older aircraft which have served for some time and are gradually being replaced by the standard types of the period; and third, new types which have passed all their trials and have been commissioned by certain lines, but which have not yet been adopted on a large scale.

Throughout the world, the U.S.-designed Douglas DC-3 21–28-seat two-motor monoplane is in wide use. It has served for over ten years and is gradually being replaced by newer types.

The most important replacements include the post-war British 21–27-seat Vickers-Armstrongs Viking; the four-motor Douglas DC-4 of greater seating capacity; and the two U.S. two-motor 35–40-seat aircraft—the Convair-Liner and the Martin 2-0-2. In Scandinavia, the Swedish SAAB Scandia is replacing the DC-3; while in the U.S.S.R., the IL-12 has taken the place of the DC-3.

The most-used four-motor, long- and medium-range transports have been the DC-4 and the Lockheed Constellation. The DC-4 is giving way to the larger and faster DC-6; and the Constellation, which is likely to be used for a considerable time, is now being joined by the new Boeing Stratocruiser, which weighs 62 tons and normally carries up to 75 passengers on regular trans-ocean flights.

Jet-propelled Air-liners

In Britain, as in other countries, much attention has been given to jet-propelled transport aeroplanes. Already Britain has produced the first turbo-propeller-driven transport aircraft, the Vickers-Armstrongs Viscount; while a second type, the Armstrong Whitworth Apollo, is being developed.

The larger 100-passenger-class transports are also being developed in Britain in the form of the Saunders-Roe Princess flying-boat and the Bristol Brabazon landplane, the former having ten gas turbines and the latter eight.

Pure jet types are also far advanced; again Britain is ahead in this field with the de Havilland Comet, driven by Ghost gas-turbines, designed for service on some of the principal British trunk air routes.

FINAL ASSEMBLY LINE at *Vickers-Armstrongs, makers of the Viking. When fitting and checking are completed, the aircraft is swung for compass adjustment and weighed.*

ARMIES OF DRAUGHTSMEN *are needed to make detailed working drawings of the airframe and thousands of components of a new air-liner before the work of building it can begin. Shown here are the drawing offices of the Lockheed Aircraft Corporation.*

CHAPTER 3

AIRCRAFT IN THE
MAKING

IRCRAFT designing is both an art
and a science. No really successful
aeroplane has ever been designed by
careful calculation and painstaking research
alone; the chief designer must also be an
artist with a flair for his work to ensure
that touch of individuality which charac-
terizes the really outstanding aeroplane.

He must also possess considerable
courage. His will be the responsibility,
quite early in the development of a new
aerop'ane, of making firm decisions on
which the success of the design will depend.
To scrap months of work on a modern air-
liner because, for instance, an apparently
better solution to design problems suddenly
presents itself, would be prohibitively
expensive; the aircraft manufacturer who
plans to build a large, long-range, fifty-
passenger air-liner must be prepared to
face an outlay of probably four-million
pounds before the first aircraft is completed.

The design of a modern air-liner is a
problem, or rather a series of problems, in
reconciling conflicting requirements. Consider, for instance, the question of speed:
in all forms of transport, most developments have aimed primarily at increased
speed. Increased speed, however, entails
greater engine-power and higher fuel consumption, unless improved design can
offset these disadvantages. Fortunately,

speed in an aircraft is not necessarily ex-
travagant. The operating cost depends
principally on the number of hours that the
aircraft flies. The passenger fares or the
charges for the carriage of freight, on the
other hand, are based on mileage. Consequently, if a greater mileage can be covered
in a shorter time, the increased speed will
return a useful dividend, enable more trips
to be flown during a given period, and, in
addition, tend to stimulate business.

Economical Cruising Speed

The designer, therefore, has the question
of cruising speed always in mind. One
method of cruising economically at high
speeds, for instance, is to fly at great
heights; as the aircraft climbs higher, so
the air becomes less dense and offers less
resistance. At a height of 40,000 ft., for
example, the density of the air is approximately one-fifth of that at sea-level. An engine power sufficient to drive the aeroplane
at, say, 200 m.p.h. at sea-level, will enable a
cruising speed of 400 m.p.h. to be comfortably maintained at a height of 40,000 ft.

Another advantage of high flying is that
above a height of about 35,000 ft. in temperate latitudes the stratosphere begins;
here, the atmosphere is virtually free from
clouds, ice and the disturbing bumps that
are evident at more moderate altitudes,
although wind gusts are sometimes en-

89

countered. The smooth flying conditions are among the most important benefits, as disturbed air can cause acute discomfort to the passengers at high cruising speeds; really high speeds would, in fact, be intolerable on most days of the year at a height between five- and ten-thousand feet. The young, fit pilot of a fighter aircraft, securely strapped to his seat, can withstand vertical acceleration which would prove disastrous to a middle-aged passenger, placidly relaxed in a comfortable arm-chair in an air-liner !

The designer, then, decides that his new aeroplane shall cruise at a height of between twenty- and forty-thousand feet. Immediately, he is faced with a fresh set of problems, among which the question of passenger comfort again asserts itself.

At the proposed cruising height, the rarefied air will contain insufficient oxygen; in fact, the average passenger would probably lose consciousness at the maximum height. The aeroplane must therefore be pressurized; that is, air must be forced into the fuselage by engine-driven blowers to maintain a reasonable pressure inside the aeroplane, whatever the atmospheric pressure outside may be.

Maintenance of Pressure

It has been found that, provided that the pressure falls slowly, passengers experience no discomfort up to a height of 8,000 ft., with an atmospheric pressure of 11 lb. per sq. in., as compared with the average pressure of 14·7 lb. per sq. in. at sea-level. Two blowers are therefore provided, each of which is capable of maintaining this minimum pressure at, say, 25,000 ft.,

SENIOR DESIGNERS *study a model of a proposed new aeroplane at a design conference. At this stage the eventual appearance of the aeroplane is still unknown. Many such models may be made before the designers have met the customer's requirements.*

METICULOUS ACCURACY *is demanded in making a modern aeroplane. Here is a standards room, where gauges are tested at frequent intervals to ensure accurate production.*

where the outside pressure is only 5½ lb. per sq. in.; or, in the case of the high-flying aeroplane just discussed, at 40,000 ft., where the outside pressure is only 2·7 lb. per sq. in.

This naturally increases the designer's difficulties, as the fuselage must be made pressure-tight; or, at least, the rate of leakage of air from joints, rivets, around the edges of doors or cargo hatches and so on, must be kept within reasonable bounds. With a pressure of up to 8 lb. per sq. in. acting all over the inside of the aeroplane, special tests are also necessary to check the mechanical strength of all components such as the skin plating, windows, doors and their sealing strips.

A complete fuselage may be set up behind a blast wall for these tests, or, if the size of the aeroplane renders the cost of this prohibitive, a representative section of the fuselage may be used; this was done in the case of the large Saunders-Roe Princess (S.R.45) flying-boat. A full-size section of the hull was enclosed between concrete end walls, each weighing 50 tons, and was subjected to a pressure of 12 lb. per sq. in. in order to provide an adequate safety margin in operation.

Air-conditioning

Pressurization alone, however, is not the complete answer to the problem of passenger comfort. In the intense cold at high altitudes some form of heating is required, while the air in the cabins must, of course, be circulated to keep it fresh. It has been found that each passenger requires 1½ lb. of air per minute. The air is changed by allowing the required amount to escape through an automatically controlled valve, each of the cabin blowers having sufficient capacity to maintain the cabin pressure in spite of this loss, so that if one blower should fail, air pressure and circulation will be maintained.

After leaving the blowers, the air passes through silencers to eliminate the noise of the blower, and then to an automatically controlled heater which warms it to the correct temperature. The air may be passed around the outside of a combustion ingenious turbine refrigeration unit, although the latter cannot, at present, be used while taxi.ing.

Finally, the humidity of the air must also be controlled within fairly close limits if the passengers are not to experience unpleasant dampness when flying at low altitudes in the tropics, or dryness of the throat and itching skin when flying high in dry, cold air. The air may be dried by

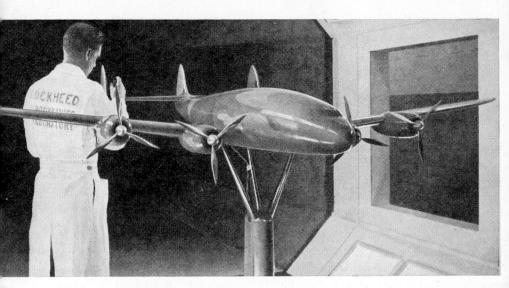

IN THE WIND TUNNEL, *a carefully finished scale model is subjected to wind speeds equivalent to* 300 *m.p.h. The model simulates the flight reactions of the full-scale aeroplane.*

chamber in which a petrol-air mixture is burnt; or, alternatively, the temperature of the air may be raised by partially restricting the outlets from the blowers, thus forcing them to work harder; the temperature of the air is then raised, in much the same manner as the air in the base of a bicycle pump becomes hot.

When the aircraft is flying at low altitudes or is waiting or taxi-ing on the ground in the tropics, however, air cooling is needed. Modern air-conditioning systems incorporate either a cooling unit charged with frozen carbon dioxide—the "dry ice" used in ice-cream tricycles—or include an passing it over a special moisture-absorbing compound, or the excess water may be condensed out of the air in the turbine refrigeration plant.

To increase the humidity, the air may be moistened by passing it over wicks dipping into water troughs, or, more simply, water may be injected into the cabin blowers, to be immediately broken up into a mist by the rotating vanes.

So far we have only touched on some of the more general problems confronting the designer. When he begins to rough out on his drawing board a preliminary design for a particular aeroplane, he will need to

SPOT-WELDING *part of an engine cowling. The upper electrode is forced down on to the lower, sandwiching the two layers of metal and fusing them at various points.*

TO ENSURE STANDARDIZATION *of all parts and components, wooden patterns are constructed to fine limits of accuracy. All similar parts are then made to the pattern.*

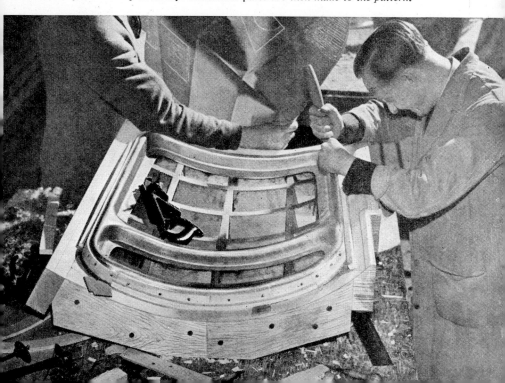

know as a starting point the approximate size of the proposed craft. Here he will have some guidance, as, nowadays, few manufacturers can afford to risk the production of large aircraft without at least a basic order. This implies that a specification has been drawn up by the prospective user, and has been considered and discussed in detail by the aircraft manufacturer, who may suggest certain alterations.

Operator's Specification

Normally, when a new aeroplane is required for air-line service, the operator issues a specification to a number of selected firms which outlines, in fairly broad terms, the speed, range, passenger- or freight-carrying capacity of the proposed aircraft and any specialized requirements, such as the ability to operate safely and regularly from small landing grounds.

The term payload features prominently in the specification. By this is meant the useful load, in terms of passengers and luggage or mail and freight, which the aeroplane can carry. This may vary between one-quarter and one-fifth of the total weight of the aeroplane. Thus the 40-passenger Hermes, with a normal gross weight of 82,000 lb., has a payload of 15,800 lb. with a range of nearly 4,000 miles. The payload is affected both by the design of the aeroplane and the conditions under which it operates.

On long flights, for instance, the amount of fuel carried will considerably reduce the payload. It is not always appreciated that an air-liner carries more fuel in reserve than the quantity actually required to complete the flight, the reserve varying according to the route and the operational conditions. Of the total fuel load carried on some

ASSEMBLING THE WING. *This picture shows an inner-wing, box-beam assembly before the skin has been attached; the trailing edge is at the top. Fuel is carried in built-in tanks, which are mounted in the box-like sections in the lower half of the picture.*

flights, for example, about 65 per cent may represent the reserve of fuel to allow the aeroplane to circle the airfield at its destination or to fly to an alternative airfield if conditions at the destination are unsuitable for landing. On a flight lasting about two hours, an allowance of one and a half hours may be made for circling at the destination, and a further one and a quarter hours for a flight to an alternative landing ground.

The project office of the firm may spend many thousands of hours on preliminary drawings before a likely-looking design is agreed on. This is submitted with an estimate of the probable cost. If the tender is accepted, work now begins in real earnest in the drawing office and calculating departments of the firm, while, simultaneously, the experimental department is preparing and testing models of the aeroplane and of individual components, as described later in this chapter; and numerous technical committee meetings are held at which the operator's technical experts are present.

From what has been written so far, it will be evident that in the modern air-liner we have a very complex structure which may weigh one-hundred tons or more, and which will be subjected to a large number of different stresses and strains. Each individual part, and the aeroplane as a whole, must be strong enough to resist these stresses: yet weight must be saved wherever possible to afford the maximum payload, in terms of passengers and freight.

Safety with Economy

To meet the conflicting claims of safety and economy in flight, the designer has to consider two types of forces which will be acting on the aeroplane: the aerodynamic forces caused by the airflow over the wings, fuselage and control surfaces; and the stresses in the various components caused by these aerodynamic loads, as well as by mechanical shocks caused during take-off and landing.

Many of the air forces acting on a wing

HIGH-ALTITUDE CHAMBER *at a de Havilland factory tests the aeroplane under the conditions of low air-pressure and intense cold which are encountered at great heights. The aeroplane and its ancillaries can be subjected to a wide range of conditions.*

or other component in flight can be accurately predicted by calculation from basic data which is already available. In some cases, however, it may be necessary to test various aerofoil sections, in addition to the usual test of a model of the complete aircraft, in a wind tunnel, in order to check these assumptions and to obtain additional information. A simple wind tunnel consists of a tubular structure, circular or oblong in cross-section, through which air is drawn at high speed by a fan resembling an aeroplane propeller, driven by an electric motor. At one point there is a gap in the tunnel, across which the air flows at high speed into the second half of the tunnel which leads to the fan. In this gap, a model of the aeroplane, a section of a wing, or any other component is suspended in the high-speed airstream so that its behaviour can be

properly observed throughout the tests.

Some idea of the large scale of an up-to-date tunnel, such as the new Vickers design, may be gauged from the fact that ten tons of air in the circuit must be speeded up to 350 ft. per sec. at the top speed; each time the fan starts up it takes in some 10,000 cu. ft. of air, and seven minutes elapse after cutting off the power before the speed is reduced to zero. Electric motors developing 1,750 h.p. are used to drive the fan, which is 24 ft. in diameter.

Powered Test Models

Because of the large loads imposed on them, models need to be of a much more exacting nature than those used in previous wind tunnels, and are almost invariably powered internally to drive propellers or jet units. They may be of any weight up to half a ton and incorporate motors developing up to 60 h.p. It will be realized that the problem of building such models to take the required two-ton load and at the same time incorporating the motors with their gear drives and control mechanisms, is no mean engineering feat, particularly when one considers that the standard of surface finish approaches closely the best that can be obtained from wooden models.

The model aircraft or component to be tested is supported on slender streamlined struts so that it is free to move slightly in all directions, just as the full-scale aircraft may be expected to climb, dive, roll or turn under the influence of air pressure acting on its wings, control surfaces and fuselage. These movements are measured by sensitive balances connected to the struts, upward movement, for example, being recorded as lift and rearward pressure as drag. By adjusting the air speed to suit the size of the model, calculations which are intended to predict the probable behaviour

PREPARING FUSELAGE *sections for alignment and mating demands great care and skill in positioning the rivet holes.*

READY FOR MATING, *these fuselage sections are all exactly alike and therefore interchangeable. The sections are subsequently brought together and joined by riveting.*

BODY SECTION *of a "double-bubble" Stratocruiser fuselage under construction. This fuselage when completed will hold about eighty passengers in its two decks.*

of the full-size aircraft can be verified.

Unfortunately, an error does intrude, known as scale effect. This is due to the fact that, although the size of the model can be reduced, the size of the particles of air which strike it or flow over it cannot also be reduced. At high scale speeds this can introduce quite appreciable errors.

The best way of overcoming the difficulty is to compress the air in the tunnel, which gives the same effect as a reduction in the size of the air particles. In a modern wind tunnel, therefore, the working section is totally enclosed and the whole tunnel is a very massive affair, as the air which is flowing around inside it is compressed to about twenty-five times normal atmospheric pressure. Every movement of the model is recorded by remote-reading instruments on an elaborate instrument panel in the control room of the wind tunnel.

Air speeds high enough to enable research scientists to investigate some of the prob-

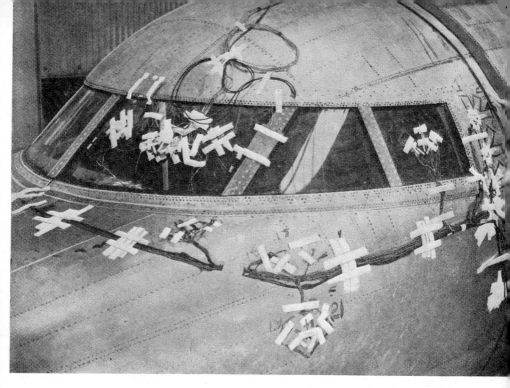

BEFORE PRODUCTION STARTS, *a full-scale specimen fuselage is given pressurization tests. Strain gauges (above) reveal any structural weaknesses, while safety pads (below) protect operators when the fuselage is tested at twice normal operating pressure.*

lems of aircraft behaviour at speeds close to and beyond the speed of sound, at which the mysterious sonic barrier is encountered, are being produced in smaller wind tunnels.

On a specially illuminated screen in a viewfinder positioned over a plate-glass window in the test chamber of the tunnel, the formation of compressibility shock waves in the air can be studied as they radiate from the wings or body of a model under test. It has long been known that changes in air density and pressure through a shock wave are intense enough to cast well-defined shadows; the method was used in the last century to photograph wave patterns from bullets at high speed. Shadowgraphs obtained by these means have frequently been used since in scientific research, and refinements in technique have been added.

A very special advantage of the principle is that it avoids placing any physical obstruction in the flow being studied, as the method depends only on passing rays of light through the air and therefore causes no interference to the flow pattern, which is very sensitive in these high-speed conditions.

On a part of the model where a shock wave is about to form, as speed increases, the picture on the screen shows what looks rather like a few short hairs moving to and fro on the surface of the model; from a strong, single shock, the shadow is much longer and is sometimes as hard as a crack in a pane of glass.

These shock waves, which can cause severe vibration and temporary loss of control, are a formidable barrier which must be surmounted before air speeds in the region of the speed of sound—760 m.p.h. at sea-level—can be attained or exceeded by air-liners in everyday flight.

Flying-boat Tests

The designer of a flying-boat or seaplane is naturally very concerned about the efficiency of the under-water form of a flying-boat hull or a seaplane float. He has, therefore, borrowed an idea from the shipbuilder, and makes use of a long tank filled with water in which models of hulls and floats can be tested.

The model is suspended from a trolley, running on rails on each side of the tank, and driven by an electric motor; it carries the observers and is equipped with sensitive balances to record the forces acting on the

LYING IN THEIR ASSEMBLY DOCKS, *these Constellation nose sections resemble giant fish. Seven other sections complete the fuselage. Note the curved ladders.*

IN THIS STATIC TEST *a Constellation fuselage is twisted out of shape by stresses far greater than are met in flight. The wrinkles disappear when the stress is removed.*

FLYING-BOAT HULLS *must not only be aerodynamically efficient but must also offer minimum water resistance. This picture shows the Saunders-Roe test tank.*

model. The wave formation caused by the model is also studied, and is often photographed by a cine-camera.

Somewhat on the lines of the hull-testing trolley is a rocket-driven trolley, running on a rail track and termed a supersonic sledge, built by Northrop Aircraft Incorporated in the Californian desert. The model to be tested is mounted on the trolley, which is reputed to attain a speed of over 1,000 m.p.h.

Any calculations of stresses, based on wind-tunnel or water-tank tests, must still be of a theoretical nature, however. A major component such as a wing, or any part in which it is necessary to verify calculations, is subjected to tests to check the accuracy of the designer's predictions. Until fairly recently, for instance, a part such as a complete wing would be mounted on trestles, and an increasing load would be applied by means of weights such as sandbags or bags of lead shot; the bending of the wing was measured, more and more weight being piled on until eventually the wing collapsed.

While this gave quite a good idea of the ultimate strength of a part, it was apt to be an expensive method of testing, especially in the case of a complete mainplane or fuselage. Moreover, it did not tell the designer the full story; he was still anxious to know just what the stress was inside certain critical spars or other components, and, of equal importance, the actual direction in which the forces were acting.

Electric Strain Gauge

The introduction of the electric strain gauge solved this problem. This consists of a very fine wire, about 25 in. in length, which has been folded in zigzag fashion, without any of the turns touching, to form a flattened coil one inch in length. This is

JOINING THE WING *to the fuselage. The wing is brought up to meet the fuselage; it is carried on a wheeled cradle which runs on tracks in the floor, and then made fast.*

NEARING COMPLETION, *the air-liners in the foreground have had engines installed. The great size of these aircraft makes it necessary to fold down the fin and rudder on to the starboard tail plane to permit them to pass through the hangar doors.*

cemented to a strip of paper, which is in turn glued to the surface of the component to be tested, such as the side or web of a spar, or a section of the metal plating on a wing or fuselage.

When the component is subjected to any stress, it will either be slightly stretched or compressed, as will the wire, because it is glued firmly to the surface. If the wire is stretched, even very slightly, its resistance to the passage of an electric current is increased; if it is compressed, its resistance is decreased. These minute changes in the wire's resistance are measured by sensitive instruments, and the readings of the instruments are a direct measure of the stress in the part. By using a cathode-ray tube similar to that used in a television receiver, and an amplifier, a visual display can be obtained; alternatively, the variations in

stress can be photographed on a cinematograph film.

These methods of recording stresses are most generally used when it is necessary to measure the vibration in a part; vibration, of course, results in alternate tension and compression of the material, and these rapidly alternating stresses will cause fracture or weakening of the part more quickly than a steady strain in one direction. On the screen of a cathode-ray tube, the stresses trace a zigzag line which is a visible picture of the frequency and magnitude of the vibration in the part.

Many parts of an aeroplane are particularly susceptible to vibration; the structure cannot be made really rigid without at the same time rendering it too heavy, so that vibration must be tracked down and cured at its source before it can set

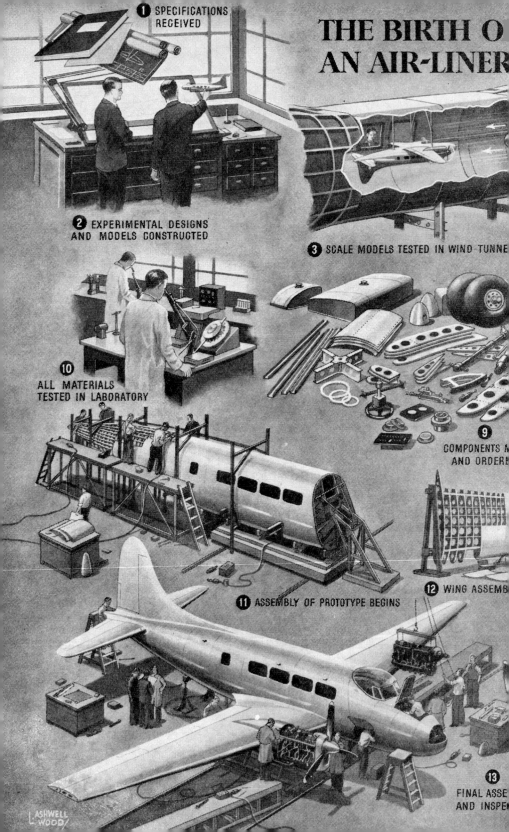

1 SPECIFICATIONS RECEIVED

THE BIRTH O
AN AIR-LINER

2 EXPERIMENTAL DESIGNS AND MODELS CONSTRUCTED

3 SCALE MODELS TESTED IN WIND-TUNNE

10 ALL MATERIALS TESTED IN LABORATORY

9 COMPONENTS M AND ORDERE

11 ASSEMBLY OF PROTOTYPE BEGINS

12 WING ASSEMB

13 FINAL ASSE AND INSPE

L.ASHWELL WOOD

5 HUNDREDS OF DRAWINGS PREPARED AND BLUE-PRINTS MADE

4 DESIGNERS AND DRAUGHTSMEN DEVELOP THE AEROPLANE

8 JIGS AND FIXTURES ENSURE STANDARD PARTS

6 FULL-SCALE MOCK-UP BUILT OF CARDBOARD AND PLYWOOD

7 SPECIAL TOOLS DESIGNED AND MADE

15 COMPLETED AEROPLANE SWUNG FOR COMPASS ADJUSTMENT AND WEIGHED

SEATS, CARPETS AND OTHER INTERIOR FITTINGS INSTALLED

16 WITH GRUELLING TEST FLIGHTS COMPLETED, THE AEROPLANE IS READY FOR SERVICE.

other components vibrating in sympathy. Typical examples are an out-of-balance propeller, excessive engine vibration, or shock waves set up by the air flung from the propeller blades striking the fuselage, wings or tail plane.

Here, the visible and photographic records of a number of strategically placed strain gauges are invaluable. Using portable equipment, it is even possible to record the vibrations in such items as the individual blades of the propellers while the aircraft is in flight. Another type of instrument called a vibrograph, in which a pen traces a record of the vibration on a chart, is also used to investigate vibration problems.

Altitude Tests

Even now, the story of the painstaking research that goes into the design of a modern high-flying air-liner is not complete. Further test equipment is required, in the form of an altitude test chamber, in which the atmospheric conditions at great heights can be reproduced on the ground.

Among the experimental uses of the altitude chamber are: investigating the performance of electrical and hydraulic equipment at low temperatures; the examination of rubber seals and the effects of contraction upon the fit of various components; tensile, bending, fatigue and vibration tests on riveted joints at low temperatures; the effect of high altitudes and rates of climb upon fuel systems; the effect of low temperature upon mechanical controls; the adhesion of paints at low temperature; and medical research, such as the effect of rapid rate of climb and of high altitude upon human beings.

The outer shell of the test chamber consists of a huge cylindrical steel tank, insulated externally. Inside this is constructed a completely insulated internal test chamber, usually fitted at the front end with double-hinged doors. The front end of the outer shell can also be completely removed, thus making it a simple matter to place large and heavy components in the inner chamber.

The working substance for the refrigeration machinery is either ammonia or Freon 12 gas, the two compressors being driven by electric motors which are connected in parallel so that only one compressor need be used for light duties.

A motor-driven fan circulates air, cooled by the refrigeration plant, through louvres into the inner chamber. Louvres in the sides and roof of the inner chamber allow the air to circulate through the space between the outer shell and the inner chamber, to the air cooler. Thus the refrigerated air not only cools the inner test chamber but also the mass of the outer shell, allowing a considerable amount of refrigeration to be stored when the machinery is stopped. The louvres are controlled from an external panel.

Inspection windows are built into the chamber so that tests can be observed in certain cases without the need for personnel to subject themselves to the severe conditions in the test chamber. A steam heater, including a small circulating fan, is fitted so that, if necessary, the louvres can be closed and the inner chamber brought up rapidly to normal or tropical temperatures.

The real value of the plant is that it can be used not only to control temperature but also pressure, as it is fitted with a vacuum pump. Thus, the conditions obtaining during a steady climb to great heights can be simulated by simultaneous operation of pump and of refrigeration.

Damage by Birds

The designer must take another risk into consideration—the possibility of the aeroplane striking a bird in flight. Damage to R.A.F. aircraft by birds was estimated recently to have totalled £20,000 in a year; in 1945 it was as high as £120,000. The majority of such accidents are caused by birds crashing through windscreens into

FIRST FLIGHT TEST *demands that the fuselage of the air-liner be converted into a flying laboratory. Here, test engineers record every aspect of the performance.*

control cabins at low altitudes when the aeroplane is taking off or landing, and, as a result, peregrine falcons are being used to rid some aerodromes of bird flocks.

Aircraft manufacturers, however, cannot afford to ignore the problem of providing a bird-proof windscreen. The windscreen on the Bristol Brabazon, for instance, is much more than a simple sheet of transparent plastics; it consists of several layers of different types of glass and a ¾-in.-thick transparent panel, with a small air gap for de-misting by circulation of hot air. It is so tough that a bird flying into it just after take-off may crack it, but will not crash through into the control cabin.

The American Convair-Liner has a steel bird-slicer fixed in the centre of the windscreen to lessen the impact of birds.

Special apparatus which hurls high-speed missiles at windscreen panels has helped to solve windscreen-design problems. For instance, the manufacturers of the Brabazon experimented continuously with a motor-driven rotor fitted with a spring-operated release mechanism at its tip. Synthetic birds, weighing approximately four pounds—equivalent to the heaviest bird likely to be encountered on most aerodromes—are attached to the rotor and released at high velocities, samples of windscreen materials being positioned to receive the full impact of the flying missile. The recipe for a synthetic bird? Take an outer bag of canvas to represent the skin, insert a ½-in. layer of soft sponge rubber to form the flesh, and add sand filling as required to make up the correct weight of the bird to be simulated!

on, a so-called mock-up of the aircraft is also built at a fairly early stage. This consists of a full-scale model, built as economically as possible of wood, plywood and canvas, in which actual components and items of equipment can be positioned as a check on the drawings. The representatives of the prospective operator are, of course, interested spectators at this stage, and will have numerous criticisms and suggestions to offer when they are able to examine the mock-up, walk about in the cabin, seat themselves in the pilot's and navigator's positions, check the accessibility of vital parts for maintenance purposes, and so on.

In America, however, actual chicken carcases are fired at velocities of from 50 to 450 m.p.h. from a cannon operated by compressed air. The chickens are painlessly electrocuted just before being loaded into the gun, and a high-speed camera photographs the effect of the impact on the windscreen—and on the chicken! Turkeys weighing up to 16 lb. can also be fired by this gun.

An alternative scheme used in Great Britain is to mount the test panel on a trolley propelled by a battery of rockets, and to suspend a bird carcase in its path. The trolley attains a high speed and is decelerated, after the panel has struck the bird, by two scoops which dip into long, water-filled troughs, and is finally brought to rest at the end of its track by a buffer attached to a piston acting in a water-filled cylinder. While this development work is going

Marking-out

When the drawing office has prepared the thousands of drawings necessary for the manufacture of every part of the aircraft, these are issued to the workshops so that production may begin.

The copying by hand of the essential lines and dimensions from the drawings to the actual sheets of metal—a process known as marking-out—is both slow and costly for large-size items. In many factories, however, this is immensely speeded up by printing the drawings on to the metal sheets by means of a photographic process.

The photographic emulsion is supplied on large sheets of paper, similar to normal photographic printing paper. The surface of the sheet of metal from which the component is to be made having been thoroughly cleaned, the paper is laid on it, with the emulsion in contact with the metal, and is pressed with a hot iron; this softens the emulsion and causes it to adhere to the metal. The paper is then carefully stripped off, and the prepared sheet, which is now virtually a photographic plate, is placed on an easel in the camera room.

The easel may be a large, absolutely flat metal plate measuring about eight feet long by six feet high, on the face of which are a number of grooves connected to a vacuum pump. The suction created by the pump causes the sensitized sheet to adhere firmly to the metal plate, without the slightest trace of buckling or distortion.

A negative, made by photographing the original drawing, is placed in a projector similar to an enlarger or a magic lantern, and the image is projected on to the sensitized surface of the sheet. The sheet is then taken to the developing room, where it is lowered by a crane into successive developing, fixing and washing tanks, after which

it can be issued to the shops, to be cut and drilled in accordance with the photographic markings on it.

While the main design work and wind-tunnel tests are proceeding, the production department is busy designing and building the jigs or fixtures in which the fuselage, mainplanes and other components are built. It will be evident that, to ensure interchangeability, the parts must be assembled in rigid steel structures which will ensure the correct contours of the metal plating and accurate positioning of vital attachment points on the wings, fuselage and other components. A million pounds may be spent on this initial preparation of jigs and tools, but this is a sound investment if production subsequently flows smoothly.

Test Flight

At last, the first completed aircraft, or prototype as it is termed, is ready for its test flight. The layman, whose knowledge is perhaps based on sensational films, is apt to imagine the test pilot's job as essentially a hazardous gamble with a somewhat fickle fate; but in practice it is apt to be an uneventful succession of flights in admirably behaved aircraft. Moreover, test pilots are skilled men of extremely wide experience.

BIRD-PROOF WINDSCREEN GLASS *is tested at the Bristol factory by this machine, which flings a synthetic bird against the test panel. Birds are a real menace to fast aircraft.*

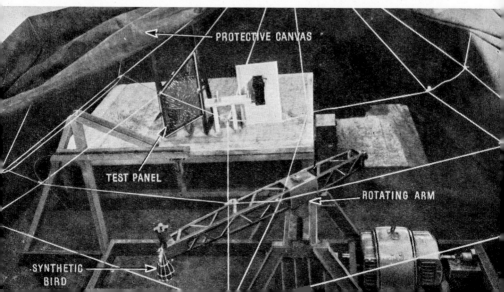

It cannot be denied, however, that there must always be some element of risk when the prototype of a new aircraft is coaxed into the air for the first time, in spite of the most meticulous system of inspection which can be devised. If something goes amiss during the test flight, the pilot will make every effort to land the aircraft intact, even at the risk of his life, in order to preserve the vital evidence of the cause and effect of a faulty part. A number of test pilots have met their deaths in this manner.

Prototype to Production

If the first flights of the prototype are successful, the production of the remaining aircraft on order, which are probably fairly far advanced, now proceeds quickly. Any alterations necessitated as a result of the prototype trials are incorporated, as are the various modifications which are usually demanded by the prospective user from time to time as production proceeds.

Each aircraft is, of course, rigorously tested as soon as it is structurally complete. As already suggested, the testing of a pro-duction aircraft is generally looked on merely as a job of work by the test crew, consisting of the pilot, a flight engineer and a radio-operator navigator. Each pilot accepts an aeroplane from the production line, and, on an average, gives it four test flights of thirty minutes' duration. It is then sent for furnishing and painting before having its final check flight.

The following are the tests which are generally undertaken: first comes the ground check, consisting of a very careful inspection; this is followed by running the engines up to full power on the ground, to check the instrument readings. If all is well, the aeroplane takes off and climbs to the altitude at which it is designed to operate. The maximum speed is now checked. Next, power is reduced until the aeroplane stalls, when its behaviour and ease of recovery are noted. Each propeller is then feathered in turn; this means that the blades are rotated so that their faces are in line of flight. With all engines restored to full power, the aircraft is put into a dive, and the maximum permissible speed is reached.

COUNTERPART *of the Stratocruiser, this Boeing Stratofreighter is here seen just after taking off on its first flight. Test pilots must at all costs endeavour to land their aircraft intact.*

IN A FAST TURN, *the Handley Page Hermes V shows its paces in a flight test. Maximum permissible speed is reached in a dive with all engines at full throttle setting.*

Next comes an instrument check, including the radio and radar equipment. During the engine check which follows, engine speeds, temperatures and pressures must be recorded under varying flight conditions. Engine or propeller vibration must be particularly noted. The flying controls can now be checked, including the operation of the automatic pilot. Next comes a test of the emergency undercarriage operation. With the wheels down, the aeroplane is now ready to make a trial landing.

Test Report

After each flight, the pilot makes out a report sheet in which he lists the faults which he has noticed in the aeroplane; these are corrected by the ground engineer, who signs for the work. This, in turn, is checked by the inspector, who signs in the next column. On the following flight the pilot makes sure that the remedies of the ground engineer have effected a cure for each fault.

As an alternative to the recording of innumerable figures by the crew during the testing of new types of aircraft, several automatic cinematograph cameras may be used to provide a continuous record of the instrument readings, which can be later analysed in the laboratory. An even more advanced version of this system, already used in practice, is to install a small television camera-transmitter, focused on a brightly lit panel containing a wide range of instruments; a moment-to-moment picture of what is happening in the aircraft is thus available to technicians on the ground.

The manufacturing and testing methods so far described have related mainly to the conventional type of modern air-liner. They are, however, also applicable to the less conventional civil aircraft, such as helicopters and the so-called flying-wings. A number of manufacturers are actively engaged on developing both these types.

Flying-wing Advantages

As its name suggests, the flying-wing type of air-liner takes the form of a large wing, shaped rather like a boomerang, into the forward edge of which are built the cabins and crew compartments. Also buried in the wing are the jet-propulsion units or turbo-propeller engines; the latter are employed to drive propellers mounted on the forward or rear edge of the wing.

This type of air-liner has a number of

advantages, chief among which is greatly improved fuel economy due to the clean design of the wing. Most of the parasite drag in a normal aeroplane—that is, drag which is not caused by the wing itself—is caused by the body, tail unit and engine nacelles. In a flying wing, or tailless aircraft, of course, these sources of drag do not exist.

If a wing having a very low drag, called a laminar-flow wing, were used in an aeroplane of this kind, the ideal conditions would be achieved. But if passengers and power units are to be accommodated in the wing itself, this must naturally be extremely thick. Thus the aircraft must be very large, having a wing span of about 160 ft.

The Armstrong Whitworth design team designed a tailless glider with an all-up weight of 6,000 lb. and a span of only 53 ft. This glider provided a great deal of useful information, but naturally the problems brought about by high speeds could not be investigated with it. The next step was to design and build a medium-sized tailless aeroplane—the A.W. 52. With two Rolls-Royce Nene jet units, this has a take-off weight of 33,000 lb., a span of 90 ft., a maximum speed of 500 m.p.h., and a maximum range of 1,500 miles. Although it is purely a research aircraft, it also has possibilities as a very fast mail- or freight-carrier, having provision for the accommodation of up to 4,000 lb. of load. The ultimate step is now the building of a large, tailless transport embodying all the lessons learnt with the glider and the A.W. 52.

In a similar category was the de Havilland 108, built to obtain experimental data for the large de Havilland Comet air-liner. The D.H. 108 was an outstanding example of the advantages of close collaboration between the scientist and the aircraft designer.

Helicopter Development

The helicopter also has numerous advantages within its own particular sphere of use. It is by no means perfected, however, and research is being carried out to determine the best methods of simplifying controls, increasing payload, and eliminating the vibration set up by the rotating blades which lift it into the air. In order to study the airflow past the blades under different conditions of flight, use is made of smoke released from a generator above or below the blades.

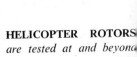

HELICOPTER ROTORS are tested at and beyond normal operating speeds by this 50-ft. tower at Bristol. Observers are ascending to the observation platform just below the rotor. Heavy steel netting gives protection in the event of a rotor breaking at speed.

VISUAL DISPLAY *of rotor performance is given by this smoke test, by which the slipstream from the helicopter rotors can be studied on the ground. Great skill is needed by the pilot in keeping the helicopter as close as possible to the smoke generator.*

To study the conditions during hovering flight, for instance, the smoke generator may be attached to the end of the jib of a 60-ft. crane, beneath which the helicopter hovers at a height of 40 ft. above the ground. The accurate positioning of the helicopter beneath the generator, at the same time keeping the rotor blades clear of the crane structure, calls for accurate piloting and control by signals from the ground; the fact that such a feat is possible indicates the controllability of a helicopter.

Tests during normal flight are carried out by fitting a smoke generator inside the fuselage, and releasing the smoke from a number of holes in a tube projecting horizontally beneath the rotor blades. The thin threads of smoke form beautiful patterns trailing from the rotor as they reveal the vortices set up in the air by the blades.

COCKPIT OF A DC-6, *a modern air-liner, gives a vivid impression of the complexity of the controls. Even the roof of the cockpit is covered with instruments and switches.*

114

CHAPTER 4

MASTERY OF THE AIR

BEFORE describing how and why an aeroplane flies, let us look over the pilot's shoulder and see what he does in the course of a flight round the aerodrome.

The same basic aeronautical principles apply whether we are flying an elementary trainer or a four-engined air-liner; but as there is so much more to do and remember in the larger type, our flight will be made in a single-engined trainer.

Before we can even enter the aircraft, a comprehensive exterior check-up must be made. Chocks must be under the main wheels so that the aeroplane does not start moving forward when the engine is started; a glance at the undercarriage legs and tyres will tell us if they are in order; and engine cowlings, petrol-filler caps and other external fittings must be securely fastened. Finally, the pitot head must be uncovered; this piece of mechanism, which looks like a poker sticking out, usually from one of the wings, is the air intake of the air-speed indicator—a vital instrument.

Having clambered into the aircraft and sat down, we go through our cockpit drill; we see that the windows are clean, the brakes on, and, in an aeroplane having a retractable undercarriage, that the undercarriage selector lever is in the "down" and the flaps in the "up" position.

Next, the controls are checked to see if they all move freely. We see that when the pilot pulls the control column—or stick— towards him, the elevators move upwards; and when he pushes it forward, they move downwards. Side-to-side movements of the stick control the ailerons; a movement to the left causes the aileron on the left, or port, wing to come up and the one on the right, or starboard, wing to go down. Pushing the stick to the right has, of course, the opposite effect. Then the rudder pedals; if you look back out of the window, you will see the rudder move to the right when the right pedal is operated, and then it will be seen to move to the left as the opposite pedal is pushed forward.

Cockpit Check

These tests completed, the engine controls and fuel cocks are set; "Petrol on, throttle closed, switches on . . . CONTACT!"—and the propeller is turning. While the engine is warming up, a complete cockpit check is made. All hydraulic levers, indicators and emergency-system levers are seen to be in the correct position, the trimming devices for elevators, rudder and aileron are checked and adjusted. Next, the pilot tests the engine controls and instruments, the blind-flying panel instruments, brake pressure, fuel level, intercommunication system, electrical switches and adjustment of the seat. Then we strap ourselves in.

Now the engine is run up to see that the propeller control and magnetos work properly and the engine delivers the correct power. Satisfied that all is in order, we give the signal to the ground engineer to remove the wheel chocks; the throttle is partly opened and we taxi out for take-off.

We taxi down-wind, so the stick is kept well forward to depress the elevators; with elevators right down, there is no danger of the wind getting under the tail and tipping the aeroplane on to its nose. The rudder, with perhaps gentle use of the brakes, steers us to the runway; but before we get there we stop across wind and the brakes are applied. One more quick check is made; the throttle is opened to clear the plugs of any oil which may have formed while taxi-ing; the flaps are put down a little to give us more lift; and then, having looked first down-wind and then all round us to ensure that we shall not baulk approaching aircraft, or run into obstacles, we turn into wind ready for take-off.

Obtaining Lift

The take-off is normally made into wind because, before the wings can obtain sufficient lift to support the aeroplane, the air must flow over them at a certain speed. Obviously, if the take-off is made into an oncoming wind, the required speed is reached much more quickly.

When taking off, the stick is held slightly back and the throttle opened smoothly to its full extent. As we gather speed, we keep straight by using the rudder and ease the stick forward. The increasing speed raises the tail and soon the aeroplane has assumed its flying position and then reached its flying speed. The pilot gently eases the stick back until—imperceptibly to the passenger—the aircraft has left the ground.

At first, the pilot keeps the aeroplane flying level to gain speed and raises the undercarriage; but once we are moving a little above the correct climbing speed, the stick is brought farther back and our aeroplane is in its correct climbing position. We gain height as quickly as we can by maintaining the best climbing speed for the type of aeroplane we are flying. The engine-throttle lever is set at the position for climbing and the propeller is adjusted to the correct revolutions-per-minute reading. We then trim the elevators to take the load off the stick, and at about 400 ft. raise the flaps and readjust the trim to keep the aeroplane in the correct climbing attitude.

At 1,000 ft. the pilot throttles back the engine to cruising power and at the same time eases the stick to a central position

FLYING DUTCHMAN *is the name applied to all K.L.M. air-liners—in this instance a DC-6 long-range air-liner of orthodox design. The small windows light the upper berths.*

BRITAIN HAS ALWAYS BEEN *a leading manufacturer of flying-boats. This is a Short Solent. Flying-boats, although posing many design problems, need no expensive runways.*

so as to adopt a level flying attitude; then the r.p.m. are adjusted to cruising conditions and the trim is again adjusted. Soon we are ready to make a turn to the left—most aerodrome circuits are left-handed—and thus enter the cross-wind leg of our circuit. Before turning, we look round to ensure that we will not obstruct other aircraft flying nearby.

Making a Turn

There are three phases in a turn. To perform the first phase—going into the turn —the stick is moved to the left until the aeroplane is banked sufficiently for the degree of turn it is wished to make. When the aeroplane is banked at the correct angle, the pilot centralizes the stick to maintain the angle of bank required, and at the same time moves the rudder to the left.

Turning the aeroplane makes the nose tend to drop, so this is countered by easing back on the stick to keep the nose up. Of course, all these movements, although described separately, are co-ordinated in one smooth operation.

To stay in the turn—the second phase— the angle of bank is kept constant with the ailerons by moving the stick sideways. If the nose drops, the stick is eased back to raise the elevators and less rudder is applied; if it rises, we put the stick gently forward and apply a little more rudder.

The last phase—coming out of the turn —is performed by applying opposite rudder and stick; the tendency of the nose to rise is checked by forward pressure on the stick. When the aeroplane is straight and level again, both rudder and stick are returned to their central positions.

Now we are flying across the wind; and soon we make another turn to fly down-wind and can see the aerodrome ahead of us on our left, apparently coming nearer. A further cockpit drill ensures that we are correctly strapped in; brake pressure is checked and the undercarriage lowered. The mixture control, which varies the proportions of the petrol-and-air mixture going into the engine, is set to give the rich, take-off mixture in case we have to go round again. The propeller control is set to give maximum permissible r.p.m. Speed is then reduced by throttling back, flaps are lowered to the slow-flying position and the elevators retrimmed.

As we again turn to fly across wind, this final check is completed and the pilot starts to throttle back to lose height. He gauges the strength of the wind and applies full flap so that the final approach begins in a straight line at the correct distance from the point on the landing strip at which it is desired to touch down.

To touch down on the correct spot requires practice, skill and judgment. We must glide in at a constant speed and also control our rate of descent. We have arranged to land into wind so as to make our speed over the ground as low as possible; and our flaps act as a brake and enable us to approach even more slowly. The elevators and throttle also help us to control our speed and rate of descent. But at the moment we are maintaining our correct speed by using the elevators, and regulating the angle of approach and rate of descent by opening or closing the throttle. If we find that we are under-shooting, for instance, we open the throttle and raise the nose slightly.

The ground seems to be coming up slowly to meet us and we begin to flatten out our gliding angle by pulling the stick back until the aeroplane is flying level just above the ground. The throttle is closed gradually; now the aeroplane is being held off the ground by bringing the stick back,

and the tail is falling; the aeroplane is now only a yard or so above ground and in almost the same attitude as when at rest. With the throttle completely closed, and the stick right back, we sink to the ground on all three wheels. Coarse use of rudder, assisted by brake if necessary, corrects any tendency to swing. We get clear of the landing path, raise the flaps, and taxi away to the allotted parking place.

Now we are on the ground again, let us find out a little about the reasons why a heavier-than-air machine can fly, and see what forces were acting upon the aeroplane in which we made our flight.

Principles of Flight

An aeroplane is able to rise into the air and to stay there by means of the force exerted by the air moving in relation to the aeroplane. This fact can be demonstrated quite simply. If you take a flat, rigid surface such as a piece of cardboard and push it through still air so that it is inclined slightly to the direction in which you are moving you will discover that the cardboard will tend to move upwards and backwards because of the force exerted on it by pushing it through the air. The upward part of this force is called lift and the backward, drag.

You may find that the lift is sufficient to raise the cardboard and keep it in the air. The cardboard, in fact, will be acting like the wings of an aeroplane. If you release it, the cardboard may continue its flight for a short distance, but eventually it will stop moving forward and flutter to the ground. This shows that to obtain lift the cardboard requires a force to push it through the air. In aircraft, this force is derived from the power of the engine.

If you try the same experiment on a day when the wind is blowing, you will find that you can achieve the same results by holding the cardboard stationary: again you will feel the upward lift and the backward drag. The experiments demonstrate the fact that it is movement *relative to the*

118

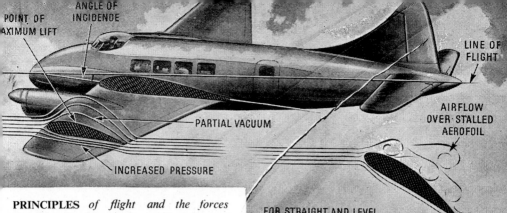

POINT OF
MAXIMUM LIFT

ANGLE OF
INCIDENCE

LINE OF
FLIGHT

PARTIAL VACUUM

AIRFLOW
OVER·STALLED
AEROFOIL

INCREASED PRESSURE

PRINCIPLES *of flight and the forces acting on the flying and control surfaces of an aeroplane are illustrated in this drawing.*

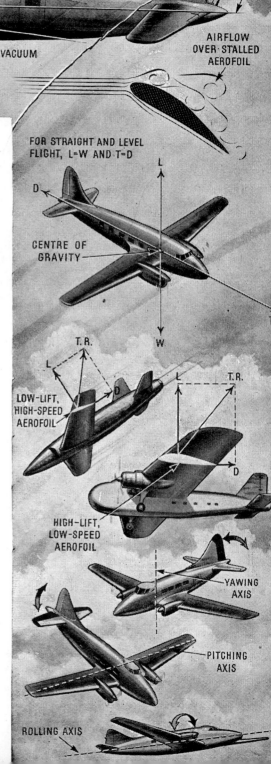

FOR STRAIGHT AND LEVEL
FLIGHT, L=W AND·T=D

L

D

CENTRE OF
GRAVITY

T

W

T.R.

L

LOW-LIFT,
HIGH-SPEED
AEROFOIL

D

L

T.R.

D

HIGH-LIFT,
LOW-SPEED
AEROFOIL

YAWING
AXIS

PITCHING
AXIS

ROLLING AXIS

air which matters when studying the principles of flight.

We have become so used to relating speed and direction of movement with the ground that we must now expand our thoughts to include the fact that although an aeroplane has movement relative to the ground it can remain in the air only because of its movement relative to the air. The speed at which an aeroplane moves through the air is known as the air speed; and the speed at which it moves over the ground is known as the ground speed.

To illustrate this important point, imagine two places, A and B, 200 miles apart. The wind is blowing at 25 m.p.h. from B to A. An aeroplane with an air speed of 225 m.p.h. flies from A to B. Although its air speed is 225 m.p.h., its ground speed will be 200 m.p.h. and it will reach B in one hour. On the return journey its air speed will still be 225 m.p.h. but the ground speed will be 250 m.p.h. and it will reach A in 48 minutes.

Aerofoil Shape

So far we have dealt with a flat surface for our experiments but, as everyone knows, the wing of an aeroplane is not a flat sheet but a curved or cambered surface known as an aerofoil. An aerofoil is so shaped for two main reasons: first, the curved surface gives greater lift, and it follows the streamline principle which

119

PARTICULARLY NEAT *is this arrangement* (above) *of instruments and controls, seen in the flight deck of the American Curtiss Wright CW-32 cargo-transport project.*

DE HAVILLAND DOVE *control cabin* (below). *As the first pilot sits on the left, the flying instruments are grouped in front of him; the second pilot is then free to operate the radio and navigate the aeroplane, which can, however, be flown by one pilot alone.*

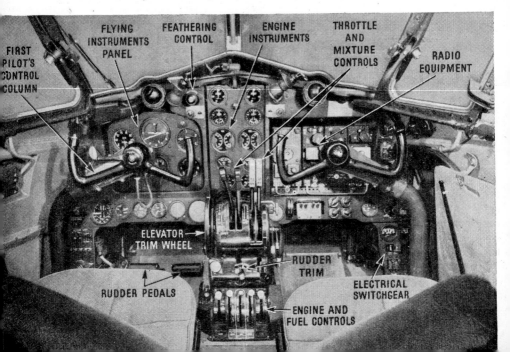

SMALL BUT COMFORTABLE, *the de Havilland Dove is designed to operate stages of 200-300 miles with eight to eleven passengers. It is in service all over the world.*

enables it to pass through the air with the minimum of resistance; second, thickness is required to lend strength to the structure.

To understand how lift is obtained, it is necessary to know what occurs when the airflow meets an aerofoil inclined towards it. Engineers have given much study to this, and by various methods they have discovered what happens.

The airflow is divided by the aerofoil; some air passes over the top and the remainder underneath the aerofoil. The air passing below the aerofoil is compressed; it therefore increases in pressure and imparts a thrust upwards, but the pressure of the air passing over the top is reduced, producing a vacuum which has a sucking effect. It has been found that about two-thirds of the whole upward pressure, or lift, is due to this sucking effect and one-third to the increased pressure below the aerofoil.

Lift is obtained from all over the aerofoil, although not equally; the lifting forces are greatest towards the front and they drop to nothing at the rear or trailing edge; so if the amounts of lift all over the aerofoil are added together and shown dia-

grammatically as a line rising from one point on the wing, the line would appear at about one-third of the way along the chord of the wing section from the leading edge. This point is the centre of pressure.

Aerofoil Characteristics

As the curved surface gives lift, so the design of the aerofoil decides the amount of lift which can be obtained. Thicker aerofoil sections may produce a lift quantity which is considerably greater than that of a much thinner section; however, as was mentioned earlier, the effect of the force exerted by the air is not entirely lift, there is the backward force, drag, as well. Therefore, although the thicker aerofoil section may produce a greater lift quantity than the thinner section, the latter may produce a better ratio of lift to drag than the thicker section. So aircraft designers have to consider carefully what they require in an aeroplane before they decide on the type of aerofoil they mean to employ. For example, the thicker wing section mentioned above may have been designed for a slow freight-carrying aeroplane, while the thinner section might be

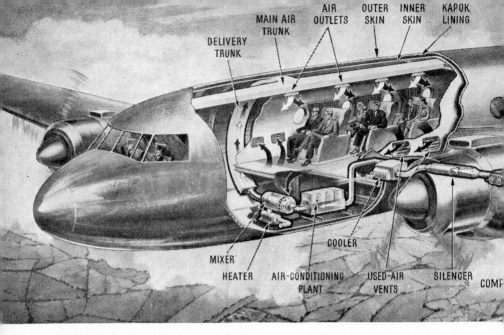

DELIVERY TRUNK · MAIN AIR TRUNK · AIR OUTLETS · OUTER SKIN · INNER SKIN · KAPOK LINING · MIXER · HEATER · AIR-CONDITIONING PLANT · COOLER · USED-AIR VENTS · SILENCER · COMF

more suitable for the faster fighter aircraft.

The direction of lift is always considered to be at right-angles to the airflow, and the direction of drag to be parallel to the airflow. The combined or total effect is known as total reaction.

The amounts of lift and drag vary according to the angle at which the aerofoil meets the airflow. This angle is known as the angle of attack or angle of incidence. If the aerofoil is at a small angle to the airflow, the majority of the force is represented by lift; but if the aerofoil presents a large angle of attack, a larger proportion of the force is felt as drag.

Angle of Attack

The lift increases as the angle of attack increases up to a certain point, this point being dependent upon the type of aerofoil. After this point the lift is reduced rapidly as the angle of attack is increased. The angle at which the lift begins to fall off is called the stalling angle.

Earlier in this chapter it was stated that the force which drives an aeroplane through the air is derived from the power of the engine. The engine drives the propeller,

which pushes the air behind it, thus moving the aeroplane through the air. We now come to two other important forces besides lift and drag: the forward force from the propeller, which is known as thrust, and the force of gravity acting on the aeroplane which is dependent upon the weight of the aeroplane, so the word weight is used to describe it.

Each force is regarded as acting in a constant direction. It has already been stated that lift is considered to act at right-angles to the airflow and drag parallel to the airflow. Thrust is regarded as acting along the length of the aeroplane from tail to nose; and weight, as acting vertically downwards. We have now established the principles of the forces concerned.

Before considering these forces too deeply, it is necessary to mention the centre of gravity, which, explained simply, is that point on or within the aeroplane where, if you placed a pivot, the aeroplane would balance perfectly. We have already mentioned the centre of pressure, which has the same relationship to lift as the centre of gravity has to weight. Similarly, thrust is regarded as acting from the

ALVE

USED-AIR EXHAUST

FRESH-AIR INTAKE

FRESH AIR
USED AIR

PRESSURIZATION *is a vital feature of the modern air-liner. Without it, flight at great altitudes would be impossible; passengers suffer discomfort at heights above about 8,000 ft. The air-conditioning plant is part of the pressurization system.*

centre of thrust and drag from the centre of drag. To maintain steady flight, these forces must be balanced and the aeroplane is then said to be in a state of equilibrium.

Balanced Forces

In order to maintain a constant height, lift and weight must be equal; if the weight were greater than the lift the aeroplane would lose height, and if the lift were greater the aeroplane would climb. To maintain a steady speed, the thrust must equal the drag. If the drag were greater than the thrust the speed would steadily decrease, and if the thrust were greater than the drag the speed would steadily increase.

An aeroplane is so built that when the state of equilibrium is upset it readjusts itself so that it reaches a new state of equilibrium. It does this by changing the angle of attack of the wings to the airflow; when this happens it alters the lift, drag and air speed (the latter changes because a change in drag acts, as the word implies, as a brake). The weight, of course, does

SLEEPERETTE SEATS *are an economical alternative to bunks on long-stage journeys. By day the Sleeperette is a comfortable chair; at night it becomes virtually a bed.*

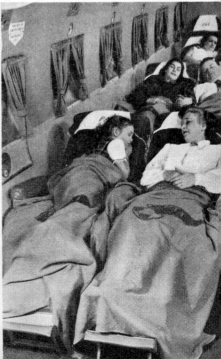

not change except over a period of time due to using up fuel. However, the new state of equilibrium may not be the state which the pilot desires. In this event the controls are moved to regulate the forces so as to adopt the conditions the pilot requires.

As an example, if an aeroplane is flying level at 180 m.p.h. and the pilot wishes to stay at the same height without altering the attitude of the aeroplane, but to increase speed to 200 m.p.h., he will open the throttle to increase the thrust. If he does nothing to alter the angle of attack he will find that, although he has obtained an initial increase in speed, the aeroplane will try to return to equilibrium; and in most aircraft he will find that the nose will rise and the aeroplane will begin to climb because the lift has increased due to the change of angle of attack. To counteract this, the pilot will reduce the angle of attack of the wings by using the controls which will be described later. So whenever the pilot changes the equilibrium of the aeroplane, he uses the controls to achieve the new state of equilibrium.

Before describing the controls, it is necessary to mention a further factor which a pilot must understand. It was stated earlier that as the angle of attack increases so the lift increases up to the stalling angle. To describe the condition known as stalling we must recall how the air flows smoothly over the wings in normal flight, and how lift is obtained.

Air Eddies

So long as the airflow is smooth over the aerofoil, lift is maintained; but if the airflow is disturbed, the sucking effect is lessened. The greater the disturbance caused by the motion of the aerofoil through the air, the less the lift. The disturbed airflow eddies and whirls over the top of the aerofoil and some of the air even moves from under the aerofoil up over the top from the trailing edge towards the front. When a wing is in such a state, it is said to be stalled. The stalling angle is immediately beyond the angle of maximum lift, and depends, of course, upon the particular design of the aerofoil.

When flying, we refer to the stalling of the aeroplane, which is dependent upon the stalling of the aerofoil surfaces, of which the wings form the greatest portion. Let us now examine one condition under which an aeroplane stalls.

Suppose our aeroplane is flying straight

MORE PAYLOAD *in baggage and cargo can be carried when the boat-shaped Speedpak is fitted to the fuselage of a Constellation. The Speedpak is shown ready for attachment.*

and level and the wings are presenting a small angle of attack to the airflow. In this condition, the lift obtained by the wings just counterbalances the weight of the aeroplane. Remember that the lift depends upon the speed of the airflow over the wings, the design of the wings, the angle of attack and the density of the air through which we are flying. The latter factor requires some explanation before proceeding further with our study.

Air Density and Pressure

The density of a gas, in this case the air, varies directly as to the pressure, and inversely as to the Absolute temperature. Air containing water vapour is less dense than dry air, and varying density causes convection currents in the air, the heavier air descending and the lighter (or less dense) air rising. It is thus obvious that air density changes with change of place and time of day, and it decreases with height. This, of course, affects aircraft performance, particularly in regard to engine performance and the amount of lift obtained. Now reduce the speed of the airflow by throttling back and so reducing the thrust provided by the engine; by reducing the speed of the airflow we have also reduced one of the factors which give us lift and, therefore, the lift is lessened. Thus, unless we move the controls to prevent it, the aeroplane will begin to lose height and the nose will drop as the aeroplane tries to return to equilibrium.

However, if we wish to continue in level flight, we must keep the amount of lift the same as it was before we reduced the thrust. The only way this can be achieved is by altering the angle of attack of the wings by easing back on the stick; but by so doing we are losing speed, and as the speed falls away so the lift decreases, and to maintain our lift we must increase our angle of attack even more. If the speed keeps falling, we must continue to increase the angle of attack to hold our lift.

Eventually, the angle of attack reaches the angle of maximum lift and then the stalling angle; the wings and aeroplane stall, the aeroplane shudders, the nose drops very quickly, and, in many aeroplanes, the dropping of the nose is accompanied by the aeroplane heeling over to one side or the other if one wing stalls slightly before the other.

Normally, except for landing and for training, an aeroplane is not stalled deliberately, because when the wings are

AIRCRAFT DESIGNED SPECIFICALLY *for freight-carrying are increasing in numbers. Here, a Bristol Type 170 is loaded. This aircraft operates a cross-Channel car-ferry service.*

stalled the loss of lift is so great that height can be lost rapidly before full control is regained.

Now that we have some knowledge of what keeps an aeroplane airborne, there is another term which requires explanation; a term in common use and which you are bound to meet again; it is load factor.

An unladen aeroplane has a certain weight; it also has varying weights when laden with passengers, crew, fuel, luggage, mails, etc. As already described, in normal flight this weight has to be maintained in the air by lift derived mainly from the wings. It is possible, therefore, to establish a relationship between the wing area and the weight of the aeroplane and arrive at a wing-loading resultant of a certain number of pounds per square foot. Remember, this is the wing loading in normal, straight and level flight; in this condition the lift per square foot equals the weight per square foot.

But the aeroplane is not always in straight and level flight, and in certain manoeuvres the wing loading increases; these changes in wing loading are referred to as a ratio to the weight and are known as load factors. For example, a load factor of 3 means that three times as much lift is necessary as when flying straight and level.

Another Force

By now no doubt you have already thought of some manoeuvres that necessitate a great increase in lift; if not, think for a few moments of what must occur in a steep turn.

All are familiar with the pressure felt when travelling in a motor-car or omnibus which turns a corner rather fast; we can feel a force acting on our bodies. This is the force which keeps a body turning in a circle and acts towards the centre of that circle.

The force required to keep an aeroplane airborne has been described; it will be apparent that any force needed to change the aeroplane's direction must be additional to this, for the lift has not only to counter the weight of the aeroplane, but also has to provide for the extra force required to maintain the aeroplane in a turn. The amount of the force depends upon the square of the speed of the aeroplane and varies inversely as the radius of turn. For example, if we continue to fly at the same air speed but tighten our turn by turning in half the radius, the force needed to keep us in the turn is doubled.

Effects of Controls

Having an idea of why an aeroplane flies, by examining the effect of the controls we shall discover quite a lot about *how* it flies. But before we consider the effect of the controls, it must be remembered that their action will be described without reference to the horizon. The controls always have the same primary effect, no matter what the aeroplane's position may be relative to the ground, except when it is stalled.

The main control surfaces which are under the pilot's control from the cockpit are the ailerons, the elevators and the rudder; the action of each will be described separately.

The ailerons are hinged along their forward edge and are part of the wings. They are located on the trailing edge of both port and starboard wings, and are linked so that as one moves up the other moves down, this movement being effected by side-to-side movements of the control column. As the stick is moved to the left, the left, or port, aileron is raised and the starboard aileron is lowered. The starboard aileron thus presents an increased angle of attack to the airflow, so having more lift; but the port aileron presents a lesser angle of attack and has reduced lift. Therefore the port wing drops and the starboard one rises and the aeroplane rolls to the left round a line drawn through the

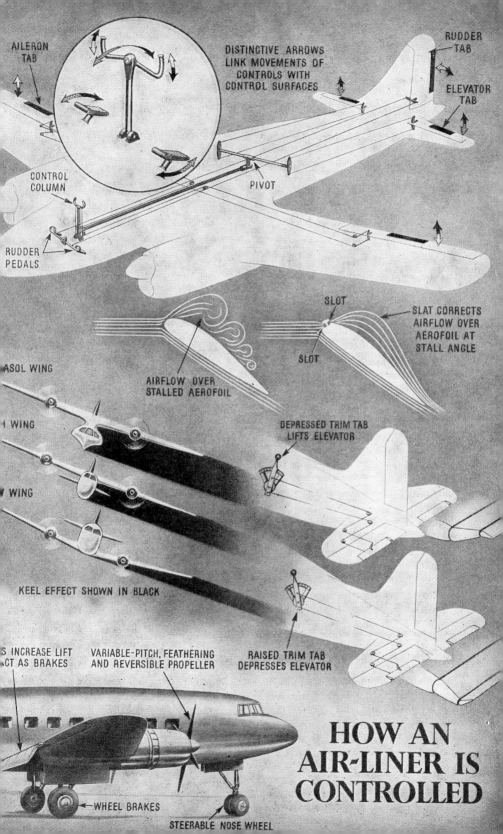

AILERON TAB

DISTINCTIVE ARROWS LINK MOVEMENTS OF CONTROLS WITH CONTROL SURFACES

RUDDER TAB

ELEVATOR TAB

CONTROL COLUMN

PIVOT

RUDDER PEDALS

SLOT

SLAT CORRECTS AIRFLOW OVER AEROFOIL AT STALL ANGLE

SLOT

AIRFLOW OVER STALLED AEROFOIL

ASOL WING

DEPRESSED TRIM TAB LIFTS ELEVATOR

H WING

W WING

KEEL EFFECT SHOWN IN BLACK

RAISED TRIM TAB DEPRESSES ELEVATOR

S INCREASE LIFT CT AS BRAKES

VARIABLE-PITCH, FEATHERING AND REVERSIBLE PROPELLER

HOW AN AIR-LINER IS CONTROLLED

WHEEL BRAKES

STEERABLE NOSE WHEEL

AT THE END OF *World War II, Britain was forced to rely on converted bomber aircraft for her air services. This B.O.A.C. Lancastrian is descended from the famous Lancaster.*

aeroplane from nose to tail. This is known as movement in the rolling plane, and an aeroplane lying at an angle in the rolling plane is said to be banked.

The elevators are part of the tail plane and are located and hinged in the same way as the ailerons. They are raised and lowered by the action of the stick moving backwards and forwards. As the stick is moved forward, both elevators are depressed, the tail rises and the nose of the aeroplane goes down. As the stick is moved back both elevators rise and offer resistance to the airflow. The pressure of the air causes the tail to fall and the nose to rise. This is known as movement in the pitching plane.

Operation of Rudder

The rudder is hinged to the rear, or trailing, edge of the fin and it can be moved to the left or right, and is controlled from the rudder pedals. As the left rudder pedal is pushed forward by the foot, the rudder moves to the left and offers resistance to the airflow. Therefore the tail of the aero-plane is pushed to the right and the nose moves round to the left. The reverse occurs as the opposite pedal is operated. This is known as movement in the yawing plane.

An aeroplane is designed to be stable whilst flying; that is, it should tend to hold the attitude into which it is placed by the pilot and to return to it if temporarily upset by disturbances in the air, thus saving the pilot much effort.

Stability in the rolling plane is obtained by placing the wings into the fuselage at a slight upward angle known as the dihedral angle. Should the aeroplane become banked when flying straight, it will begin to slip through the air towards the lower wing. The lower wing will present a greater angle of attack to the airflow than the upper wing and thus have more lift; this lift will bring the aeroplane back to the level position.

In the pitching plane, stability is achieved by means of the tail plane. The tail plane is an aerofoil, usually of symmetrical section and normally set in the fuselage at zero angle of attack to the airflow. Should the tail plane be displaced downward from the line of level flight due to an air disturbance, it will have positive lift and therefore return to the level position. If it is displaced upwards, it will have negative lift and so fall back to the level position.

The reason for this is that, if an aerofoil is moving downwards as well as forwards, its effective angle of attack in relation to the airflow is increased. If it is moving upwards as well as forwards, its effective angle of attack to the airflow is reduced. Therefore, in the first instance, the aerofoil will have more lift; and in the second, less lift. In conventionally designed aeroplanes, the tail plane is well behind the centre of gravity and controls the stability of the whole aeroplane in the pitching plane.

Directional Stability

The fin and the sides of the fuselage (known as the keel surfaces) provide stability in the yawing plane. Should the aeroplane move in the yawing plane, resistance to such movement is offered by the fin and keel surfaces, and the rear portion of the aeroplane, pivoted around the centre of gravity, tends to be forced back to the former position by the airflow.

This is described as directional stability.

The engine, driving the propeller, provides the power to keep the aeroplane in the air. The propeller drives the aeroplane through the air by pushing backwards the air immediately behind it; this air is called the slipstream. In consequence the speed of the airflow over the tail is greater than that over the wings. Therefore the degree of effect of the rudder and elevators varies with the speed of the engine and propeller. The greater the speed of rotation of the propeller, the greater the effect of the elevators and rudder.

The slipstream twists round in corkscrew fashion. If a propeller turns clockwise when viewed from the rear, the aeroplane will yaw to the left because of the slipstream meeting the upper fin surface on the port side. This effect is allowed for by offsetting the fin or, alternatively, by some form of rudder bias so that, when cruising, the aeroplane will fly straight without pressure being applied to the rudder. In consequence, at full throttle the aeroplane will have a tendency to swing to the left; and with the throttle closed when gliding it will tend to swing to the right.

In addition to the main controls of

NEW AIR-LINER TYPES, *such as the Marathon 1, soon appeared after the war. Shown here is the Marathon 2, a similar airframe powered by two turbo-propeller engines.*

STRATOCRUISER CONTROL CABIN *has no fewer than* 19 *windows! All instrument panels are hinged to allow easy servicing, and radio racks can be serviced in flight.*

ailerons, elevators and rudder, aeroplanes have subsidiary controls known as trimming tabs. These are fitted to the main controls and vary in design, some being a spring loading which tends to pull the elevator or rudder in a certain direction; others are a separate movable part of the ordinary control surface. The trimming tabs are normally under the pilot's control, although on some aeroplanes the rudder and aileron tabs are pre-set on the ground. The most used tab is the elevator trimmer, and its object is to relieve the pilot of strain in maintaining the desired attitude of the aeroplane in the pitching plane. The tab and the control surface move in opposite directions. If the tab is moved down it will force the elevator up, and this will, of course, force the tail down.

Some aircraft have a small, subsidiary aerofoil fitted in front of the leading edge of the wing; this is called a slat. The space between the slat and the wing is called the slot. The slat is so made that its angle of attack is less than that of the wing. When the wings are at normal angles of attack, the slat lies flat against the leading edge, but when the angle of attack of the wing approaches the angle of maximum lift, it leaves the leading edge, so opening the slot. The air rushes through the slot and is deflected by the slat over the top surface of the wing, so preventing the airflow becoming turbulent. This, of course, postpones the stall and allows the angle of attack of the wing to be increased beyond the angle at which stalling would occur if the slat were not fitted.

Placed in the trailing edges of the wings between the ailerons and the fuselage, and on some aeroplanes extending below the fuselage, are control surfaces known as flaps. In general, a flap is a surface hinged at its forward end to some part of the wing and is lowered below the line of the wing by means of a control in the pilot's cockpit. The flaps under both wings go down evenly at the same time, and the degree to which they are lowered is controlled by the pilot.

Flaps differ in design, but the purpose is always the same. As the flaps are lowered, so the angle of attack to the airflow is increased and therefore the lift and drag from the wings also increase. Whether the lift increases more than the drag or vice versa is dependent upon the angle through which the flaps are lowered and also partly upon the design of the flaps.

Flaps are put to their main use in approaching to land and landing, and with some aeroplanes they are also used during take-off. When approaching to land, the flaps have two uses: they enable an aeroplane to glide at a steeper angle and at a lower speed; and, when an aeroplane is being held off—that is, being flown just above the ground prior to touching down—the drag produced by the flaps enables speed to be lost quickly and lessens the length of the landing run. Similarly, the drag aids the aeroplane to come to a standstill more quickly after touching down.

For taking off, flaps, if used, are lowered through only a small angle so that more lift is obtained at the minimum cost in extra drag, thus lowering the take-off speed.

Ground Manoeuvring

In addition to these controls, most modern aeroplanes are fitted with wheel brakes to assist in controlling the movement of the aeroplane on the ground. It is normal for the brakes to be interconnected with the rudder pedals so that, if it is desired to turn to port, the left rudder is operated and when the brake is applied it acts only on the port wheel, thus holding it back whilst the starboard one is free to turn. Brake levers may be either hand-operated or operated by the toes, the levers in the latter case being attached to the rudder pedals.

So far we have considered an aeroplane to be flying with a visible horizon.

The pilot is normally accustomed to positioning the attitude of his aeroplane, at various speeds and loads in relationship to the horizon; the horizon thus provides a natural check for the pilot, once he becomes accustomed to the attitude of the particular type of aircraft, which saves constant reference to instruments and thus makes flying much simpler.

Instrument Flying

But what enables a pilot to fly in cloud, or bad visibility, when there is no visible horizon? The answer, of course, is his instruments. Flying by instruments is a most important part of every pilot's work, and, in consequence, thorough training is given to pilots in this aspect of flying, and constant practice is undertaken both in the air and on the ground. The latter practice is carried out in a machine known as the Link trainer, which simulates instrument-flying conditions. The aim of this training and practice is to enable the pilot to fly and manoeuvre his aeroplane without external visual aids.

The standard instrument-flying panel consists of six instruments: the artificial horizon, direction indicator, air-speed indicator, sensitive altimeter, vertical-movement indicator and turn-and-slip indicator. Another instrument to which reference is made from time to time whilst flying by instruments is the magnetic compass.

The artificial horizon is the master instrument, and it will record accurately up to 90 deg. of bank and 60 deg. of climb or dive. It is normally worked by a gyro wheel spinning on a vertical axis in a frame

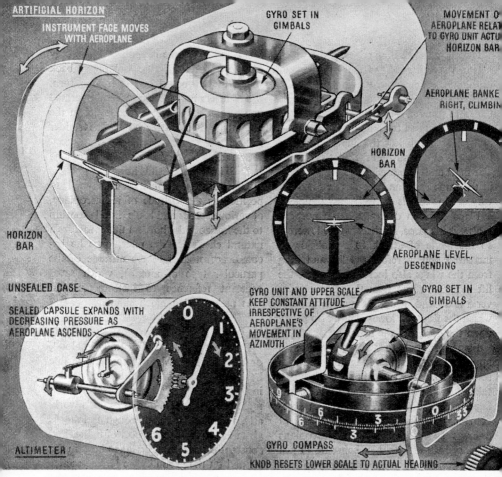

INSTRUMENT FACE MOVES WITH AEROPLANE

GYRO SET IN GIMBALS

MOVEMENT O AEROPLANE RELAT TO GYRO UNIT ACTU HORIZON BAR

AEROPLANE BANKE RIGHT, CLIMBIN

HORIZON BAR

HORIZON BAR

AEROPLANE LEVEL, DESCENDING

UNSEALED CASE

SEALED CAPSULE EXPANDS WITH DECREASING PRESSURE AS AEROPLANE ASCENDS

GYRO UNIT AND UPPER SCALE KEEP CONSTANT ATTITUDE IRRESPECTIVE OF AEROPLANE'S MOVEMENT IN AZIMUTH

GYRO SET IN GIMBALS

ALTIMETER

GYRO COMPASS

KNOB RESETS LOWER SCALE TO ACTUAL HEADING

ESSENTIAL TO THE PILOT *are these six main flying instruments. The artificial horizon indicates the general attitude of the aircraft when the ground is invisible, the altimeter measures the height of the aeroplane, and the gyro compass its heading. The speed of the*

pivoted on a fore-and-aft axis. The frame is joined to an artificial horizon which comprises the dial seen in the cockpit. The pilot is given a realistic picture of the attitude of his aeroplane, as an aeroplane image is set against the artificial horizon. As the frame moves, so the artificial horizon moves, and the relationship between the artificial horizon and the aeroplane image records on the dial the attitude adopted by the aeroplane in relation to the real horizon, which the pilot cannot see.

The direction indicator, or gyro compass, helps the pilot to keep a straight course and

is also a steering aid when turning. A free gyroscope spins on a horizontal axis and is linked to a dial marked with degrees of the compass, the dial being the part of the instrument which faces the pilot. The instrument can be locked, or caged, as it is called. When on the required compass course, it is set to correspond with the magnetic compass reading and uncaged: then, if the aeroplane moves off its course, the dial will indicate the amount of turn in degrees.

It has the advantage of not being subject to the errors of the magnetic compass. It

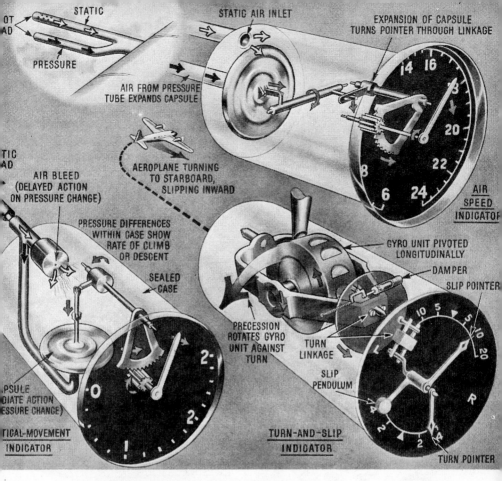

OT AD

STATIC

PRESSURE

STATIC AIR INLET

AIR FROM PRESSURE
TUBE EXPANDS CAPSULE

EXPANSION OF CAPSULE
TURNS POINTER THROUGH LINKAGE

AIR
SPEED
INDICATOR

TIC AD

AIR BLEED
(DELAYED ACTION
ON PRESSURE CHANGE)

AEROPLANE TURNING
TO STARBOARD,
SLIPPING INWARD

PRESSURE DIFFERENCES
WITHIN CASE SHOW
RATE OF CLIMB
OR DESCENT

SEALED
CASE

GYRO UNIT PIVOTED
LONGITUDINALLY

DAMPER

SLIP POINTER

PSULE
DIATE ACTION
ESSURE CHANGE)

TICAL-MOVEMENT
INDICATOR

PRECESSION
ROTATES GYRO
UNIT AGAINST
TURN

TURN
LINKAGE

SLIP
PENDULUM

TURN-AND-SLIP
INDICATOR

TURN POINTER

*aeroplane and its rate of climb or descent are shown by the air-speed indicator and vertical-
movement indicator respectively; while rate of turn and amount of inward or outward slip
are shown on the turn-and-slip indicator, which consists of two instruments in one case.*

has, however, to be checked and re-set
about every fifteen minutes as, owing to
friction in the bearings and to the earth's
rotation, it wanders from its setting.

Operation of A.S.I.

The air-speed indicator, or A.S.I. as it
is commonly known among pilots, was
mentioned briefly at the beginning of the
chapter. There are different types of A.S.I.,
one of the most common being the pitot-
static type. Two tubes face into the airflow,
one the pressure (or pitot) head and the
other the static head. The former is open

at the end and is subject to pressure because of the airflow; the latter has a closed
end and a number of holes around its sides.

Thus, when the aeroplane is flying, there
is a pressure difference in the tubes which
is fed to the A.S.I. via a metal aneroid
capsule, the static side to the container and
the pressure side to the inside of the capsule.
Subsequent expansion of the cell is conveyed to an indicator on the graduated dial
in the cockpit. The A.S.I. is invaluable to
the navigator as it enters into all his calculations for fixing the aeroplane's position.

The altimeter is an aneroid barometer

HANDLEY PAGE
HERMES IV

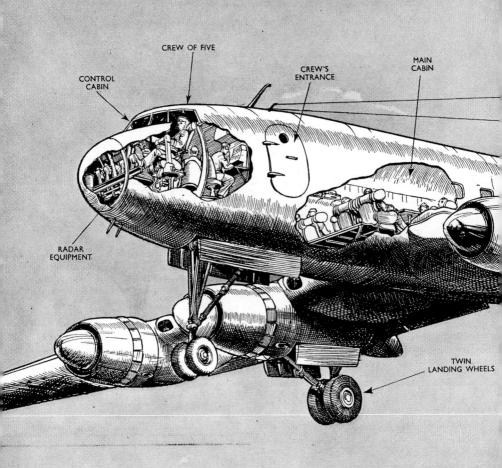

CREW OF FIVE

CONTROL CABIN

CREW'S ENTRANCE

MAIN CABIN

RADAR EQUIPMENT.

TWIN LANDING WHEELS

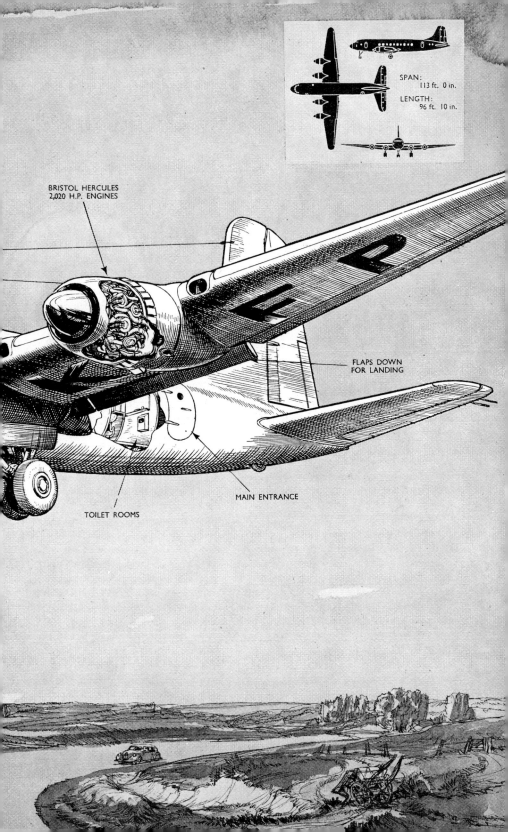

SPAN:
113 ft. 0 in.

LENGTH:
96 ft. 10 in.

BRISTOL HERCULES
2,020 H.P. ENGINES

FLAPS DOWN
FOR LANDING

MAIN ENTRANCE

TOILET ROOMS

which is calibrated in terms of height in feet instead of units of pressure. There are two main types of altimeter: that in which the relationship between pressure and height is used to graduate the instrument on the assumption that temperature is constant at all heights (50 deg. F.); and, second, the type which is calibrated by the I.C.A.N. law, which assumes that air temperature falls from a ground-level temperature of 15 deg. C. at 6.5 deg. C. per kilometre. Errors in the instruments caused through temperature changes can be easily calculated from computers carried in the aircraft.

The altimeter can be set to any particular pressure on a small scale at the bottom of the dial. If the altimeter is set on the ground so that the instrument's scale records the height of the aerodrome above mean sea-level, the instrument will show the height above mean sea-level in flight.

For landing purposes, the pilot may require to set the altimeter to the height above the aerodrome at which he is landing. He can do this by obtaining by radio the pressure at the aerodrome and setting this figure on the small scale; the altimeter will then record the height above that particular aerodrome.

Measuring Rate of Climb

The vertical-movement indicator measures the rate of change of pressure. By means of a diaphragm connected to an indicator on the dial of the instrument, the pressure in a chamber is recorded in relation to the outside air pressure, the chamber being linked to the air outside by a small hole through which the air passes. The indicator thus tells the pilot the rate at which height is being gained or lost and serves as a check on the other instruments.

The turn-and-slip indicator has two needles on a dial; in straight and level flight, the two needles show as a vertical line hinged at the centre. The top needle works on a damped pendulum; in a correctly banked turn the needle remains stationary, but moves in the direction of any slip or skid should the turn not be correctly banked.

The precession of a gyroscope is the principle on which the bottom needle works. When the aeroplane turns, the gyro turns about its vertical axis, which is set in a frame pivoted on a horizontal axis; this results in a precessional movement of the frame. The movement is recorded on the dial by the bottom needle to show a left or right turn and the rate of turn. This instrument is most valuable to a pilot when used in conjunction with the artificial horizon.

The use of the magnetic compass is described elsewhere in this book, but for the purpose of instrument flying reference to it is normally made only to check the setting of the direction indicator.

Instrument Skill

The instruments have been described separately; as, however, a pilot sometimes has to fly for long periods using instruments as his only guide, it is essential that he should be able to do so with the minimum mental strain. Therefore he develops the art of reading the complete panel and uses the artificial horizon as the master instrument, by which he integrates the readings of the whole panel. He knows the position in which the artificial horizon should be for each manoeuvre he has to make, and, by using his controls, is able to make small adjustments until all the other instruments read correctly for each attitude of the aeroplane.

To assist in the relief from strain the dials of the instruments are usually fitted with special lighting which renders the instruments easily readable without any glare or reflections in the cockpit.

Having learned so much about aeroplanes, let us now see what is required of the men who fly them. The captain of a

LINK TRAINER *simulates control reactions of a real aeroplane and can spin, bank, dive and even give a violent imitation of a sideslip. Once the fully equipped cockpit is closed, the pilot must rely entirely on his instruments for the " flight." Duplicate instruments on the controller's desk reflect his progress. The device in front of the controller is the electrically controlled "crab"; this traces the pilot's course on a large-scale map.*

137

modern air-liner has learned his job through many years of study and hard work, and has to pass examinations, both theoretical and practical, to prove his competency before he is permitted to fly public-transport aircraft. In addition, he has to undergo a strict medical examination each time his licence to fly is renewed. For public-transport flying, the licence is renewable every six months.

Physical Standards

In the case of applicants for a pilot's licence to fly public-transport aircraft, the medical examination is conducted by specially qualified medical officers. General requirements must be fulfilled before the detailed examination takes place; that is to say, the pilot must have complete and full use of all four limbs, both eyes, and be free from any medical or surgical dis-

ability or infection. Following the general check-up a detailed questioning concerning family and personal history takes place, together with a complete and thorough check of the nervous system. This is followed by a thorough general surgical examination and then by a general medical examination. If the candidate passes, he has still to undergo a strict examination of the eyes, ears, and nose, throat and mouth: his binocular vision, ocular poise, field of vision of each eye and colour perception must be normal. With regard to the nose, throat and mouth, he must possess free nasal and tubal entry on both sides.

At present, the pilot of a public-transport aircraft has to possess a licence permitting him to carry out such duties. In Britain only he must hold a pilot's licence class B. To obtain this licence, he must undergo practical tests and a techni-

PUPILS *attending instruments class at a British flying-training school. The working of the many instruments used in a modern air-liner must be fully understood.*

EMPIRE COLLEGE OF AERONAUTICS *provides a two-year course for selected students. Here, in the cockpit of an Anson, two students are seen under instruction.*

cal examination. In the latter, theoretical knowledge refers particularly to the type of aeroplane which the pilot wishes to be authorized to fly, and to the types of engines with which the aeroplane is equipped. He must have a knowledge of the various parts of the aeroplane and their assembly and functions, together with a knowledge of the theory of flight and also be able to complete practical tests on rigging.

He must also know the functions of the numerous parts of an internal-combustion engine and know the construction of an engine and how various parts are adjusted, the causes of faulty running and the use of the various engine controls.

In addition to this knowledge of rigging and engines, he must be able to satisfy the examiners as to his knowledge of the instruments fitted on modern aeroplanes.

This is just a small portion of the knowledge which the pilot must possess. He must also know the distress, urgency and safety signals and those signals made and seen during flight, markings and ground signals, and aircraft and marine lights. He must also be familiar with all the information contained in the official publication *Air Pilot* relating to such subjects as air-traffic control and telecommunications.

Knowledge of Regulations

There are other general regulations which he is required to know; such things as licensing of aircraft crews, log books, documents to be carried, general safety provisions for aircraft in flight, Customs requirements, accident regulations, and airworthiness requirements and the pilot's responsibility in connexion with them. This means, in effect, that he must be

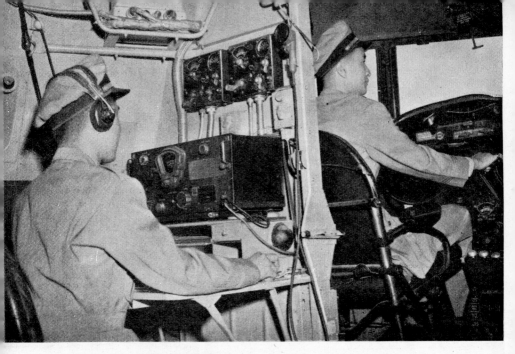

PILOT AND RADIO OFFICER *of one of China's CNAC DC-4s are seen in the control cabin. China was an early entrant in the field of civil air transport.*

thoroughly familiar with the Air Navigation Order and the various Directions issued following the Order. In addition to the above, a pilot is required to have a knowledge of the meteorological organization and meteorology.

Most public-transport pilots, besides possessing the B licence, are also holders of a navigator's licence. This licence requires further study and a very comprehensive knowledge of the science of navigation, including form of the earth, maps, charts and tides, astronomical navigation, aircraft navigation instruments, the earth's magnetism and compasses, radio navigation, signalling and meteorology.

The practical-flying tests for the pilot's licence determine his ability to land without use of the engines within fixed limits of a predetermined point; ability to make accurate turns to both right and left at low altitude, spinning and recovery from spins; cross-country flights with obligatory landings and forced landings, night flying, instrument flying; and, on multi-engined aircraft, ability to fly and manoeuvre with each engine in turn inoperative.

New Licence Classification

However, following agreements reached by the International Civil Aviation Organization, the various member states of that organization will be introducing new professional-pilot's licences and Instrument Rating. Replacing the existing B licence will be three different classes of licence which will be known as: the Commercial Pilot's Licence; Senior Commercial Pilot's Licence; and Air-line Transport Pilot's Licence. New regulations will require pilots, when flying under instrument-flight rules, to possess an Instrument Rating. The 2nd-class Navigator's Licence will also be replaced by an internationally agreed Flight Navigator's Licence.

The Commercial Pilot's Licence will allow a pilot to fly as pilot in charge of a

ELECTRONIC FLIGHT SIMULATOR *duplicates exactly the cockpit of a Boeing Stratocruiser. The switchboard on the right, called "Maddening Maria," simulates faults.*

public-transport aeroplane (but only aircraft of the particular types on which he is technically competent) not engaged on regular air-line services and not exceeding 12,500 lb. in maximum weight, and as second pilot of any aeroplane. Holders of this licence will have at least 200 hours' experience as pilot and will have to reach a standard approximately equivalent to that of the present B licence.

Licence Requirements

The Senior Commercial Pilot's Licence will permit the holder to fly the types of aeroplane on which he is qualified, as pilot in charge of any public-transport aeroplane up to 15,000 lb. maximum weight, and, if it is not carrying passengers, up to 30,000 lb. maximum weight. Holders of this licence will have at least 700 hours' flying experience as pilot. Examinations will be of a standard approximately equivalent to that of the 2nd-class Navigator's Licence, and the holder will have

to pass a stricter medical examination than that for the Commercial Pilot's Licence and must also undergo flying tests, and hold an Instrument Rating.

To hold an Air-line Transport Pilot's Licence, a pilot will have to have at least 1,200 hours' experience as pilot, 100 of which must be night flying, 250 as pilot in charge and 75 hours' flying solely by reference to instruments. This licence will entitle a pilot to fly as pilot in charge of any aeroplane. The ground examination will be of a higher standard than either of the others and there will, of course, be a stringent medical examination, and the candidate must possess an Instrument Rating. The licence will only be valid for types of aircraft on which the pilot is qualified.

Without an Instrument Rating, a pilot will be entitled only to fly under Visual Flight Rules, but the possession of such a rating will permit the holder to fly as pilot in charge or second pilot under Instrument

Flight Rules. An applicant for the Instrument Rating will have to be the holder of a valid pilot's licence. He will be required to pass flying tests in addition to an examination in aviation law (including legislation concerned with air-traffic control, the rules of the air, and the application of the Instrument Rating), air navigation, meteorology, signals, and flight operation.

The latter will be a new examination subject, and will be a subject in which pilots will also be tested before being granted a pilot's licence. It concerns flight planning and the safe operation of aircraft. In the case of Instrument Rating, the subject will include questions on aircraft instruments and radio aids to navigation.

Test Standards

The flying tests require a high standard and include general instrument-flying manoeuvres, the ability to deal with the situation arising from engine failure, flying on a limited instrument panel—that is, with certain blind-flying instruments covered over so that they cannot be used—and descending using an instrument-landing and approach aid. To pass the tests, a candidate will be required to fly to certain specified fine limits.

It is obvious that to attain these standards is no easy matter and requires lengthy and costly training. The cost of flying time is in itself an expensive item. Therefore, one may ask, how does a civil-air-line captain obtain his training?

Before the war there were normally two sources from which air operators drew their pilots. The first was from those who paid for the expensive training at air training schools with the intention of entering civil aviation; and the other was from those who had completed an engagement in the flying arms of the armed Services. The end of the war found some countries, such as Great Britain and the United States of America, with a surplus of trained pilots from the Services.

However, there is a fundamental difference between the approach to civil air operation and military flying. A wider degree of responsibility falls to the lot of the civil pilot, and safety and economy take a higher place in the scheme of things. The methods of handling aircraft differ considerably, and the civil pilot must have a wider knowledge than is normally to be gained in the specialized field of military aviation.

Nevertheless, pilots with experience on heavy night bombers and in Service transport Commands provided good material for a re-awakening civil aviation; but even those with several thousand hours' flying experience still required conversion to civilian methods. Most of them found that, with extra studying, their previous experience stood them in good stead, and they were able to obtain the necessary civil-pilot's licence. With even more hard work and the gaining of a civil-navigator's licence, they found that positions with civil air operators were available to them.

Conversion Experience

This, however, in spite of their licences, did not mean that they were in a position to take command of modern air-liners, particularly in the major corporations and companies. These air-line operators had experienced civil pilots who were used to train the new entrants in the methods of handling civil-transport aircraft and the practical application of the knowledge they had gained whilst studying for civilian licences. The latest recruits spent a considerable period as First Officers (second pilots) and their progress was watched and reported upon; they were given a thorough testing before they were considered suitable to be given command of a commercial air-liner.

When one visualizes how thorough is the training given to a military pilot, particularly those who fly the larger Service types of aircraft, one realizes how

IN FLIGHT *between London and Montreal, the crew of this TCA North Star Skyliner are seen at their stations. The Skyliner is, of course, a Canadair Four.*

thoroughly competent and reliable is the civil-air-liner captain. Elementary military training involves both theoretical and practical knowledge of the aeroplane and its components, the controls and their effects, and also a knowledge of the theory of flight. Practical elementary flying training involves instruction on taxi-ing, flying straight and level, climbing, gliding, stalling, turns, and taking off and landing both into and out of the direction of the wind.

Instruction is also given on spinning and recovery from spins, side-slipping, low flying, forced landings, climbing turns, steep turns, aerobatics, and also what to do should an emergency arise such as engine failure or fire on board. An introduction is also made to flying entirely by instruments.

More advanced instruction is given on heavier aircraft, and those with more complicated controls, on all the above and on other more difficult manoeuvres. Instrument flying assumes greater importance, night flying is introduced to the trainee, as also is the practice and theory of air navigation. At this stage, flying is no longer an end in itself but is automatic, and becomes a means to an end.

Continued Training

By the time he leaves his training unit and joins a squadron, the Service pilot is quite competent. However, he will still continue his training, first as second pilot and then as a captain of aircraft; but even as a captain his training has not ceased. There is always something new to be

143

DESIGNED AS *a military transport, the Avro York uses many of the components of the Lancaster bomber. This York belongs to Skyways, a British charter company.*

learned. By the time he becomes a captain, the pilot will be thoroughly versed in air navigation, radio aids, bad-weather flying and landing in turbulent conditions accompanied by low visibility and cloud ceiling.

So we have progressed in thirty short years from the pilot who navigated by following landmarks on the ground from an open-cockpit biplane, equipped with instruments regarded today as completely inadequate, and fitted with a fixed undercarriage, to the highly trained and skilled commercial pilot, and to the clean-looking modern air-liner which cruises at approximately two and a half to three times the speed of the aeroplane which first crossed the Atlantic non-stop at a speed of 118 m.p.h. in 1919. The modern air-liner carries many people at a standard of comfort undreamed of in those days.

Those thirty years have seen the introduction of fully enclosed cabins, engines of gigantic horse-power, retractable undercarriages, adequate instruments for flying blind, automatic pilots which fly the aeroplane for the pilot, and radio and radar equipment which enable landings to be made in weather conditions in which flying would not have been possible even ten years ago.

But despite the many advances made in thirty years, there are yet greater developments to be made.

New Aircraft

We have now witnessed the flight of the giant Brabazon Mark I prototype which was built by the Bristol Aeroplane Company. This aeroplane, powered by eight 2,500-horse-power Bristol Centaurus engines coupled in pairs, has a span of 230 ft. and a loaded weight of 290,000 lb. It will be used for experimental purposes only, but will be followed by the Mark II version, fitted with eight Bristol Proteus turbo-propeller engines, and designed for flight "above the weather" on the North Atlantic route. The Brabazon

Mark II will cruise at 335 m.p.h. and will be pressurized to enable it to fly at great heights without discomfort to its complement of about a hundred passengers.

Within a few years, we should also see the de Havilland 106 Comet in air-line service. With its four jet engines, this aircraft will serve the Commonwealth routes at speeds of around 500 m.p.h. and at a of a great deal of strain; for when it is put into operation it will keep the aeroplane flying along a desired flight path. Many automatic pilots utilizing hydraulics have been manufactured, but the modern trend is towards electrical techniques.

As automatic pilots became more accurate and reliable, it was natural that more and more should be asked from them.

SPECIFICALLY DESIGNED *as an air-liner, the jet-propelled de Havilland Comet is a striking contrast to the York. The beautiful lines of the Comet suggest speed.*

height in the region of forty-thousand feet.

With the innumerable things the pilot of a modern air-liner has to remember and the great distances covered in one day's flight, one may wonder how he is able to complete a flight without becoming physically and mentally exhausted. However, the development of aids to the pilot has been keeping pace with the elaboration of the highly complex modern air-liner, and one of the most useful of these aids is the automatic pilot. This relieves the pilot

If they could fly an aeroplane straight and level, could they not manoeuvre the aeroplane as the pilot wished? They could, and they did. So, following the automatic pilot which was capable of keeping an aeroplane straight and level, came the automatic pilot which could execute manoeuvres under the watchful eye of the pilot.

The operation of the automatic controls is primarily governed by two gyroscope units, one of which controls the rudder and elevators and the other the ailerons. In

145

MAXIMUM SPEED *of 124 m.p.h. makes the Fairey Gyrodyne (above) one of the world* *fastest helicopters. The propeller on the starboard wing stub counteracts rotor torque and* *at the same time adds to the forward thrust. Shown below is the Percival Prince, a two-motor* *transport of the smaller, short-stage and executive-use class.*

some modern automatic pilots, however, three gyroscope units are used. Coordinated turns are accomplished by the action of the rudder and ailerons in response to the movement of small knobs on a panel in the pilot's cockpit. Climbing or diving attitudes are adopted by the action of the elevator in response to another small knob. Thus the pilot is relieved of the strain of holding the controls for many hours and counteracting the results of every air disturbance which moves his aeroplane out of equilibrium.

Fully Automatic Flight?

The next stage of automatic-pilot development is that of complete flight control. We have already opened the door to this stage. In 1948, it will be remembered, an aeroplane took off from the United States of America, flew the North Atlantic Ocean and landed at Brize Norton aerodrome in England without it being necessary for a pilot to touch the controls. This flight was not a stunt, and such occurrences may become everyday affairs more quickly than many think possible.

Already, a very useful item of equipment has become available for commercial use; it couples the radio receivers of the instrument-landing system in the aircraft with the automatic pilot and controls the aircraft so that it follows the correct line of approach, as guided by radio signals, when an approach to land is made in really bad weather. The pilot, however, lands the aircraft manually.

The need for automatic flight control is becoming more obvious every day, particularly in areas where air traffic is dense. The modern pilot is furnished with all manner of instruments and radio and radar facilities to ensure safe operation and navigation. He has to remember many differing procedures which must be complied with in different parts of the world, and holding and landing procedures which may differ from airport to airport. Almost all information, whether supplied by his crew or from the ground, must be received by the pilot, interpreted and put into action. The time is rapidly approaching when this will prove too much for one man.

Commercially, automatic flight may not replace the pilot; but it could carry out the routine function of flying and leave the pilot free to deal with the numerous messages, Air Traffic Control instructions and procedures which are necessary today and will be more necessary in the future if air traffic is to fly expeditiously and with safety. Another pointer in the same direction is the fact that speeds are increasing rapidly; eventually, the limiting factor of human reaction will make it impossible to follow a predetermined flight path.

In the old days, a pilot could fly slowly, checking his position on a map as he went; wandering off his course a few miles did not matter. Such methods are out of date. Nowadays, a pilot must adhere to his flight plan, navigate accurately with the aid of radio, and follow an exact routine in approach and landing. At future higher speeds his problems will intensify. Just as, today, the automatic pilot manoeuvres the aeroplane to the pilot's wishes, so, in the future, it is to be expected that new automatic pilots will control the high-speed aeroplane from take-off, throughout flight, to touchdown under the control of the pilot, who, of course, will be able to fly the aeroplane manually if he so desires.

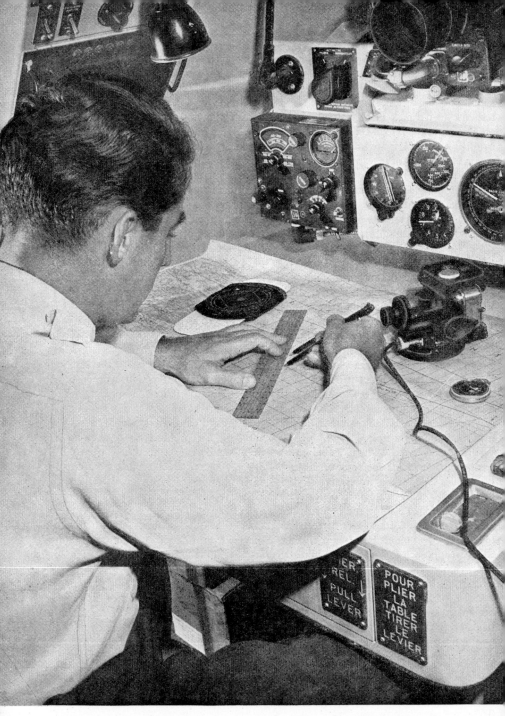

NAVIGATOR'S STATION *in a Constellation. The radio compass faces the navigator. Although radio and radar aids have done much to lighten his task, the ability to navigate by observation and calculation alone is still essential. A sextant rests on the chart table.*

CHAPTER 5

FINDING THE
WAY THROUGH SPACE

In the early days of aviation, all that a pilot needed to find his way from place to place was a compass and a map of the surrounding countryside. Even then it was not always easy, as map-reading from the air is quite a different thing from map-reading on the ground. As a rule, however, he got along fairly well as he seldom went very far, his speed was not very high and he did not frequently attempt to fly in or above cloud or out of sight of land. But today all this has changed. Flights are of short duration when compared with journeys by sea, but, nevertheless, due to the high speed of modern aircraft, many hundreds of miles are covered on a single flight; and often the aeroplane is flying high above cloud, out of sight of land or sea, for hours on end.

Anyone who has motored through unfamiliar country, or made his way on foot over the Scottish Highlands, the Cumbrian Fells or across the wilds of Dartmoor, is familiar with some of the basic principles of navigation, such as the need to keep a constant check on position, by reference to some known landmark such as a town, river, wood or distant hill, and to estimate progress by reference to direction of travel, speed of movement and the lapse of time. These same principles form the basis of air navigation, but there are many other factors which the air navigator has to take into account before he can be sure of arriving safely at his destination.

In the first place, it is important to remember that an aeroplane cannot heave to, or stop, if bad weather is encountered; nor, if the navigator loses track of his position, can he call a halt while he sorts things out. If the ground can be seen, the pilot can, of course, circle round a town or other landmark and stay more or less in one position until it is identified on a map, but when out of sight of land the problem is not so easily solved.

Second, there is a limit to the amount of fuel which an aeroplane can carry; and, come what may, a safe landing place must be found before fuel runs out if risk of accident is to be avoided.

Air Movement

At first sight it may not be obvious why the navigator, knowing the distance and bearing of his destination airport from his point of departure, should have much difficulty in finding it. If he wants to fly from London to Amsterdam, for example, why can he not measure off the distance and bearing from a map, use his compass to head for Amsterdam and tell when he will arrive by comparing the distance to be flown with his air speed as recorded on the air-speed indicator in the cockpit? The reason is simply that the aeroplane is

149

FLYING OVER WINDSOR CASTLE *is this Percival Proctor. The Proctor, a British light aeroplane seating four persons, was designed for both military and private use.*

airborne; it is carried in the air, which itself is constantly moving across the surface of the earth in a direction and at a speed which can vary very considerably not only with height, but from hour to hour and from place to place.

Everyone is familiar with this movement of the air in the form of winds blowing across the surface of the earth, varying in strength from an almost imperceptible breeze to a gale or hurricane; but it is not so generally known that wind speeds tend to increase with height and to change direction as well. Also, of course, winds are

often purely local; an aeroplane, flying perhaps from London to Bristol, may well start off in a light north-westerly airstream and arrive in a south-westerly gale an hour or so later, having left the fine weather behind.

The effect of the wind on an aeroplane should not be confused with its effect on, say, a ship, which is in contact with the water and thus offers resistance to the wind. The aeroplane is carried in the air and thus offers no resistance whatever to the force of air in movement, being carried along with it whichever way it blows.

A LANDMARK *seen from the air. This is Windsor Castle as seen by many air-line passengers using London Airport. Note the railway station (bottom left) and main-road traffic.*

There are, in fact, three forces acting on the aeroplane. One is the force of gravity, pulling it towards the earth, and how this is overcome is explained in another chapter. The second is provided by the engine or engines, driving it forward through the air. The third is the wind. It is important that the effect of the wind be fully understood, and one or two analogies may help to make things clear.

Allowance for Drift

Suppose, for example, a goldfish decides to swim in a straight line from south to north across its bowl of water, a distance of perhaps nine inches. It does so; and, provided that the bowl itself is stationary, the goldfish will arrive over a point on the floor nine inches north of its starting place. But if, while it is swimming, someone carries the bowl from the west to the east side of the room, the point on the floor below the goldfish when it finishes its swim will be, not nine inches north, but probably ten feet almost due east of where it started. The goldfish corresponds to the aeroplane; the water in which it swims, to the air through which the aeroplane flies; and the movement of the water across the room represents the wind or movement of the air over the ground.

Another illustration is that of a man swimming across a river which flows, say, from west to east. If he starts from the southern bank and swims due north, he will not reach the other bank at a place opposite to his starting point. Although he is swimming north, the current is carrying him east and he will thus arrive at the opposite bank at a point downstream.

For a third illustration, imagine a man walking to and fro along the corridor of a train. After half an hour or so he may be in precisely the same position in the train as he was when he started, but his

FLYING LOWER *over the castle, details can easily be picked out—some of them unexpected. Few people realize, for instance, that the large tower is not truly circular in cross-section.*

"ground position" may be 30 miles or so away. This shows what happens to an aeroplane circling above cloud without any landmark to help the pilot to maintain his position relative to the ground. If a wind is blowing at 60 m.p.h.—and such speeds are by no means uncommon at high altitudes—at the end of half an hour he, too, will be 30 miles from where he started circling. This shows the importance to the navigator of making an adequate allowance for the effect of wind.

Pre-flight Planning

In good weather, of course, a trained pilot or navigator can find his way from one aerodrome to another by drawing a line on his map to show the required track over the ground and keeping to this track by looking over the side from time to time and checking his progress on the map. But this is not good enough for the air-line pilot, who is required to keep to a set time-table. He must work out what heights, speeds and courses to fly before he takes off and check his progress much more carefully if he is to arrive on time at his destination. Also, he will wish to take advantage of any favourable winds and avoid head-winds as far as possible, so as to avoid unnecessary waste of fuel. And, for the comfort of his passengers, he will plan his flight so as to fly above or below any turbulent layers, and to skirt any local storms which lie on or near his normal route.

In order to do all this, he will consult the weather forecaster before taking-off and obtain full details of the weather he may expect to meet on his journey, taking particular note of wind speeds and directions at various heights along the route. This process is all part of what is known as pre-flight planning: tracks and distances are measured, bearings noted, courses to steer calculated and heights are decided having regard to winds and to high ground en route; then speeds and times are worked out, so that by the time the aeroplane leaves the ground, the captain and his crew have as complete a picture as possible of the entire flight from start to finish.

Reference has been made above to flying to a time-table, or schedule-keeping,

FUTURE AIR-LINE NAVIGATORS *study their subject in the classroom. The diagrams on the blackboard illustrate triangles of velocities, the basis of the air plot.*

as it is generally known in flying circles. While every effort is made to keep to schedule by adjusting speed and keeping accurately to the route laid down, it must be remembered that even modern aircraft cannot vary their speeds over a wide range and still operate economically. Sometimes it is not possible to keep to time in the face of strong adverse winds. At other times it may be possible to do so, but only at the expense of an uneconomically high fuel consumption. Also, for economic reasons, it is clearly desirable to take advantage of following winds; but doing so in the case of, for example, a transatlantic crossing, may mean arriving an hour or more ahead of the published time.

Value of Map-reading

The air-line companies and their staffs, of course, are kept fully informed of the aircraft's progress and are always ready to receive the aeroplane when it arrives, but it is not always easy to explain to passengers who arrive unexpectedly early, or whose friends are kept waiting for them, that such departures from the scheduled times are sometimes unavoidable.

It should not be thought that the comprehensive pre-flight planning described makes the ability to read a map no longer an essential part of the air navigator's trade. Map-reading is, in fact, one of the very first things he has to learn and it forms a most fascinating study. It is not a science but an art, which can only be mastered after careful study and considerable experience. The best of instruments may fail from one cause or another, and, after all, there is nothing so reliable—or reassuring—as the positive identification on a map of some landmark, although seen, perhaps, from a distance of several miles through a small gap in the clouds.

The pilot or navigator must be able to do two things before he can consider himself an efficient and experienced map-reader. The first is to judge, from their

PILOT AND NAVIGATOR *discuss the route in the cockpit. The navigator holds a computer, which simplifies his calculations. The pilot and navigator must work as a team.*

presentation on a map, what various objects are going to look like from the air, so that he will readily pick them up as he passes overhead; the second is to be able to identify quickly and accurately on his map any landmark which appears.

Anyone who has flown will know how different familiar objects look when viewed from above instead of from ground level. Hills which form prominent landmarks to the pedestrian or the motorist can be easily missed if the aircraft is flying at, say, 5,000 ft. and the hills themselves are only a few hundred feet above the general level of the ground.

Before taking off, then, the first task is to study a suitable map and look for landmarks on or near the route to be followed which are likely to be easily recognized. Among these may be included lakes,

153

A PIN-POINT FIX can be obtained through a break in the cloud. The Percival Prince shown here is at too great a height to allow recognition of small ground features.

reservoirs, railways, rivers and canals, coastlines, large towns and large woods of distinctive shape. The last-mentioned, however, should be treated with some caution, as deforestation can swiftly change a first-class landmark into something quite unrecognizable. Roads must also be treated with care, since a tarred highway, particularly if overhung by trees from place to place, is by no means always as easy to see as might be thought; also, after a heavy fall of rain such roads look rather like rivers or canals, particularly when seen against the light.

Deceptive Landmarks

This is not the only way in which roads can be deceptive. Quite minor roads in chalky country—even cart tracks over moorland—sometimes show up with extraordinary clarity. Often they may be seen stretching away for miles into the distance, although, from a road-transport point of view, they may be of such little importance

that they do not appear on the map at all.

There are times when a map can be most useful even though no definite landmark can be identified. This may sound paradoxical, but an excellent example is to be found on the East Anglian coast. During World War II, many a pilot returning to England across the coastline between the Wash and the Thames Estuary was able to obtain a check on his position by comparing the direction of the coast with his compass. Even on a dark night the coast is usually visible; and if, for example, it is seen to be running roughly from south-east to north-west, then the aircraft must be in the vicinity of Mundesley, between Cromer and Great Yarmouth. Similarly, if the coastline beneath the aeroplane runs north and south and, to the north, it is seen to turn towards the east, then reference to a map will establish the pilot's position as in the vicinity of Dunwich, about halfway between Lowestoft and Orfordness.

Another example is to be found when crossing an estuary such as that of the River Severn. By noting the time taken to cross from one shore to the other, it is possible to make a fairly accurate estimate of the width of the estuary at the point of crossing. Reference to the map will then tell, almost with certainty, just where the crossing was made.

So much for map-reading. When suitable landmarks are plentiful, it is fairly easy for an experienced navigator to find his way across country in reasonably good visibility by map-reading alone, but when a flight is to be made across the open sea or above cloud out of sight of land it is necessary to fly by dead reckoning—D.R. navigation, as it is usually called.

Dead Reckoning

There is no magic about D.R. We have already seen that, in the absence of wind, the path of an aeroplane over the ground can be estimated from the compass in the cockpit whilst the air-speed indicator and a watch or clock will tell us the distance travelled. Suppose, for example, we pass over Flamborough Head, flying due east at 180 m.p.h. at dawn on a still summer's day. Ten minutes later our D.R. position will be 30 miles east of Flamborough Head, since we are travelling eastwards at a rate of three miles a minute. Using the correct map scale, the navigator draws a line due east from Flamborough Head representing a distance of 30 miles and this is the beginning of what is known as an air plot. In conditions of no wind, of course, "air positions" and "ground positions" are coincident.

Now suppose that a steady wind is blowing from the south-west at 30 m.p.h.; we shall still have flown 30 miles eastwards through the air but in the same time the air itself has moved a distance of five miles over the ground from south-west to north-east. Our D.R. position at the end of the ten minutes is therefore five miles north-east of the air position and, at the end of an hour, our D.R. position over the ground

PART OF *the kind of map in common use with air navigators. The area enclosed by the rectangle is shown on page 156 as it appears on a map of much larger scale.*

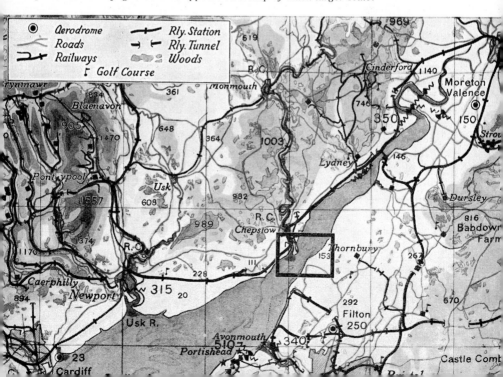

BEACHLEY POINT *as seen by the navigator. Compare this photograph with the two maps, on this and the preceding page.*

will be 30 miles north-east of the corresponding air position however many times we may have altered course in the meantime.

The condition of no wind is, of course, extremely rare. Even when there is little more than a slight breeze at ground level there is usually an appreciable wind blowing at higher altitudes, and the art of navigating an aeroplane accurately depends on an accurate knowledge of wind velocities. Weather forecasts obtained before take-off will, of course, contain estimates of wind velocities at all heights required along the proposed route, whether it be from Land's End to the Scilly Isles or from Prestwick to Gander in Newfoundland across the North Atlantic. Such forecasts, however, cannot always be accurate and the navigator must therefore check them continually as he flies along. This is normally done by "fixing position" as explained later and comparing the "fix" with the D.R. position.

Provided that courses have been ·accurately flown and the aeroplane has been kept to its correct height and air speed, any discrepancy between a reliable fix

LARGER-SCALE MAP *(above) shows the area in which the two photographs were taken. With a map to this scale, unlike that on page 155, detail features can be recognized.*

and the corresponding D.R. position reveals an error in the wind velocity used for estimating the D.R. position. The actual wind velocity must be worked out at once, as a change of course will probably be necessary to bring the aeroplane back on track for its destination. In the case of an air-liner flying a scheduled service, a change of speed may also be necessary to ensure that the destination is reached at the required time.

Before describing some of the methods of fixing position it will be as well to explain what is meant by a line of position, or position line, as these terms will be frequently used. A position line is always associated with a given time and when a navigator draws a position line on his chart it means that, at the stated time, his aeroplane was somewhere along that line, although he may not know just where.

A simple example of a position line is obtained from a transit bearing. Suppose, for example, that a navigator flying across the Irish Sea notes that the Point of Ayr and Maughold Head on the Isle of Man are in line with each other. He draws a straight line on his chart passing through these two headlands and thus obtains a line of position. A position line can also be obtained by means of a compass if some distant landmark is visible, but when no landmarks are to be seen the navigator has to rely on astro-navigation or on radio or radar aids of one kind or another. Most of these provide him with position lines, and by selecting two or more (preferably not less than three) which intersect each other he obtains a fix.

If it is possible to obtain two or more position lines simultaneously, then clearly

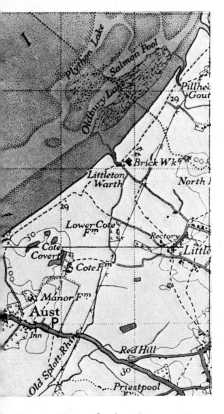

OTHER SIDE *of the Severn Estuary (right). The ferry pier can be seen at the bottom of the picture, as can two roads and most of the coastal features.*

157

AIDS TO NAVIGATION

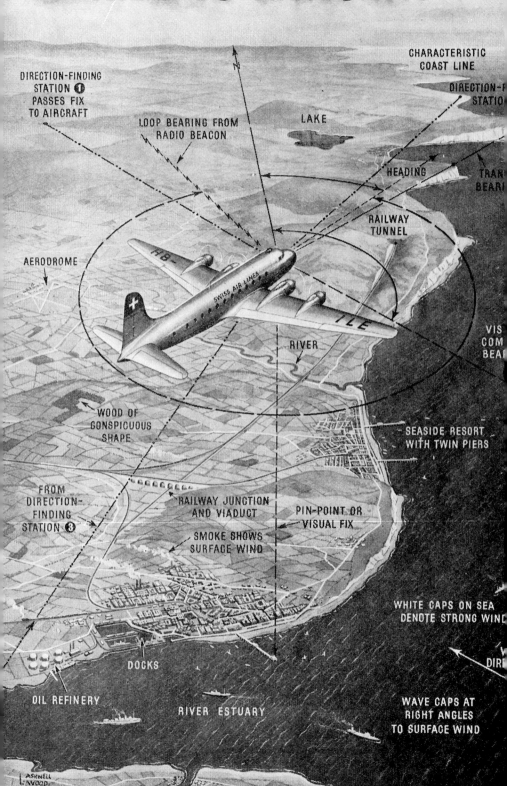

DIRECTION-FINDING STATION ❶ PASSES FIX TO AIRCRAFT

LOOP BEARING FROM RADIO BEACON

CHARACTERISTIC COAST LINE

DIRECTION-F STATIO

LAKE

HEADING

TRAN BEARI

RAILWAY TUNNEL

AERODROME

HB

SWISS AIR LINES

ILE

VIS COM BEAI

RIVER

WOOD OF CONSPICUOUS SHAPE

SEASIDE RESORT WITH TWIN PIERS

FROM DIRECTION-FINDING STATION ❸

RAILWAY JUNCTION AND VIADUCT

PIN-POINT OR VISUAL FIX

SMOKE SHOWS SURFACE WIND

WHITE CAPS ON SEA DENOTE STRONG WIN

DOCKS

W DIRI

OIL REFINERY

RIVER ESTUARY

WAVE CAPS AT RIGHT ANGLES TO SURFACE WIND

the point of intersection represents the position of the aeroplane at the time the observations were made. Normally, however, this is not possible, and when a period of time elapses between observations, allowance must be made for the distance travelled between them. This is done by drawing a "transferred" position line parallel to the line of position first obtained, the distance between the two parallel lines representing the distance flown over the ground between the two observations.

From the foregoing it will be seen that the basis of all air navigation is fixing the aeroplane's position at regular intervals, so that checks can be made on the wind, and, if necessary, alterations can be made to the course and speed being flown.

As already stated, the easiest, and most positive, method of fixing position is by map-reading; but when the navigator is precluded from using this simple means, resort must be made to other fixing devices. In the following paragraphs, therefore, details are given of the various fixing facilities available to a navigator, and the method of employing them.

Light Beacons

A navigator flying over or near the sea at night can, of course, get a considerable amount of help from the many lighthouses and lightships to be found in all parts of the world. If he is traversing unfamiliar ground, however, he would be very well advised to make quite sure that those he hopes to use will in fact be visible from above, since they are installed, of course, for shipping and are beamed horizontally as a general rule.

There are, however, numerous so-called aerial lighthouses and aerodrome beacons operating specifically for the use of aircraft. These are designed to throw the maximum amount of light upwards in a wide inverted cone so as to be seen not only from great heights but also from a

considerable distance away. To facilitate identification they are usually coded, not as are marine lights, but simply by flashing a single- or two-letter characteristic in morse code.

What are known as aerial lighthouses are provided for general navigation purposes and are of high power. The aerodrome beacons are usually of lower power and are installed on or near to individual aerodromes to assist pilots in making their final approach to the aerodrome itself. They may also be used in some circumstances as a holding point round which aeroplanes may circle whilst awaiting their turn to land.

Astro-navigation

Astronomical navigation is an art which has been practised for a great number of years. It is of great value to long-distance air navigation, since it enables the navigator to fix his position almost anywhere and at any time provided, of course, that the sky is not completely obscured by cloud. Long-distance aircraft, however, normally fly at high altitude "above the weather" so that at night the stars and planets can usually be clearly seen, whilst by day the sun can be used, or, if visible, the moon.

Another advantage of astro-navigation is that, whilst radio aids may suffer from interference and other troubles of various kinds, the stars and other heavenly bodies are always there and can be relied on at all times. There are, however, two drawbacks, but both of these can be overcome by constant practice. The first is that plotting an astro fix takes some time—although this, of course, is not serious on a long-distance flight.

The second difficulty, which can be most baffling, is that an aeroplane in flight does not form a very good platform from which to take astro sights. For reasons explained later, it is necessary to measure very accurately, by means of a sextant, the angle subtended between the horizontal and the star or other body used, and it is by no means easy to do this unless the aeroplane is flying absolutely straight and level at a constant speed. Any slight change in speed or direction will cause an error and, for this reason, modern aircraft sextants are designed to give the average of a large number of readings taken in rapid succession.

The information which the navigator gets from a single astro sight is a single line of position. In order to obtain a fix, therefore, it is the practice to measure the altitudes of two or three different stars and to fix position, as previously described, by plotting the position lines obtained on a chart and noting where they intersect, due allowance being made for the distance travelled by the aeroplane in between successive "shots."

To understand the basic principle of astronomical navigation, it is necessary to know just how a position line is obtained by measuring the altitude of a star. In the brief explanation given below, reference is made to the substellar point, which is the point at which a straight line joining a given star to the centre of the earth cuts the surface of the earth. Thus, if one is standing at the substellar point of a star it will be immediately overhead; in other words, its altitude will be 90 deg.

Substellar Points

Owing to the rotation of the earth about its own axis and round the sun, the stars appear to move across the sky so that the substellar points are constantly moving, but tables have been prepared showing exactly where the substellar points of the various stars will be at any instant of time throughout the year. Knowing the substellar point, it follows that the distance and bearing of any point on the earth's surface from any such point can also be determined in advance.

We saw earlier on that, at the substellar point, the altitude of the star would be 90 deg. If the altitude is measured and found to be *less* than 90 deg., it follows that the observer is somewhere on the perimeter of a circle centred on the substellar point and that the radius of this circle will depend on the altitude measured, the altitude becoming steadily less as the observer moves away from the substellar point.

And so the navigator plots an astro sight thus: first, he selects the star he wishes to use and measures its altitude by means of his sextant, noting the time to the nearest second and the altitude to the nearest minute of arc, that is, to the nearest sixtieth of a degree. He then plots his D.R. position at that instant on his chart and finds from his tables the bearing, or azimuth, of the substellar point from his D.R. position. This line is drawn on the chart through the D.R. position and corresponds to a section of the radius of the circle mentioned in the last paragraph.

Astro Calculations

Now, from his tables, he can also find out the exact length of this radius from the substellar point to the D.R. position and the corresponding star altitude. By comparing this "assumed" altitude—that is, the altitude for his assumed, or D.R., position—with the altitude he actually measured with his sextant, he can find out just how much farther from, or nearer to, the substellar point he was at the time of making the observation. If, for example, the sight obtained is less than that calculated from the tables, then he is farther away from the substellar point than his D.R. position, and vice versa.

Suppose his calculations show him to be six miles farther away, then a line drawn at right-angles to the azimuth line already plotted, cutting this line at a point six miles from the D.R. position and on the opposite side of it to the substellar point, will be his required position line. In actual fact, the position line is an arc

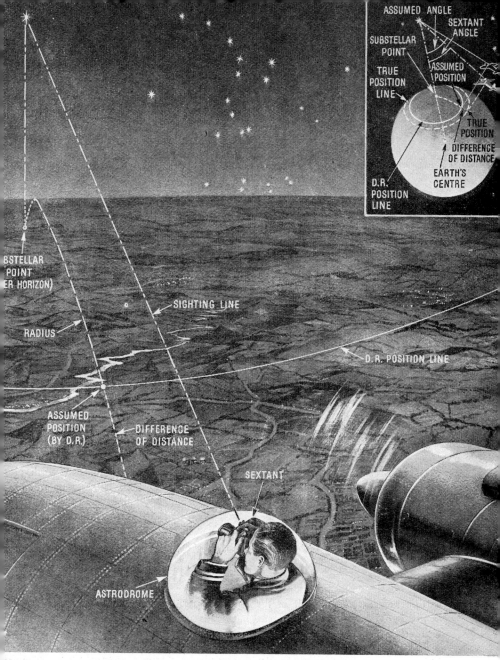

ASSUMED ANGLE
SEXTANT ANGLE
SUBSTELLAR POINT
ASSUMED POSITION
TRUE POSITION LINE
TRUE POSITION
DIFFERENCE OF DISTANCE
EARTH'S CENTRE
D.R. POSITION LINE

BSTELLAR POINT
ER HORIZON)

SIGHTING LINE

RADIUS

D.R. POSITION LINE

ASSUMED POSITION (BY D.R.)

DIFFERENCE OF DISTANCE

SEXTANT

ASTRODROME

ASTRO-NAVIGATION. *The navigator is measuring a star's altitude with a sextant. He compares this angle with that for his assumed position and then converts the angles into a difference of distance from the substellar point. The difference is applied to the line joining the assumed position and substellar point to give a radius of the true position line. The point of intersection of a succession of such astro position lines gives a fix.*

F

ONE OF THE EARLIEST *means of navigation, the stars are still used as a means of finding position. An air-line navigator is here seen using a sextant in the astrodome.*

of a circle centred on the substellar point with a radius equal to that found from the tables, plus six miles; but the radius is normally so great that for all practical purposes the small arc of the circle drawn can be drawn as a straight line.

The Pole star is of particular interest to the navigator since its substellar point lies very nearly at the North Pole and so changes little with the rotation of the earth. The measured altitude of the Pole star can thus be very easily converted into latitude, by means of a small correction given in the tables, since parallels of latitude are circles centred on the Pole itself.

Position lines are obtained from the sun, moon and planets in a similar way to that described for star sights, but additional calculations have to be made as they are much nearer to the earth and

because the moon itself revolves round the earth; and the planets, like the earth, also revolve round the sun. The stars are much more simple to use because they are so far away that all rays reaching the earth are parallel to each other and their apparent movement across the surface of the earth is much less complex.

Direction-finding Methods

Radio direction-finding, or D.F., to use the common abbreviation, has provided aircraft with valuable navigation information from very early days. There are two forms of D.F., one in which bearings are found by the aeroplane and the other in which radio bearings are obtained by ground stations and passed back to the aeroplane, usually by W/T—wireless telegraphy. As a matter of interest, the term wireless is seldom used nowadays, but the abbreviation W/T remains. It has not been changed to R/T possibly because this is the accepted abbreviation for radio telephony; that is, the transmission and reception of radio messages by voice instead of morse code.

Most multi-engined aeroplanes, as well as some single-engined machines, are fitted with a loop aerial and associated radio receiver. By means of this loop, which is generally rotatable, the navigator or his radio operator can determine the bearing of a distant transmitting station in relation to the fore-and-aft line of the aeroplane. The heading of the aeroplane (its direction in relation to north) can be found from the compass so that the radio bearing can easily be converted to a bearing from north.

Loop Bearings

Suppose, for example, that an aeroplane is on a heading of 225 deg.—in other words, is flying due south-west—and a loop bearing of 080 deg. is obtained on the B.B.C. station at Brookmans Park. Starting from north, we measure 225 deg. to get the fore-and-aft line of the aircraft, then add a further 80 deg. for the loop bearing and find that Brookmans Park bears 305 deg. from the aeroplane. Now, the position of the transmitter is known, but not that of the aeroplane, so to obtain the required position line we must plot the reciprocal bearing (305+180 deg.) from Brookmans Park. Thus we are somewhere on a line bearing 485 deg. from the transmitting station. This, of course, is the same thing as 125 deg., as 360 deg. make up a complete circle.

It is not proposed here to explain in detail how the loop works, but, very simply, the principle is that when the loop itself lies at right-angles to the direction of the signal received, both sides of the loop receive identical signals and these are made to cancel each other out. With the loop in any other position, one side of it receives the signal a fraction of a second before the

other side, and a minute signal voltage is developed between the ends of the loop winding, and registered by the equipment.

A rotatable loop is always installed to show zero deg. when it lies across the fore-and-aft axis of the aeroplane and the operator reads off the bearing on the scale provided when he has found the precise setting at which signal strength is weakest.

Some aircraft carry automatic D.F. equipment (known as A.D.F.) in the form of a radio compass. As its name implies, this equipment finds the bearing automatically whenever tuned in to a radio station, and a special circuit is incorporated, as in the case of most manual loop installations, to make sure that the true, and not a reciprocal, bearing is found. Without this sensing device, as it is called, the loop might register zero when the source of the signals received was dead astern instead of dead ahead.

So far reference has been made to broadcasting stations which, when on the air, can

GROUND D.F. STATION *which provides navigational assistance. A transmission from the aeroplane is received by the operator, who determines the bearing of the aeroplane from his particular ground station.*

of course be used provided that their radio frequencies and precise positions on the chart are known. In most countries, however, radio beacons are provided specially for aircraft. These often work twenty-four hours a day, and are sited on or near aerodromes and at other useful positions so that whenever possible a navigator is within range of at least two of them and can thus obtain a fix. They vary in size and power, but all transmit a steady note, with which the operator can find the minimum reading, with a morse code identification signal radiated at regular intervals. They are variously referred to as medium-frequency (M.F.) beacons, radio beacons or non-directional beacons. The last-mentioned term is used to indicate that the beacon itself does not give bearing indication; it merely transmits a signal in all directions, and bearings are found by the loop equipment in the aircraft. This term

distinguishes them from various forms of rotating beacon which tell the navigator his bearing without any need for a loop aerial. There have been several kinds of such directional beacons, but for various reasons they are not entirely satisfactory.

Ground D.F. Stations

The second form of D.F. is that in which bearings are taken by ground stations on signals transmitted by the aeroplane. These stations may work singly, in which case the aeroplane is given position-line information. This can be used for plotting purposes in the same way as any other bearing, or for homing, that is, flying towards the beacon site. When used for homing it is customary for the ground station to pass to the aeroplane a series of bearings, each of which is the reciprocal of the bearing it finds. These bearings can thus be directly used by the pilot to home to the ground

RADIO AND RADAR *play an important part in navigation, and the radio officer, here shown in a Viking, provides much of the information required by the navigator.*

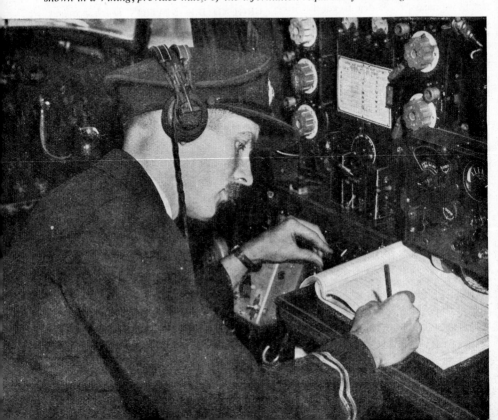

station. A series of bearings is needed because, unless the pilot makes due allowance for any drift due to wind, he will not remain on a constant bearing and might miss the station altogether without frequent corrections to bring him safely overhead.

A more elaborate form of D.F. assistance is provided when three or more ground stations work together to form a so-called fixer service. The ground stations, which are many miles apart, are linked together by telephone lines and all take bearings simultaneously when the aeroplane transmits a signal. In the case of a three-station chain two of the stations pass their bearings by land-line to the master, or central, station, where all three bearings are plotted on a special table. In practice, they will rarely precisely intersect at one spot, owing to numerous small errors which creep in, but in most cases the position of the aircraft can be estimated with a considerable degree of accuracy, and this radio fix, usually expressed in latitude and longitude, is radioed back to the aeroplane.

Radio Range

The radio range is a special form of ground station which was originally developed in the United States of America and is still widely used to mark the civil airways in America and in many other countries of the world. The radio range is likely to remain in use for many years, for it requires a bare minimum of airborne equipment. Where routes are marked by radio ranges, in fact, they can be followed accurately by aircraft fitted with no more than a simple radio receiving set. The range stations also serve as radio beacons for aircraft fitted with loop equipment or A.D.F.

As already stated, the ordinary non-directional radio beacon transmits in all directions; in other words, it emits radio waves in a circular pattern. The radio-range station, however, by means of a special aerial arrangement, sends out waves in the form of four lobes, rather like four petals

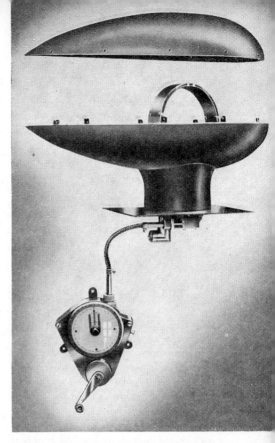

LOOP AERIAL. *The casing, fitted externally, contains the rotatable loop. The angular position of the loop is shown on the circular scale inside the aeroplane.*

of a flower. Four sectors are thus formed and in two of these which oppose each other, say one north-east of the station and the other south-west of it, the transmitter sends out a repetition of the letter A in morse (· —), interrupted at intervals by the station's identification signal. In the other sectors letter N is radiated (— ·).

Where the sectors overlap, the two signals merge into a steady note. This area of overlap is known as the equisignal zone. The station just described can thus be used to mark two air corridors or airways, one running from north to south and the other from east to west. The pilot keeps to his required route by listening to the

165

radio signals and flying along the virtual beam formed by the equisignal path.

A radio-range station can provide only four beams; while these beams need not necessarily be exactly at right-angles to each other, they work best that way. What is known as an omni-range is being developed, and this, when used with the special airborne equipment designed for it, provides the pilot with an almost infinite number of beams radiating in all directions from the transmitter site. It has the added advantage that it works on much higher radio frequencies than the ordinary radio range and is therefore less susceptible to interference. It is also less likely to suffer from distortion caused by such things as

THE GEE NAVIGATION SYSTEM is based on a network of curves, each representing a constant difference of distance between two points. The aeroplane shown in the diagram below is all the time 20 miles farther from A than it is from B. It is thus following a line of constant distance difference, called a hyperbola. Other similar curves of constant difference can be drawn, as shown on the left of the illustration.

mountain ranges and large lakes or areas of mineral deposits; these sometimes cause the beams of the radio range to become bent, to be split into a number of false beams, or to waver from side to side.

The omni-range station is, however, much more elaborate and expensive than the relatively simple four-course range, as the radio range is often known, and cannot be used unless the aeroplane is fitted with a special radio receiver which sorts out the signals and feeds the information to instruments specially designed for this function situated in the cockpit.

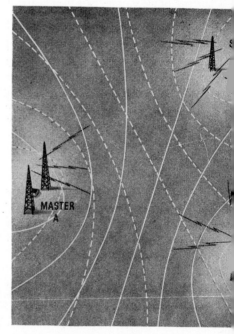

GEE GROUND STATIONS, *Master A and Slave B, send out timed pulses of radio energy. If a further slave station, C, is added and made to operate in conjunction with Master A, two sets of hyperbolae are formed, and these make a lattice or network of radio lines. This lattice is overprinted in colours on a special navigation chart, and each curve is numbered. A simplified representation of such a chart is shown on page 167.*

THE GEE SET *in the aeroplane detects the radio pulses forming the lattice as they arrive, and measures the time interval between their arrival. This information is translated into Gee numbers, which are used by the navigator—in the same way as a motorist uses map references—to determine his position on the lattice and thus on the chart.*

Radio ranges can be used up to distances of about 150 miles from the transmitter, but the beam, of course, becomes wider as the distance from the station increases. In the vicinity of the station the width of the beam is about 50 ft., but it increases to seven miles or so 100 miles away. The omni-range cannot be used at such great distances, unless the aeroplane is fairly high, since the very short waves used do not follow the curvature of the earth but shoot off into space. Ordinary broadcast stations use waves more like those of the radio range and can thus be received at ground level many miles away.

Another radio aid to navigation is the Consol system. This works in the medium-frequency waveband and uses high-power transmitters which can be received hundreds of miles away. With Consol, a special map is generally used, and the navigator obtains a position line from a Consol station by listening to the signals received and counting a number of dots and dashes. On his map he finds a series of radial lines drawn from the transmitter site and finds the particular line which corresponds to the number of dots and dashes he counted. To obtain a fix, it is, of course, necessary to receive signals from two different Consol stations and note where the two position lines intersect.

At the present time there are Consol stations in various parts of Europe, one at Bushmills in Northern Ireland and another at Stavanger in Norway, providing fixing cover over most of the British Isles. Others are installed on the French and Spanish coasts and additional stations to provide coverage over the North Atlantic

RADIO OFFICER'S DESK *in a Canadair Four of the type in service with B.O.A.C. is shown here. This high-power equipment is built in units for ease of servicing.*

have been considered and may be built.

Like the radio range, Consol has the advantage that the signals can be received without any special airborne equipment and they can be heard over long distances. The accuracy, however, decreases with distance and the signals are, in certain conditions, liable to be blotted out by atmospheric disturbances.

We have dealt so far with various radio aids which can provide the navigator with bearing information or with radio beams and have seen how ground D.F. stations, when working together, can fix the position

of an aircraft and tell it where it is. It is proposed now to describe what are known as hyperbolic systems of navigation which do not depend on bearings and which provide the navigator with a fix at any instant anywhere within their coverage.

Hyperbolic Navigation Systems

There are three systems which come under this heading: they are known as Gee, Loran and Decca. The first two, although not strictly radar systems in that they do not depend on the reception of reflected radio signals, are usually referred to as radar systems since they use radio pulses—radio energy transmitted in short bursts—instead of continuous transmission. Decca works on a somewhat different idea but so far as the navigator is concerned the results are comparable with those provided by Gee and Loran.

All these systems require two or more ground stations many miles apart and rely on the fact that radio waves travel through air at a constant speed of 300,000,000 metres, or about 186,000 miles, per second. If two such ground stations send out signals simultaneously, and the aeroplane's special receiving set computes just how much the signal from one arrives before that from the other, this information can be converted into a position line. This is because there is only one line on a map at any point on which the difference in distance of two given points (in this case, the sites of the transmitting stations) is the same. The position line is a particular form of curve which is known in geometry as a hyperbola; this is why these systems are described as hyperbolic.

Two stations thus give a position line. A second position line, to give a fix, can be obtained either by two other stations, as in the case of Loran, or, as with Gee and Decca, by adding a third station. When three stations are used in this way, one is usually known as the master and the others as slaves. Readings are taken from the master and each of the slaves simultaneously so that an instantaneous fix is obtained. There is thus no need to transfer any position line as when plotting a fix from two or more position lines taken in turn. This, of course, is of great advantage to the

LORAN AIRBORNE EQUIPMENT, *here shown, is a hyperbolic system, as are Gee and Decca. The navigator is viewing the cathode-ray tube through a visor which excludes extraneous light and thus makes the tube easier to read.*

navigator, who is often working against time in somewhat cramped quarters.

The three systems differ in the method used to convert the received signals into readings which the navigator can use. In the earlier Gee sets and in Loran, readings are taken from a cathode-ray tube fixed in the aeroplane. In a later and improved Gee set, the readings are shown on small drums revolving behind a window opening. In the Decca system, dials with revolving pointers somewhat like clock faces are used.

Special maps with the hyperbolae printed on them are provided for use with Decca, Gee and Loran so that the navigator can, as in the case of Consol, readily plot his position from the readings obtained.

Although minute measurements of time are involved, hyperbolic systems are all extremely accurate, and with them it is

TRANSPORTABLE RADIO *ground installation for providing navigational aid on bush air-strips in the Far East. Sponsored by a number of British manufacturers, it provides D.F. and communications facilities.*

possible to tell easily and quickly whether the aeroplane is one side of an aerodrome or the other. Even at great distances, the accuracy is quite high; and Loran (which stands for Long Range Navigation) is used by many air-liners throughout the crossing of the North Atlantic. Even in mid-Atlantic it is still possible to obtain a fix accurate to within two or three miles. This degree of accuracy is, of course, quite sufficient in the middle of a long flight.

Radio Distance-measurement

There is still one kind of navigational information with which to deal. We have referred to systems which give position lines in the form of bearings, and to hyperbolic systems in which position lines take the form of hyperbolae running in sets, each formed by a pair of ground stations. Position lines formed by visual means, transit bearings and compass bearings, and position lines obtained from measuring the altitudes of the stars have also been described. The development of radar has made it possible to produce equipment in an aeroplane which, working in conjunction with a suitable ground station, can give distance information; that is, can give a position line which is in fact an arc of a circle, rather like the astro position lines mentioned earlier but centred on a ground station instead of a substellar point.

Although other forms exist for special purposes, distance-measuring equipment designed for civil aircraft enables the airborne navigator himself to measure his distance from ground station or beacon. Thus, D.M.E. is classed as an air-interpreted aid, such as the Loop, Decca and Gee, as distinct from ground-interpreted aids such as the D.F. fixer system.

By making the system air-interpreted it is not only possible for the navigator to take a reading just at the moment it best suits him, but, more important, a large number of aircraft can use the system at the same time; a D.F. fixer system, on the

AIRCRAFT RADIO INSTALLATION. *Marconi lightweight radio transmitting and receiving equipment as installed in the instrument panel of a de Havilland Dove.*

other hand, of course, can deal with only one aeroplane at a time, and although the operators are very highly skilled and can deal with a great number of aircraft over a period of an hour, ground-interpreted aids do tend to become saturated just when the weather is at its worst and many aircraft may be in need of assistance.

Like the hyperbolic systems, D.M.E. depends on the fact that radio waves travel at a constant speed. An airborne transmitter is used which radiates signals in all directions; these signals, on reaching a ground-based responder beacon, as it is called, cause the beacon itself to send out an answering radio signal. The equipment in the aeroplane enables the navigator to measure the time taken for the signal to travel to the beacon and back. This time is converted into terms of distance.

Clearly, a single responder beacon cannot provide the navigator with a fix, but only with a line of position. In order to fix his position the navigator must obtain two distance measurements or, alternatively, cross a D.M.E. position line with another position line obtained in some other way.

R. Theta System

We have already seen how the hyperbolic systems provide "carpet" cover; in other words, how they provide fixing information over a wide area as distinct from, say, radio ranges, which give tracking indication only along a limited number of set routes. Such carpet cover can also be provided, but in a different way, if a number of ground stations is dotted about the country, each having a D.M.E. beacon and an omni-range transmitter. This combination gives what is often spoken of as R. Theta, R standing for radius measured by D.M.E., and Theta for angle or bearing measured from the omni-range. An aeroplane suitably equipped can thus obtain a fix even though within reception distance of

171

OUTWARD BOUND, *this Pan-American Airways Stratocruiser Clipper is seen over the skyscrapers of New York, heading, perhaps, for one of the airports of Europe.*

SHANNON AIRPORT, *shown below, offers an unrestricted approach to transatlantic air-liners. This airport was associated with many early transatlantic flights.*

only one of the sites, as the combination of distance and bearing gives positive indication of position over the ground.

In civil aircraft the size and weight of any radio equipment carried must be kept down to the absolute limit to ensure a maximum payload. During recent years, therefore, the efforts of scientists and radio manufacturers have been devoted to producing not only more accurate and reliable radio equipment, but also much smaller and lighter sets which can be used even by a pilot flying without an assistant.

International Standards

Attempts are being made through the International Civil Aviation Organization (I.C.A.O.) to select standard navigation systems for world-wide use on international air routes. What particular system will be finally decided upon naturally depends on many factors. Both hyperbolic and R. Theta systems have much to commend them; the former are generally more accurate, but the latter, of course, have the advantage that fix information can be provided from one small site, which might be on an island miles away from any other land. The advantages of having a common system are, of course, considerable because without it aircraft need to carry more than one different type of airborne set if they are to make the best possible use of the ground facilities provided in the various countries of the world over which they fly.

It might be thought from the foregoing that the task of the air navigator is simple now that there are so many aids at his disposal. In fact this is not so. Air navigation remains an art in which success depends on an ability to make the best possible use of all information which can be collected on the way, by eye or by ear, to assess the probable reliability of position lines obtained by astro, radio or other means, to plot with great accuracy and keep a constant watch on height, speed and direction and, most important, time. The navigator must also learn to understand all the implications of a weather map and to read the signs of the sky so as to be prepared for deterioration in weather, forecast or not, and he must be able to make rapid calculations to tell, for example, whether his aeroplane will be able to reach its destination in the face of increasing adverse winds. If he fails to act in time his aeroplane may be unable either to reach its destination or to return to its point of departure before the fuel is exhausted, and this may mean a forced landing in the sea.

The air navigator who takes a pride in his task, however, can and does obtain a feeling of satisfaction, of "something attempted, something done," at the conclusion of a flight. And the more difficulties he has had to overcome the greater the pride he can justly feel in his profession. Air navigation is, indeed, a job worth doing and worth doing well.

ORANGE-PEEL NACELLE *is a striking feature of the Convair-Liner's engines. The four panels can be opened quickly and easily, exposing every part of the engine for inspection and servicing. At the upper left of the engine, one set of exhaust pipes can be seen entering the bell-shaped mouth of the exhaust-thrust augmenter. There are two of these tubes which end at the trailing edge of the wing. It is claimed that this "jet-exhaust" system adds substantially to the speed of the aeroplane by using power otherwise wasted.*

CHAPTER 6

SOURCES OF POWER

SINCE the earliest days of flying, all power-driven aircraft have been jet-propelled. This somewhat surprising statement will probably provoke the average reader to argue that jet propulsion is a comparatively new development. This is true as far as the jet-propulsion unit itself is concerned. Strictly speaking, however, even propeller-driven aircraft are propelled by a jet.

The explanation lies in the fact that an aeroplane is propelled through the air by the reaction from a mass of air flung backwards by the jet-propulsion power unit, or by the propeller of a conventional piston-engined aircraft. The only difference between the two forms of propulsion is that the "jet"—the slipstream from a propeller—consists of a large quantity of cold air, whereas that from a gas turbine is a concentrated, high-speed jet of hot gas.

Why does the jet drive the aircraft forward? At first the answer may seem a simple one. Obviously, one would say, the reaction or thrust of the jet or slipstream against the atmosphere causes the forward movement.

It is here that the term reaction, while strictly correct, is misleading. The reaction does not take place against the atmosphere, in the same manner that a gardener's feet thrust against the ground when he pushes a barrow.

It is a natural law that every action has an equal and opposite reaction, as exemplified by the recoil of a gun when it is fired, the rotation of a lawn sprinkler by the jets of water issuing from its arms, and the difficulty in holding steady a fire hose from which a high-pressure jet of water is issuing. In each case, the reaction is not taking place outside, but inside the gun, sprinkler arm or hose nozzle.

The simplest method of understanding this reaction from a jet of gas or liquid is to consider what causes an inflated toy balloon to zigzag about the room when the neck is released and the air allowed to escape in a jet. When the balloon is inflated, the air pressure inside it presses equally all over its inside surface. Immediately the neck is released and the air begins to escape in a jet, the internal pressure is relieved at this point, although pressure is still exerted over the remainder of the inside surface. Consequently, at a point immediately opposite to the neck, there is now an unbalanced pressure which is sufficient to drive the balloon forward at high speed.

How Jet Propulsion Works

To prove that the jet does not propel the balloon by reaction against the atmosphere, consider what would happen if the balloon were re-inflated to its original pressure and the experiment repeated at a high altitude. At sea-level the pressure of the atmosphere is approximately 14·7 lb. per sq. in., whereas at a height of 40,000 ft., due to the rarefied atmosphere, it is reduced to 2·7 lb. per sq. in. Consequently, the difference between the pressures inside and outside the balloon would be greater by 12 lb. per sq. in., resulting in an increased unbalanced pressure when the neck of the balloon was released. In practice, of course, the difference in pressure would probably burst the balloon and so put an end to the experiment. The principle will, however, now be clear; the thrust would be at its maximum, in fact, if the experiment could be repeated outside the earth's atmosphere, or in a vacuum.

To apply the same principle to a jet-propulsion unit, it is necessary to obtain sufficient internal pressure by burning paraffin, petrol or any other suitable liquid fuel in combustion chambers which communicate with a jet pipe. The air expands when heated, producing a greater pressure inside the combustion chambers than exists outside them, just as in the case of the balloon. The air also supplies the oxygen required to support combustion of the fuel. The method of maintaining a constant supply of air is explained later.

Meanwhile, it must be remembered that since a jet unit, unlike our experimental balloon, needs oxygen for combustion purposes, its efficiency begins to fall off at very great heights owing to the smaller amount of air which can be drawn into the engine from the rarefied atmosphere. A rocket, which is another form of jet-propulsion unit using chemical fuels containing the necessary oxygen, does not suffer from this disadvantage, reaching its maximum efficiency in outer space beyond the earth's atmosphere.

Propeller Principles

So much for the basic principles of jet propulsion. How does a propeller, driven by a piston engine or gas turbine, exert its thrust? The reaction from the mass of air which is flung backwards by the blades causes an increased pressure on the rearward surface of each blade. Due to the special aerofoil shape of the blades, a reduced pressure is also created in front

ENGINES, TOO, *pass through a mock-up stage. Here is shown a mock-up of the Armstrong Siddeley Mamba propeller-turbine engine, as installed in the Apollo air-liner. In spite of its compactness and small size, the Mamba can develop over 1,000 h.p.*

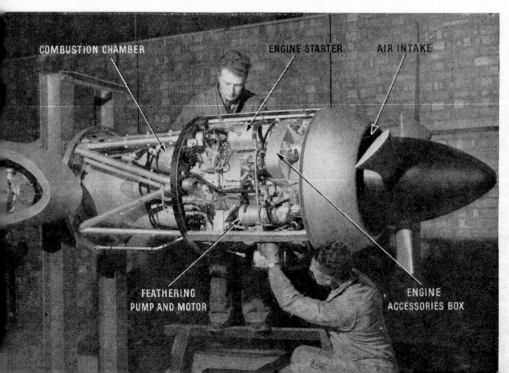

COMBUSTION CHAMBER — ENGINE STARTER — AIR INTAKE — FEATHERING PUMP AND MOTOR — ENGINE ACCESSORIES BOX

MAMBA PROPELLER-TURBINE ENGINE, *flanked by piston engines, is installed in the nose of this flying test-bed Lancaster. The difference in frontal area between the two types is noticeable. Below is shown a Rolls-Royce Nene gas-turbine installation.*

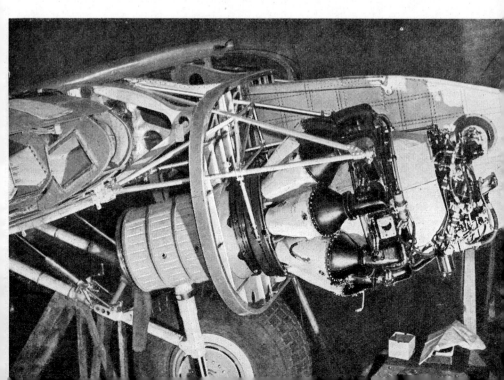

TESTING THE FUEL FLOW *of the Brabazon's engines is done by means of the mechanism shown above, which simulates various conditions of the engines while they are in service.*

CHINOOK JET ENGINE, *a product of Canada's expanding aviation industry, is put through its paces on the test bed. An observation window can be seen on the left.*

INSIDE A GAS TURBINE. *This cut-away section of the Mamba engine reveals the compressor drum, bristling with propeller-type blades which compress the air.*

of each blade. The forward thrust is transmitted to the hub of the propeller, and so to a thrust bearing in the nose of the engine or in a gearbox attached to the wing of the aeroplane if the propeller is driven by a shaft from the engine or gas turbine, as in some of the latest air-liners.

Increasing Thrust

It will already be evident that the designer of a modern air-liner has a choice between several different types of engine. There is the pure jet-propulsion unit; the gas turbine which is used to drive a propeller; and the piston engine driving a propeller. The choice is further widened by the present tendency to combine the different types of engine for increased efficiency.

For many years it has been known, for instance, that a useful increase in power and speed can be obtained by fitting rearward-facing exhaust pipes to a piston engine so that the exhaust gases create a number of small, high-speed jets. At maximum speed, fighter aircraft can obtain an increase of 15 per cent in maximum power in this manner.

On the engines fitted to some present-day air-liners a similar effect is obtained by directing the exhaust gases into the open mouths of one or more large jet pipes which pass through the engine nacelle. The advantage of this system is that the exhaust gases, as they are ejected into the jet pipe, draw in air which adds to the mass of the jet, and which also cools the engine as it flows around the cylinders towards the mouth of the jet pipe.

Small gas turbines, too, driven by the exhaust gases, have been in use for some

POWER PLANTS

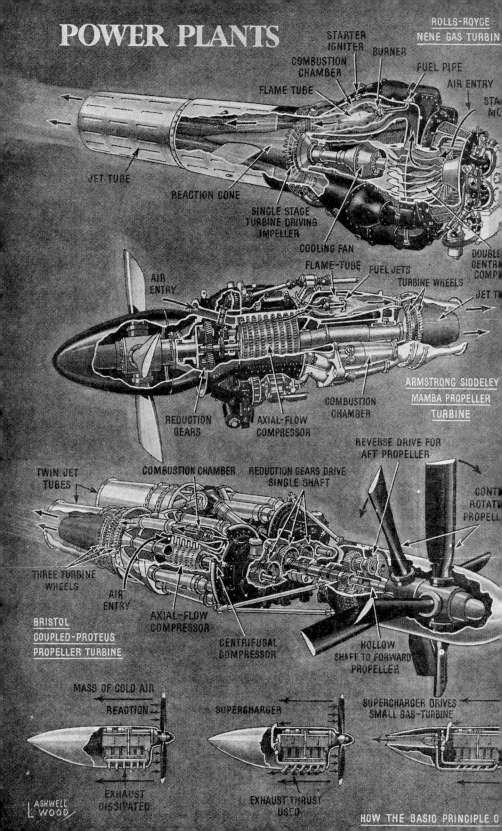

ROLLS-ROYCE
NENE GAS TURBIN

STARTER IGNITER

BURNER

COMBUSTION CHAMBER

FUEL PIPE

FLAME TUBE

AIR ENTRY

STA
MC

JET TUBE

REACTION CONE

SINGLE STAGE TURBINE DRIVING IMPELLER

COOLING FAN

DOUBLE
CENTRA
COMPI

FLAME-TUBE

FUEL JETS

TURBINE WHEELS

AIR ENTRY

JET T

REDUCTION GEARS

AXIAL-FLOW COMPRESSOR

COMBUSTION CHAMBER

ARMSTRONG SIDDELEY
MAMBA PROPELLER
TURBINE

REVERSE DRIVE FOR AFT PROPELLER

TWIN JET TUBES

COMBUSTION CHAMBER

REDUCTION GEARS DRIVE SINGLE SHAFT

CONT
ROTATI
PROPELL

THREE TURBINE WHEELS

AIR ENTRY

AXIAL-FLOW COMPRESSOR

CENTRIFUGAL COMPRESSOR

HOLLOW SHAFT TO FORWARD PROPELLER

BRISTOL
COUPLED-PROTEUS
PROPELLER TURBINE

MASS OF COLD AIR

REACTION

SUPERCHARGER

SUPERCHARGER DRIVES SMALL GAS-TURBINE

ASHWELL
WOOD

EXHAUST DISSIPATED

EXHAUST THRUST USED

HOW THE BASIC PRINCIPLE O

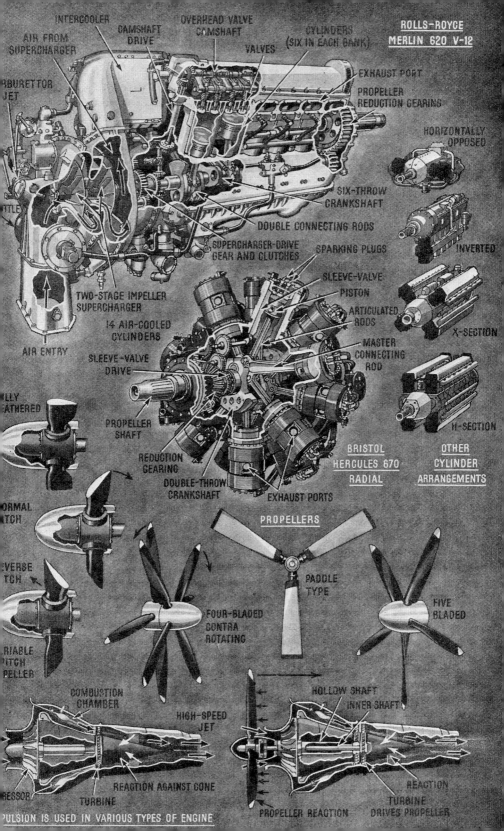

ROLLS-ROYCE
MERLIN 620 V-12

INTERCOOLER

CAMSHAFT DRIVE

OVERHEAD VALVE CAMSHAFT

VALVES

CYLINDERS (SIX IN EACH BANK)

AIR FROM SUPERCHARGER

CARBURETTOR JET

EXHAUST PORT

PROPELLER REDUCTION GEARING

HORIZONTALLY OPPOSED

THROTTLE

SIX-THROW CRANKSHAFT

DOUBLE CONNECTING RODS

SUPERCHARGER-DRIVE GEAR AND CLUTCHES

INVERTED

AIR ENTRY

TWO-STAGE IMPELLER SUPERCHARGER

14 AIR-COOLED CYLINDERS

SLEEVE-VALVE DRIVE

SPARKING PLUGS

SLEEVE-VALVE

PISTON

ARTICULATED RODS

X-SECTION

MASTER CONNECTING ROD

FULLY FEATHERED

PROPELLER SHAFT

REDUCTION GEARING

DOUBLE-THROW CRANKSHAFT

EXHAUST PORTS

BRISTOL HERCULES 670 RADIAL

H-SECTION

OTHER CYLINDER ARRANGEMENTS

NORMAL PITCH

REVERSE PITCH

VARIABLE PITCH PROPELLER

PROPELLERS

FOUR-BLADED CONTRA ROTATING

PADDLE TYPE

FIVE BLADED

COMBUSTION CHAMBER

HIGH-SPEED JET

HOLLOW SHAFT

INNER SHAFT

COMPRESSOR

TURBINE

REACTION AGAINST CONE

PROPELLER REACTION

REACTION

TURBINE DRIVES PROPELLER

...PULSION IS USED IN VARIOUS TYPES OF ENGINE

years to drive superchargers which force additional air into the engine at high altitudes. On some of the most recent engines, to be described later, exhaust-gas turbines are coupled to the engine crankshaft, in order to recover more of the energy normally lost in the exhaust gases.

Inside a Gas Turbine

As some of these terms may be confusing it might be helpful to examine the individual types of engine in greater detail, beginning with the jet-propulsion gas turbine.

We have seen that to obtain a propulsive jet it is necessary to burn a liquid fuel in one or more combustion chambers, to which a large quantity of air must be supplied. The air is drawn in at the front of the engine by a type of fan termed an impeller. In some engines, such as the de Havilland Ghost, this takes the form of a large disk of light-alloy metal, from whose face a number of vanes radiate. The disk is rotated at high speed and the air between the vanes is thrown outwards, just as a stone attached to a string and swung round in a circle attempts to fly outwards under the influence of centrifugal force. This type of air compressor is therefore termed a centrifugal impeller. On some engines, such as the Rolls-Royce range of gas turbines, the impeller is double-sided, air entering both at the front and at the rear of the disk.

An alternative type of compressor takes the form of a drum on which are mounted a number of small propeller blades; these

IMPELLER BLADES *of a D.H. Ghost engine are tested by moving a detector over the blades, vibrated by the device shown, and displaying the vibrations on a cathode-ray tube.*

FIRST TURBO-PROP *air-liner to be granted a Certificate of Airworthiness, the Vickers Viscount is powered by four Rolls-Royce Dart engines in slim nacelles.*

are, in effect, a series of fans, one behind the other. Stationary blades, attached to the casing surrounding the drum, project between the rows of rotating blades to straighten the airflow and improve the efficiency of the compressor. These are termed axial-flow units, as the air flows along the axis or centre-line of the compressor.

When the engine is first started, the compressor shaft is rotated by an electrical starting motor. Leaving the compressor, the air is forced into a number of combustion chambers called flame tubes; in one or two instances, one large chamber surrounding the engine is used. Fuel, generally paraffin, is sprayed into the combustion chambers through jets; it mixes with the air, and is ignited by a spark from an electrical sparking plug. Within a few moments,

however, the intense heat of the flame from the burning fuel heats the flame tube to a temperature which is sufficient to ignite the fuel, so that the sparking plugs can be switched off.

From the flame tubes, the expanding gases are ejected at high speed through nozzles which direct the gas streams on to the vanes of a turbine wheel which is carried on the same shaft as the impeller. The jets rotate the turbine wheel at high speed just as the wind revolves a windmill, or, more accurately, as steam rotates the turbines in a power station or ship. Since the turbine wheel rotates the compressor through their common shaft, the starter motor can now be disengaged and the engine runs under its own power.

After passing through the turbine, the

FEW THREE-MOTOR *air-liners are in operation today. Here is the Junkers-Ju 52, a widely used machine designed in Germany and powered by three 660-h.p. B.M.W. engines.*

gases escape from a jet tube at a speed of over 1,000 m.p.h. Inside the tube, behind the turbine wheel, is a cone against which the gases react. Through this cone the thrust is conveyed to the engine and so to the aircraft, which is thrust forward.

This, briefly, is a gas-turbine jet-propulsion unit in its simplest form—an extremely compact, light, but tremendously powerful engine. Its power is measured, not in horse-power, but in terms of thrust. A modern jet unit, such as the de Havilland

TEST TUNNEL FOR ENGINES *at a K.L.M. base supplies, by means of the fan on the left, an artificial cooling airstream equivalent to that encountered under flight conditions.*

Ghost or the Rolls-Royce Nene, will produce a thrust equivalent to a weight of over 5,000 lb., or nearly 2·4 tons.

It is difficult to convert this into the more familiar terms of horse-power, used in connexion with a piston engine, as the speed, altitude and the efficiency of the propeller used with a piston engine must be taken into consideration. To provide the same thrust as a jet unit developing 5,000 lb. at a speed of 600 m.p.h., however, a piston engine developing 15,000 horse-power would be needed.

Since the largest piston engines, at present in the development stage, can produce only 5,000 horse-power, it has been estimated that a 15,000-horse-power engine, if it could be built, would weigh about seven tons and would be extremely complicated — a striking contrast to the jet unit, which weighs under one ton and is only about 4 ft. in diameter !

The tremendous power of the jet unit is not obtained, however, without some drawbacks; chief among them is its heavy fuel consumption at low altitudes and moderate speeds. It is not really an economic proposition for civil air-liners (where costs must be carefully watched) at speeds of less than 450 m.p.h. and at heights below 30,000 ft. Since, for all practical purposes, these figures are still well outside the range of air-liners now in use, the propeller engine can still offer very considerable advantages for normal operation.

Turbine-propeller Engines

Engine designers, however, have not been slow to combine the lightness and simplicity of the gas turbine with the efficiency of the propeller at normal speeds and heights; this combination promises to prove superior to the piston engine and propeller for any but very short- or very long-range flights.

In the turbine-propeller engine, or turbo-prop, as it is generally termed, the shaft

ENGINES of a Constellation are run up on the flight line at the Lockheed Air Terminal. This American air-liner is powered by four Wright Cyclone engines, each driving three-bladed braking propellers. The output of the four engines totals 10,000 h.p.

JET-PROPELLED, *the de Havilland Comet air-liner owes its speed of more than 450 m.p.h. to its exceptionally clean lines and its four Ghost turbo-jet engines.*

WING TEST RIG (*below*) *is specially designed to enable the Armstrong Siddeley Python gas-turbine propeller engine to be tested under conditions approximating to those experienced in actual flight. Note the contra-rotating, four-bladed propellers.*

TESTING a Wright Turbo-Cyclone 18 compound engine. In this design, three small turbines, driven by exhaust gas, are coupled to the crankshaft, thus recovering exhaust power otherwise wasted. The propeller blades have been cut at the tips to relieve stresses peculiar to testing.

which carries the impeller and the turbine wheel is extended at the front to drive a gearbox, which in turn drives the propeller. The gearbox is necessary because of the very high speed of rotation of the turbine shaft, which is about 7,750 r.p.m. in some engines, to 18,000 r.p.m. in others. This must be reduced to a speed of about 1,500 r.p.m. for the propeller.

Part of the energy of the gases passing through the turbine wheel is thus transmitted to the propeller, resulting in a useful propeller horse-power and a small residual thrust in the form of a jet. Alternatively, nearly all the power may be absorbed by the propeller as in the Bristol Proteus.

Advanced types of turbo-propeller have two turbine wheels, one behind the other. The first drives the compressor and the engine auxiliaries, while the second drives the propeller. In addition, these units often have both a centrifugal and an axial compressor for added efficiency, while the air may also pass through a heat exchanger, where it picks up heat from the exhaust gases so that its temperature is raised before entering the combustion chambers, thus economizing in fuel.

The modern jet or turbo-propeller unit is, in fact, constantly being developed and improved. The first gas turbines were somewhat temperamental, with relatively short lives between overhauls, but nowadays increased power is not obtained at the expense of reliability. A new unit must pass a rigorous type test before it may be used in a transport aeroplane.

Combined Type Test

It is easy to talk glibly about engine type tests, but how many know precisely what are the requirements of the combined civil and military type approval test, as it is officially called? To take a typical example, when the Armstrong Siddeley Mamba turbo-propeller unit was ready for the test, the manufacturers first had to declare the power and thrust they thought would be achieved running under various conditions, the r.p.m. figures and the fuel and oil pressures and engine temperatures.

187

Of the series of five- and ten-hour test periods under various running conditions which make up the 150-hour endurance test, the easiest consisted of five hours at varying cruise conditions. More arduous was a ten-hour run at "maximum climb," while a further ten hours was run with alternate five minutes at "take-off" and "idling," with accelerations and decelerations from one condition to the other.

Halfway through the test the unit was run for 15 minutes at maximum jet-pipe temperature, and overspeeded up to 15,450 r.p.m. During the test, 155 accelerations were made from zero to full power. Each had to be timed and the average was five seconds. At the end of the endurance test the number of starts was made up to a hundred, and the initial performance curve was repeated in full.

When producing the fuel-consumption and power curves the shaft horse-power was obtained from the torquemeter readings. The torquemeter was not a part of the test equipment, but an integral part of the engine reduction gear. The actual total running time was 165 hours, which the Mamba completed in 8½ days. The whole test was roughly equivalent to a flight from London to Paris and back every day for three months, while the time spent running at cruising and maximum climbing revolutions was the equivalent of 12 Atlantic crossings. During the test, over 2,000 tons of air passed through the compressor.

After further flying experience the Mamba was ready for its 500-hour endurance test, which was also carried out under the supervision and control of the Air Registration Board. The total 500 hours was made up of 34 periods, each of five hours' duration, and 33 periods of ten hours. During each five-hour period, 18 minutes were spent on initial starts, idling,

PARTLY CUT AWAY, *this Rolls-Royce Merlin 620 is a liquid-cooled, in-line piston engine with the cylinders arranged in two banks forming a V. It develops 1,760 h.p.*

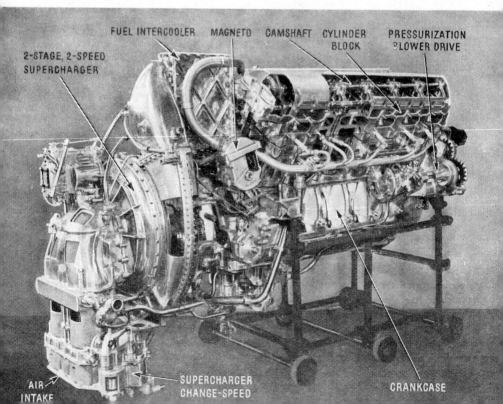

2-STAGE, 2-SPEED SUPERCHARGER — FUEL INTERCOOLER — MAGNETO — CAMSHAFT — CYLINDER BLOCK — PRESSURIZATION BLOWER DRIVE — AIR INTAKE — SUPERCHARGER CHANGE-SPEED — CRANKCASE

SUGGESTION OF POWER *is given by this Avro Tudor II as engines are run up prior to take-off. The Merlin engines are of the type shown on the preceding page.*

taxi-ing and acceleration conditions; three minutes were devoted to maximum take-off and 30 minutes to maximum cruise; 60 minutes were run at 70 per cent of the take-off power and similar periods at 65, 60, and 55 per cent. Tests of final acceleration and taxi-ing conditions occupied nine minutes. In the ten-hour periods, the cycle was repeated twice.

During the test more than 70,000 instrument readings were taken. The test was equivalent to flying 150,000 miles, or six times around the earth at the equator. The compressor and turbine made 370,000,000 revolutions and each turbine blade travelled a greater distance than that from the earth to the moon, at an average speed of 600 m.p.h.

One of the chief reasons for the development of the gas turbine was the constant demands made by aircraft designers for yet more power to drive high-speed, high-lying air-liners. Whereas, in 1940, a piston engine which developed 1,000 horse-power was among the most powerful available, nowadays designers are using power out-

puts of 3,500 horse-power; while one or two advanced types of piston engine will develop as much as 5,000 horse-power.

These very large engines, however, are necessarily complicated, since there is a practical limit to the size of an engine cylinder, with the result that any substantial increase in power calls for a larger number of cylinders. The 12-cylinder, in-line engine, or the 9- or 18-cylinder radial engines, have therefore grown up, having

STRAIN GAUGES, *cemented to the blades and wired to slip-rings in the hub, measure propeller vibration during flight.*

24 and 28 cylinders respectively, and developing about 3,500 horse-power. The experimental 5,000-horse-power engines have as many as 36 cylinders.

Most readers will have some idea of the working principles of a piston engine, as used in motor cycles and cars, in which a mixture of petrol and air, burnt in a cylinder, expands and drives a piston downwards. The piston rotates a crank-shaft through a connecting rod, converting a reciprocating movement into a rotary one. Due to its working principle, the piston engine is often referred to as a reciprocating engine.

Other essential parts of the engine are a carburettor to mix the petrol and air, or an injection pump and injectors to force the petrol into the airstream entering the engine, or directly into the cylinders; sparking plugs, which are supplied with a high-voltage electrical current from a magneto driven by the engine, are needed to ignite the petrol-air mixture in the cylinders; and valves, mechanically-operated by a shaft which is geared to the crankshaft, must be timed to admit the mixture, to close the cylinder while it is compressed and fired, and then to open it to allow the exhaust gas to escape.

More Powerful Engines

These essentials make up the simple, small engine of the type used in light aircraft, which may have only four or six cylinders arranged vertically in line or disposed horizontally on each side of the crankshaft. The more powerful engines, however, are much more complicated.

Thus, to keep the length of the engine within reasonable bounds the cylinders of a 12-cylinder in-line engine are arranged in two banks, inclined towards a common crankshaft so that the engine forms a V. When 24 cylinders are used, the most general arrangement is an engine in the form of a capital H lying on its side, with two banks of 12 horizontally-opposed

cylinders, six a side; each bank drives its own crankshaft, the two crankshafts being geared together.

Belonging to a different family of engines are the radial designs, so called because the cylinders are arranged radially around the crankshaft like the spokes of a wheel. A moderately powered engine of this type, developing, say, 400-450 horse-power, may have seven or nine cylinders. If a greater number of cylinders is required, a second bank is arranged behind the first, with the cylinders opposite the spaces between those of the first bank. Thus a 14- or 18-cylinder engine is obtained giving a power output of from one to three thousand horse-power. Still more power is given by a four-bank, 28- or 36-cylinder radial engine, with seven or nine cylinders in each bank.

Cooling Systems

The choice between in-line and radial engines depends largely on the type of cooling system adopted. A cooling system is an unfortunate necessity; if all the heat which is developed in the cylinders could be effectively employed, the petrol engine would be very efficient indeed. In practice, however, only from one-quarter to one-third of the energy in the fuel can be used. Power is lost due to friction and also to the loss of heat—which represents fuel—in the exhaust gases. Some of the latter may be regained by compressing the mixture of petrol and air in the cylinder to a greater degree, but this raises the temperature of the mixture and combustion chambers.

If the temperature of the cylinders and combustion chambers becomes too high, the fuel ignites spontaneously instead of burning progressively. It explodes or detonates with the effect of a hammer-blow on the piston, instead of imparting a steady push. The white-hot flame and violent blows of a detonating mixture will quickly damage, or even wreck, an aero engine.

In spite of an efficient lubrication system, friction between the various sliding and

SUPERCHARGER FAN   ROCKER   VALVE SPRING   PISTON   VALVES   AIRSCREW SHAFT

VALVE CAMS

CYLINDER BARRELS   CRANKSHAFT

CONTRAST IN TYPES *is afforded by these two pictures. The Pratt and Whitney Double Wasp (above) is an American air-cooled motor of radial design developing 2,400 h.p. Shown below is the enormously powerful Rolls-Royce Eagle, of 3,500 h.p. The Eagle, like most of the larger in-line engines, is liquid-cooled. The cylinders are in four banks, forming an H.*

FUEL INJECTION TO SUPERCHARGER   TWO-SPEED, TWO-STAGE SUPERCHARGER   CONSTANT-SPEED UNIT   HEADER TANK, MAIN COOLING SYSTEM

CYLINDERS CAST IN TWO BLOCKS OF TWELVE

TWIN SPARKING PLUGS

MAGNETOS (2)

REDUCTION GEAR FOR CONTRA-ROTATING PROPELLERS

COOLANT PUMP

ENGINE SUMP HOUSING AUXILIARY UNITS

AIR INTAKE TO SUPERCHARGER   OIL-HEATED THROTTLES   FUEL-INJECTION PUMP

DE HAVILLAND DOVE *is powered by two D.H. Gipsy Queen engines of 340 h.p. The six in-line inverted cylinders are seen at the bottom of the nacelle (above). A complete change of power unit (below) can be made by two men in just over an hour.*

rotating parts of the engine also causes heat and loss of power. Consequently, some means of carrying away the excess heat is needed. A liquid, such as ethylene glycol, or a mixture of glycol and water, may be circulated around the cylinders and combustion chambers by a pump, and then passed through a radiator placed in the airstream flowing over the engine nacelle or the wing of the aeroplane. This is the usual method of cooling the more powerful V-type or H-type in-line engines.

Alternatively, the cylinder barrels and heads may have a large number of cooling fins cast or shrunk on to them, thus providing a very large radiating area. The fins are exposed to the air blast of the slipstream from the propeller, suitably directed and controlled by sheet-metal baffles and cowlings. Small in-line engines and all types of radial engine are air-cooled.

The internal design of the engine is a major factor in obtaining the last ounce of power without causing detonation. The valves, for instance, are critical items. They may be of the so-called poppet type, like inverted mushrooms, whose heads project into the combustion chamber to seal the inlet and exhaust ports. The exhaust valves normally work at a dull red heat, and are generally cooled by inserting a special salt inside the hollow stem and head. This salt becomes liquid when heated and splashes up and down inside the valve, thus helping to conduct the heat away from the head to the stem, and so through the valve guide to the cylinder head, cooled by air or liquid.

Sleeve Valves

Some engines have sleeve valves instead of poppet valves. These take the form of steel sleeves inside the cylinder with inlet and exhaust ports to match those cut in the cylinder walls. The sleeves are reciprocated and slightly rotated by small cranks to bring their ports opposite those in the cylinders at the correct moment. The large area and adequate lubrication of the sleeves help to prevent overheating.

A further important mechanical item on all but the smallest engines is the supercharger. This is a centrifugal air compressor similar to the impeller of a gas turbine, which forces the petrol-air mixture into the cylinders under pressure; it thus makes

FREE-EXIT COWL of the Bristol Hercules 672 radial engine. Air entry is speeded by the ring mounted with impeller blades behind the propeller. The holes in the inner cowling give easy access to the sparking plugs and convey air from the rear of the cylinder heads to the (just visible) exhaust stubs.

G

FIRE HAZARDS *are best reduced by practical tests of extinguishing methods and materials. Here, fire-fighting experiments on Rolls-Royce engines are observed.*

up for the reduced density of the air as the aeroplane climbs, and enables normal power to be maintained up to a considerable height. Without a supercharger, of course, the engine power would be progressively reduced owing to the smaller quantity of air drawn into the cylinders.

High-altitude Superchargers

A height will eventually be reached, however, at which even the supercharger is unable to supply sufficient air to the engine. On high-flying aircraft, this difficulty is overcome by providing two alternative gear ratios in the supercharger drive; a second, higher ratio can thus be engaged when the critical altitude is reached to speed up the supercharger and enable the aircraft to climb still higher. On very powerful engines, two or more superchargers may be used in series, thus providing two-speed two-stage supercharging.

Since this high degree of compression so heats the air that the weight of the charge entering the cylinders is reduced, a cooling radiator, termed an intercooler, is needed between the supercharger and the cylinders, and sometimes between the two stages of supercharging.

A further essential item is the boost control. A moment's reflection will indicate that if a supercharger is capable of maintaining sea-level conditions inside the engine at a considerable altitude, it will force in too much air when flying at lower heights.

Consequently, a collapsible metal bellows from which the air has been evacuated is placed in an airtight container connected by a pipe to the outlet side of the supercharger. The bellows controls, through a valve, an hydraulic piston which operates the linkage by which the pilot controls the power output and speed of the engine.

EXACTLY SIMILAR *to the flight-engineer station of a Lockheed Constellation air-liner, the cockpit shown (right) never leaves the ground. In this cockpit, flight engineers under training go through all the normal and emergency procedures; thus a thorough knowledge of emergency action can be gained without the necessity of putting an aeroplane in danger.*

ENGINES *are fitted (below) to a Boeing Strato-cruiser air-liner. The engines are Pratt and Whitney Wasp Majors, each of 3,500 h.p. The four-bladed propellers are reversible in pitch, and can thus be used for braking and deceleration when the aeroplane is approaching to land.*

If the pilot moves his control lever to the fully-open position at sea-level, the pressure built up by the supercharger collapses the bellows and reduces the power output of the engine to a safe figure. As the aeroplane climbs, the bellows gradually expands and allows the engine to maintain the required power without the necessity of altering the position of the pilot's control lever.

Compounded Engines

As mentioned at the beginning of this chapter, the power of the exhaust gases which is normally wasted may be used to drive an exhaust-gas turbine which in turn drives the supercharger; this results in a useful saving of fuel. The latest trend in design is to use both a turbo-supercharger and exhaust-gas turbine geared to the engine crankshaft. A reduction in fuel consumption of as much as 20 per cent can be obtained from a power plant of this type, which is known as a compounded engine.

Mention has already been made of the carburettor or injection equipment. The carburettor is, in effect, a scent-spray or atomizing device, in which fuel is drawn from a nozzle as a mist and mixed with the airstream entering the engine. Modern carburettors, however, are complicated units, containing a number of jets to meter the fuel so that the correct mixture is obtained under all conditions of flight.

Mixture-control Mechanism

The pilot is provided with a control which enables him to select the required mixture; rich for take-off and maximum power, fairly rich for climbing and normal full-power flight, as weak as possible for economical cruising, and a suitable idling mixture when the engine is running slowly.

The preselected mixture is maintained automatically at all heights by a control operated by atmospheric pressure. It will be appreciated, of course, that as the air

becomes less dense at high altitudes, less petrol must be mixed with it if the petrol-air ratio is to remain the same.

The automatic mixture control, therefore, embodies a pressure-sensitive capsule, similar to that used in an aneroid barometer, which is linked to valves controlling an hydraulically operated piston which moves the carburettor mixture control.

A similar control is fitted to the injection pump when a fuel-injection system is used instead of a carburettor, and to the fuel-injection system of a gas turbine. The petrol-injection system on a piston engine consists of a pump, driven from the engine, which feeds petrol under pressure either to an injection nozzle fitted at the centre of the supercharger casing, or to nozzles spraying into the individual cylinders. A modified scheme is the injection-type carburettor, in which the fuel, instead of being drawn from the jets by suction, is sprayed under pressure into the throat of the carburettor.

Petrol - injection systems have been adopted, in spite of their greater complexity, owing to the liability of ice formation in an ordinary carburettor. The constant vaporization of fuel particles in the throat of the carburettor, coupled with the reduced air pressure in this region, encourages the rapid building up of ice when the aircraft is flying in ice-forming conditions. Although the air intake can be heated, the injection system is a better safeguard.

Propeller-design Problems

To absorb the great power of modern engines, a large area of blade on each propeller is necessary. The diameter of the propeller cannot be indefinitely increased, due to the very high speed reached by the tips of the blades. When the tip speed exceeds the speed of sound, a serious loss of propeller efficiency occurs. The smaller circle described by the tips of shorter blades results in the tip speed being kept below this figure, while the height of the

POWERED BY *two Pratt and Whitney Double Wasp engines, each developing* 2,400 *h.p., the Martin* 2-0-2 *is an American air-liner carrying about* 36 *passengers.*

aeroplane's undercarriage can also be reduced representing a considerable saving in weight. Although a small-diameter propeller is less efficient than a large-diameter one it does offer an overall improvement in efficiency.

It is necessary, however, to increase the number of propeller blades to compensate for the reduction in diameter; thus four- and five-bladed propellers are now fairly common. As five blades represent the practical limit, the next step in absorbing increased power is to arrange two propellers on the same hub, rotating in opposite directions, and driven by gears from one engine. Contra-rotating propellers are now usual with high-powered gas-turbine and piston engines. Usually, the shaft driving the first propeller passes through the hollow shaft which drives the second propeller.

For the Bristol Brabazon air-liner and the Saunders-Roe Princess multi-engined flying-boat a coupled Proteus power unit has been developed, consisting of two Proteus units arranged with their shafts parallel and driving a coupling gearbox which, in conjunction with a reduction gearbox, drives the two co-axial shafts for the contra-rotating propellers. The aircraft accessories are driven from the coupling gearbox through a shaft-and-bevel box which may be used to drive a cabin blower or generator.

The small diameter of the Proteus units and their compact lay-out enable the coupled unit to be installed entirely within the wing of the aeroplane. Reduction gear and propeller shafts are enclosed in a faired stalk projecting forward from the wing.

The air intakes are situated in the leading edge of the wing on either side of the propeller stalk, where full advantage is

CONSOLIDATED VULTEE
CONVAIR - LINER

MAIN ENTRANCE

LAVATORY

40 PASSENGERS

PAA

N 90658

CARGO COMPARTMENT

PRESSURIZED MAIN CABIN

JET EXHAUST

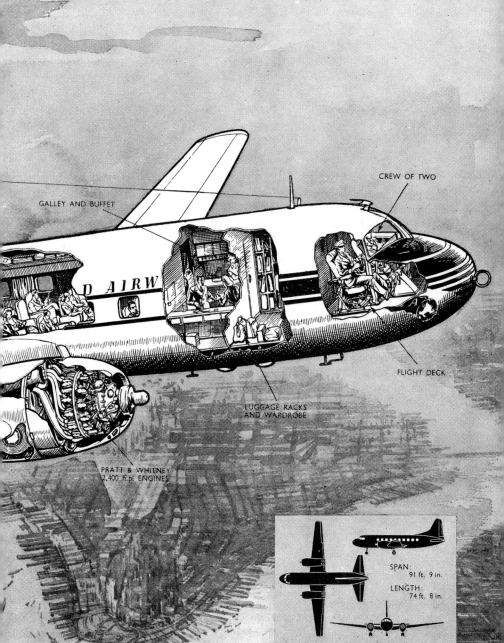

GALLEY AND BUFFET

CREW OF TWO

D AIRW

FLIGHT DECK

PRATT & WHITNEY
2,400 h.p. ENGINES

LUGGAGE RACKS
AND WARDROBE

SPAN:
91 ft. 9 in.

LENGTH:
74 ft. 8 in.

10,000 H.P. *drives the propellers in this picture, which shows four of the eight Bristol Centaurus engines of the Bristol Brabazon. The engines are coupled in pairs. A later version of the Brabazon is to be powered by coupled turbine-propeller engines.*

taken of the aeroplane's speed and the propeller's slipstream to provide a high intake ram pressure. These ducts feed the turbines and the accessories. Since the air intake is toward the rear of the Proteus the engine air is led by the intake ducts to a so-called plenum chamber, which surrounds the air intake of the coupled pair of units, thus providing a uniform air entry.

Coupled power units of this type are likely to be used increasingly on large aircraft in the future, owing to the clean aerodynamic design of the installation.

Reversible-pitch Propellers

A further development is the reversible-pitch propeller, in which the blades can be turned through an angle which is sufficient to reverse the airflow through them, so that the propeller can be used to slow up the aeroplane after it has landed (the pitch of a propeller blade is the angle at which it meets the air); this design also facilitates manoeuvring when taxi-ing, particularly in the case of flying-boats.

Reversible-pitch propellers can also be useful during normal flight. When the angle of the blades is reversed, the braking effect of the propeller enables the aircraft to descend safely at a much steeper angle than would otherwise be possible, without an increase in forward speed. Besides being useful in an emergency, this could also enable an aircraft to approach an aerodrome without making a long descent at a shallow angle, thus reducing the risk of striking high ground or other obstructions near the aerodrome during periods of poor visibility.

The reversible-pitch propeller is, of course, a logical development of the variable-pitch and feathering propeller, which has been in use for many years. As an aeroplane climbs and the air becomes less dense, the propeller blades tend to lose their efficiency, beginning to slip or spin too rapidly; besides reducing the thrust, this will also cause the engine to overspeed. If the angle at which the blades meet the air is increased, however, they will throw back a greater quantity of air, thus restoring the lost thrust and slowing down the speed of rotation of the propeller.

The blades are rotated by gears operated by an hydraulic piston or an electric motor, controlled by a centrifugal governor in the propeller's hub which responds to changes in speed.

The pilot is provided with an over-riding control which enables him to reduce the pitch when maximum engine power and revolutions are required, as for instance during take-off. It is also possible to feather the blades—turn them edge-on to the airflow—to reduce drag and prevent further damage in the event of engine failure; and, as already described, to reverse the pitch of the propellers for braking purposes.

Mention has already been made of the use of ducted fans to increase the thrust of gas turbines. The ducted fan is simply a propeller in which the blades have been reduced in size and increased in number, until they resemble the blades of a single-stage axial compressor. To maintain the efficiency of the very short blades, they are enclosed in a tube which surrounds the jet tube. A ducted fan provides improved thrust at low altitudes and flying speeds,

conditions under which the pure jet engine does not show up to advantage.

With such a wide range of power plants available, how is the designer to choose the most suitable type, and what units are we likely to see in use in tomorrow's air-liners? In practice, what at first seems a wide choice usually narrows down to a decision between one or two units of a particular type, either piston, pure jet, or propeller-turbine.

Choice of Power Unit

The propeller-turbine stands out as a power plant which has advantages over both the piston and the pure jet unit. Among its disadvantages are its low efficiency at low speeds and the problem of ice formation in the air intake under unfavourable weather conditions—a problem which has yet to be completely solved. The only serious limitation, however, is that, to obtain the best results, the cruising altitude must be at least 25,000 ft., and preferably over 30,000 ft. At 35,000 ft., for example, a typical air-liner of the future may cruise at 420 m.p.h. for 3,500 miles, whereas for the same range and payload the piston-engined version could cruise at

IMPRESSION *of the Princess flying-boat in flight. Built by Saunders-Roe, the Princess is powered by ten Bristol Proteus propeller-turbine engines, eight of them coupled in pairs. The coupled engines are the four inboard units, driving contra-rotating, twin four-blade propellers. The two, single outboard engines each drive a single four-blade propeller.*

FOUR BRISTOL PEGASUS ENGINES, *each developing* 1,000 *h.p. at take-off, have speeded the passengers aboard this Hythe flying-boat safely to their destinations.*

only about 340 m.p.h.—80 m.p.h. slower.

If, on the other hand, it is necessary for any reason to cruise below 20,000 ft. at fairly low speeds, the piston engine is the most suitable, while the compound piston engine possesses certain definite advantages for ranges exceeding two thousand miles, at speeds up to 400 m.p.h. and at a cruising altitude as high as 35,000 ft. above sea-level.

For speeds in excess of 425 m.p.h. the turbo-jet is the best type of unit, although this will mean flying at 30,000 to 40,000 ft. With improved fuel consumption and reduced aircraft drag, the performance of this class of aeroplane will improve considerably, although as far as large-scale operation is concerned these developments may materialize only in the more distant future.

CHAPTER 7

ENSURING AIRWORTHINESS

THE type of aeroplane in operational service on the trunk air routes today is larger than any express railway locomotive in the world; yet, whereas the latter may weigh anything up to 250 tons our air-liner scales little over 40 tons. Remembering that the combined power of four aero-engines approaches six times that of the railway engine, you have the first requirements of safety in aircraft: great strength with light weight.

The second safety requirement is reliability under extreme conditions. As an example of these conditions, consider an air-liner operating the route from Jamaica to Gander (Newfoundland), in the winter. It taxies out for take-off in a temperature of about 120 deg. F. The passengers inside are sitting comfortably in a temperature of 75 deg., thanks to an efficient air-conditioning system. When the throttles are opened for take-off, the engines develop a total of 10,000 h.p., and in about twenty-five seconds the air-liner will have accelerated from standstill to 140 m.p.h.

In a further thirty minutes it will level off at a height of 25,000 ft., with an increase of speed to 350 m.p.h. The temperature outside will be 20 deg. below freezing point, and the atmospheric pressure only one-third of its sea-level value. The passengers, however, are unaware of the violent changes that have gone on outside; a thermostatically-controlled heater has maintained the cabin at a comfortable temperature, and the pressurization system

has been slowly "pumping up" the fuselage so that the pressure inside now corresponds to that at 8,000 ft. Thus the passengers feel no shortage of breath or other unpleasant symptoms of altitude.

Some eight hours later the outside temperature will have lowered to 72 deg. below freezing point, and even on the ground at Gander the temperature will probably be lower than 30 deg. below. At any of these temperatures an encounter with cloud would result in icing-up of the wings and engines, were it not for the efficient de-icing system which, under the worst conditions, may have to dispose of several tons of ice every minute.

Legislation for Safety

Truly, these varied conditions call for standards of materials and workmanship in the construction of the aeroplane which far exceed those required in any other medium of transport.

Who, then, is responsible in each country for ensuring that these standards are observed, and that aircraft may operate safely anywhere in the world?

All the air-going nations have a body whose responsibility is the ensuring of airworthiness. In the United States it is called the Civil Aeronautics Board and, in Britain, the Air Registration Board. The French call theirs Le Bureau Veritas.

Each of these bodies lays down legislation governing all the safety aspects of civil-aeroplane design, construction, and

203

maintenance, within its respective State. There is, of course, by reason of the international nature of air carriage, the very closest liaison between the bodies of different countries. Obviously, a nation demanding certain qualities in its own aircraft must demand similar qualities in the aircraft of other nations using its air space or airports. So, today, many of the requirements of design and performance are being internationalized through the medium of the International Civil Aviation Organization (I.C.A.O.).

To appreciate fully how closely concerned each national body is with safety, let us follow the life of an air-liner right through. For convenience, we will choose a British one.

When a specification for a new aeroplane is submitted by an operator to a constructor there are certain minimum requirements laid down by I.C.A.O. and implemented by the Ministry of Civil Aviation which must be met, regardless of other requirements of the operator.

The requirements of I.C.A.O. appear rather complex, but may be summarized thus:

(1) Depending upon the size of airfield into which the aeroplane is required to operate, it must have sufficient power and directional control to enable it to climb away after take-off, so that it will be able to reach a height of 50 ft. within a certain distance, even if one engine ceases to function from the moment it becomes airborne. If the engine ceases to function just before the aeroplane is about to become airborne, it must be capable of coming to a normal stop in the same distance.

(2) It must carry those instruments and equipment necessary for its navigation, engine handling, and safety.

(3) It must carry such equipment as is

LICENSED ENGINEERS *responsible for servicing a Viking air-liner record progress on a schedule board. Major inspections, such as that for C. of A., are carried out inside the hangar.*

NO SMOKIN

INSIDE THE HANGAR, *gantries and inspection ladders give access to every part of the aeroplane. Inspection and maintenance periods are being internationally agreed.*

necessary to enable the aeroplane to be operated in the conditions it will meet. For instance, if icing seems probable along the aeroplane's intended route, then de-icing gear is essential.

Bearing in mind the statutory requirements and those of the operator, the constructor's project team will get down to interpreting the specification into the broad features of the aeroplane, and decide upon such details as the gross weight required to meet the specification, wing loading and size and shape of the fuselage. The design of many of the major features of the machine is based largely upon practical experience, and to a certain extent upon the designers' preference.

Designing for Safety

It must not be understood from this that designers are a dogmatic race: far from it. The rapid progress of aviation demands frequently that features of virtue in yesterday's aircraft be modified or even dropped out of the design of tomorrow's to prevent them from becoming vices.

With the external details of the design completed, the lay-out of the interior is decided by the project team, with particular reference to the accommodation of the various systems necessary to actuate such components as the landing gear, brakes, and wing flaps.

The next stage is the calculation of the stresses to which the various parts and components of the aeroplane will be subjected in the worst conditions it could encounter, and the estimation of the gauge of materials and the construction necessary to withstand those stresses. This part of the design is obviously of great importance, and all calculations are checked and rechecked by the firm's Stress Office.

During this stage, the draughtsmen get down to the detailed planning, the drawings are dispatched to the various shops, and component manufacture is commenced. Each stage of component assembly is inspected thoroughly by the A.R.B., and exhaustive tests are carried out where necessary. For instance, landing gear is always mounted on a test rig and actuated several thousand times, before it is fitted to the prototype machine's wing nacelles.

Now aircraft are, for several reasons, built in sections, the main sections being the centre section, nose, tail, outer mainplanes, and landing gear. These sections are assembled in different shops, and are fitted out as far as possible while still in sections. This greatly simplifies the job, as the interior is more accessible and a larger team of men can carry out their tasks without getting in each other's way.

The sections are now brought together, put in position and joined up, and as each section has already been fitted with its appropriate electrical cables, hydraulic pipe-lines and other requisites, these are connected at each join. This system ensures that a minimum of fitting remains to be done when the aeroplane shell is in its finished state.

There are, of course, thousands of small, but very important, components in the aeroplane which are made, not by the constructor but by specialist firms under contract to the constructor. These firms supply electrical switches, gyro instruments, thermostatic controls, and hydraulic pumps and similar components. Here again, the influence of the Air Registration Board is seen. For all the individual units, when delivered to the constructor's stores, have labels attached certifying that they have been examined, tested and found to function correctly by an inspector approved by the A.R.B. whose signature appears on the label. All material used by the constructor also bears a stamp of approval.

Test Flight

The completed aeroplane is now passed over to the test flight. The test pilots' task is to prove that the designers' calculations are correct. The tests gradually become more complex, starting with taxi-ing, braking and fast taxi-ing tests, and not only supply vital data, but also give the pilot a surprisingly good forecast of how the aeroplane will behave when taking off, in the air, and landing.

These tests usually take six weeks or even more, during which time the aeroplane will be sent back to the assembly sheds time and time again for seemingly endless adjustments, until the first flying test.

INTERCHANGEABILITY *of parts, the secret of quick renewal, originates in the factory. Shown here is a mating station, where semi-complete Convair-Liner fuselages and wings are joined. A damaged wing-tip or a complete fuselage can be renewed from stock.*

This test is frequently undertaken by two test pilots, who take the aeroplane up to a safe altitude, check the calculated stalling speed, return and land. Expressed in so many words, the first flying test sounds a routine task, but no test pilot can be regardless of the enormous responsibility in being entrusted with the results of so many years of endeavour. He may be excused if he feels not a little proud on this great occasion.

From this day on, each flight is carried out with a large complement of technicians on board, and over a period of some nine months to a year every feature of the new aeroplane is tested to the full. Fuel consumption is checked, optimum speeds for various conditions are ascertained, engine performance is compared with that obtained by the makers in the test chamber. Heaters are calibrated, the pressurization system adjusted, electrical circuits regulated, and a hundred-and-one other tasks completed during these vital months of the aeroplane's life. All the statistics obtained from these flights are submitted to the Air Registration Board for examination and approval.

Finally, when all the tests have been completed and the aeroplane has been adjusted to complete efficiency, the Air Registration Board grants a Type Certificate of Airworthiness. Then, as other aircraft of the same type, built and equipped to the same standards, come off the production line they are awarded their Certificates of Airworthiness after more routine, but none the less thorough, tests.

With its Certificate of Airworthiness, the air-liner is now sent to the operator, where engineering and flying staffs are given a course in maintenance and operation of the new aeroplane.

This is not to suggest that the operator's engineers know nothing about the new aeroplane, for usually, at least from the time of the first flight, some of the maintenance personnel are attached to the maker for the express purpose of studying all the problems associated with the new aeroplane. In the case of the operator who has submitted a specification to the constructor, this liaison will probably start while the aeroplane is in the project stage.

Inspection Schedules

One of the most important results thus achieved is the compilation of Inspection Schedules. A word is necessary here on these items.

The owner of a car has a responsibility towards the general public. To discharge this responsibility, he must comply with statutory orders which require that tyres, brakes, steering and so on be efficient.

PROPELLERS *must be reconditioned after about* 1,200 *hours' flying. These, ready for service, are at a B.O.A.C. maintenance base.*

SERVICING THE ENGINES *of a Constellation at the K.L.M. main base at Schiphol. At the end of the "safe life" period, engines are removed from the airframe for complete overhaul.*

In the air, the responsibility of the carrier is patently much wider than this, and it has become a statutory requirement that an operator must submit his plan of maintenance to the Air Registration Board for approval. In other words, he does not wait until he suspects a possible breakdown before sending the aeroplane into the hangars for repairs, as is the habit of many car drivers. However well the aeroplane is running, when its time comes round for an inspection, into the hangar it goes.

Maintenance and Economy

While safety is the over-riding consideration in planning maintenance, it is also of great importance to keep cost of maintenance to a minimum. The operator therefore tries to strike a happy medium between too many and too few inspections. In the first case, the aeroplane would frequently be grounded for inspections which would show nothing and cause loss of earning power, while the second would necessitate expenditure on new units which might have been saved by a more generous schedule of overhauls.

With a new aeroplane it is obviously wiser to err on the side of too many inspections; but as the machine settles down in service, the operator will usually apply to the Air Registration Board for approval of a plan involving less inspections. If he can prove that no loss of safety will result, he will be permitted to increase the time between inspections.

The primary and most frequent inspection which the aeroplane undergoes is the refuelling and between-flight check. The inspection schedule demands that this check must be carried out after each refuelling operation, or, if the aeroplane as not been refuelled, before each flight. It is the purpose of this check to ensure that the engines can take their fill of fuel efficiently, and, therefore, the items on the schedule are mainly connected with the fuel system. There is also an examination of surfaces and other units which may have been damaged in the previous flight. Any faulty unit is repaired or replaced before the licensed engineer signs the Certificate of Safety for Flight to the effect that the aeroplane is serviceable.

Physical Inspections

There are, however, further inspections of a physical nature, which are related to the flying time of the aeroplane. Since these physical inspections involve a considerable amount of organization and time, the operator tries to plan his maintenance and inspections so that they cause the least interruption to his services, and so that inspections fall due at a time when the aeroplane arrives at a suitable base.

The time limits vary appreciably with the type of aircraft and the length of route, but, very broadly, the inspection cycle is made up of a servicing inspection at between 25 and 50 hours' flying time,

a minor overhaul at about 150 hours, and a major overhaul after approximately 500 hours of flying.

The servicing inspection consists mainly of attention to the many ancillaries, such as topping up the contents of hydraulic systems, checking the pressure of pneumatic systems, cleaning engine oil filters, checking the efficiency of electrical batteries and similar details.

The minor and major overhauls consist, broadly speaking, of a close examination of those moving parts of the machine which may require adjustment at the appropriate overhaul. Thus magnetos, fuel pumps, oil pumps, hydraulic pumps, pneumatic compressors, and the like, are inspected at a minor overhaul, while the slower-moving parts are inspected at the major overhaul.

There is one further kind of physical inspection: the annual inspection for renewal of the Certificate of Airworthiness. The Certificate of Airworthiness is valid for one year only, and can be renewed only

DRAG STRUT *is pointed out by an executive at the Lockheed plant. He is standing below the wheel well—the area into which the main landing wheels retract. The drag strut is an hydraulic damper or shock absorber designed to absorb shocks which might tend to force the undercarriage backwards in the event of a "heavy" landing.*

after the aeroplane has undergone an exhaustive and minute check. This inspection involves the almost complete stripping-down of the aeroplane for examination of the main-spar and wing structure, tail-plane structure and surfaces, fuselage formers and skinning—in fact, all those parts of the aeroplane which are under stress while operating. Defective parts are, of course, replaced by other components, the aeroplane is reassembled, and the new C. of A. granted.

In an attempt to save "dead" time, the A.R.B. has agreed to a sectionalized C. of A. inspection. Instead of an operator waiting until exactly one year has elapsed before carrying out this inspection, he is enabled to carry out his check in sections, but each section must be re-examined within the year. This is usually more convenient as it is often possible, for instance, to do the C. of A. inspection on the tail-plane section while the aeroplane is in for its routine engine changes. Other cases are constantly occurring where a clever operator can save time in this way, and therefore achieve higher utilization.

"Safe Life" of Engines

All the inspections so far mentioned have related solely to the aeroplane as a whole, and have excluded engines almost completely. Engines and certain other specialized items of equipment are treated by the operator in rather a different way.

These are granted a "safe life," as a result of tests and experience gained upon the particular component. The component is fitted to the aeroplane and used with only normal servicing until its safe life has expired, when it is removed complete and returned to the makers for stripping and overhaul. Units treated in this way usually include engines, cylinder blocks, fuel-injection pumps and carburettors, gyro and sensitive instruments, and certain pro-prietary ancillaries.

An excellent example of this system of overhaul is furnished by a well-know British engine, the life of which is 8 hours. The cylinder block for this engine has a life of only 400 hours, so that a ne cylinder block is fitted twice during the l of the engine. When a time-expired engine or cylinder block has been taken out of power plant it is sent to the makers f reconditioning before it is used agai The reconditioned engine is, for practical purposes, a new engine, and h the same life.

Propellers normally have a life of abo 1,200 hours before reconditioning, a gyro instruments about 500 hours, b tyres are limited to a number of landing

Engines and Power Plants

In preceding paragraphs the read may have been mystified by reference engines and power plants in differe senses, and possibly has wondered what the need for differentiation in terms. I fact, the engine forms part of the pow plant; the power plant also includes t radiators, fuel pumps, injection pump magnetos, oil system, propeller, aut matic boost control, air intake, engi bearers, and cowlings.

In earlier aircraft, engines were of suc simplicity that their removal involved n great work, especially as the unit weighe no more than a man could lift. Toda with the increase in weight and complexi of engines and the number of their anci laries, the removal of an engine take something like 100 man-hours. All th ancillaries have to be disconnecte pipe-lines dismantled, electrical circui broken, and the propeller removed befo the engine can be taken out of its bearer

As the power plant includes all thes components, it is very much quicker remove the power plant complete than t engine alone. For this purpose the ma fuel, oil and electric lines are disconnecte the weight of the power plant is taken by hoist and the bearers disconnected at the

AIRCRAFT SERVICING

TECHNICAL STORES

HYDRAULICS REPAIR SHOP

ENGINE REPAIR SHOP

ACCESS TO BLIND-FLYING PANEL

SERVICEABILITY SCHEDULE BOARD

ENGINE TEST BEDS

INSTRUMENT REPAIR SHOP

RADIO REPAIR SHOP

A STROBOSCOPE *used to check the rotor speed of a distant-reading compass in the British European Airways Instrument Section at Northolt Airport.*

FLYING-BOAT MAINTENANCE *and minor repairs are often carried out in a floating dock as shown below, where a B.O.A.C. flying-boat is being checked.*

feet. The whole is then placed on a special cradle which is wheeled in to the workshops, where work proceeds under conditions of good light and temperature.

A complete change of a power plant need take only about 20 man-hours.

High Utilization

The paragraphs dealing with the construction of an aeroplane described how, as far as possible, it is built in sections. The wisdom of this principle is observed many times over in the operation of the air-liner. The power plant serves as one example, but there are many others. An attendant vehicle skids into the air-liner's tail on an icy parking apron; the complete tail unit is changed in 12 hours. The compressible leg of an undercarriage develops an air leak; the whole undercarriage is changed in a similar time.

At this juncture it may well be asked why the need is so urgent, in civil aviation more than in other forms of transport, to keep the aircraft moving—or, more technically, to achieve the highest utilization.

The explanation is that the four-engine aeroplane is a very costly piece of equipment necessitating a capital outlay, today, of about £200,000. There are, of course, more expensive items in other modes of travel, but although the ocean liner or the railway cost more when new, their useful life is far longer. This is because progress of design is much more rapid in the air than elsewhere. Today's air-liner will not be seen in the air in ten years' time, because its performance will have been long outdated by faster, higher-flying and more efficient aircraft.

In practice, most operators consider the useful life of a new type of aeroplane to be only five years, and so write off one-fifth of its value each year. This is a standing

RADIO EQUIPMENT *is serviced by special maintenance technicians. This is the radio-repair shop at the B.O.A.C.-British South American Airways base at London Airport.*

AUTOMATIC PILOT *undergoing test at a K.L.M. maintenance base, after servicing. A special test bed is used, on which aeroplane controls and reactions are simulated.*

charge and continues whether the aeroplane is flying or not. There is one other standing charge, the cost of the annual Certificate of Airworthiness inspection, which again must be borne regardless of hours flown. For a machine of the type described, these two charges account for about £55,000 every year!

All the other expenses are heavy, of course, but they are incurred only by actual operating. Were it not for the standing charges, revenue would be in proportion to operating expenses, whether the operator used his aeroplane once a day or once a month. Because of the standing charges, however, the aeroplane must be made to fly for as many hours as possible, and the aim of every air-line is to achieve the highest utilization consistent with safety. Sectionalization of the aeroplane is the designer's contribution towards this aim.

So much for the aeroplane. But what of the men who design, build and maintain them? What are their qualifications?

The designer, strangely enough, is not required by the Air Registration Board to have any special qualifications. Anybody can notify the Board that he desires to build an aeroplane, provided he pays a monetary deposit at the same time. The A.R.B. will then instruct him to forward all plans of the new aeroplane for approval by the Board.

When this approval has been granted, the construction may begin. But every stage of the construction must be inspected by an A.R.B.-licensed inspector, and, since an inspector has to specialize by the nature of his work, a number of inspectors must be employed.

After satisfactory construction and flying tests, a C. of A will be granted for the aeroplane.

Naturally, this very critical supervision is not applied to firms who have demonstrated their ability to design and build good aircraft. Those who have shown this ability by constructing one or more aircraft are known as Approved Designers and Constructors. Having gained this title, they have only to notify the A.R.B. that they intend to build an aeroplane of such and such a type, and incorporating certain new features not previously used, prior to constructing it. The Board will inspect only the proposed new features or installations. All results of trials must be sent to the A.R.B. for inspection and approval, however, before the necessary Certificate of Airworthiness is granted. A firm in the fortunate position of being an approved constructor must have a design organization approved by the A.R.B.

Servicing Tradesmen

The men who build the airframe, and those who look after it during its operating career, are called riggers—a name which has been handed down from the earliest days of flying. The engine maintenance men are called fitters, after normal engineering practice.

To perform their duties, fitters and riggers need no qualification beyond that of experience, although many air-lines will take on as a member of the maintenance

RIGGER *checks the tail-control linkages of an air-liner undergoing complete overhaul.*

FROST ACCRETION *is cleared from the wings of a B.E.A. DC–3 by means of a de-frosting unit with which a liquid anti-freeze mixture is sprayed on to the affected surfaces.*

staff only those who have passed a suitable examination. However, there is no licensing examination set by the Air Registration Board for fitters and riggers. The position is similar in all the other aircraft trades, such as radio and instruments.

After World War I, when the aeroplane was first used for carriage of goods and passengers, it was appreciated that safety standards would have to be of the highest to ensure that lives of passengers and others would not be in jeopardy in the coming air age. The Air Navigation Act of 1920, therefore, laid down the basis of safety requirements, which, in spite of the great progress made in aviation since those early days, are fundamentally unchanged today.

Licensed Aircraft Engineers

In addition to introducing the various aeroplane certificates, the Act also laid down who were eligible to sign them and thus certify their responsibility for an aeroplane's airworthiness. For this purpose, the Aero-

nautical Inspection Directorate (later superseded by the Air Registration Board in its authority over civil aircraft) decided to delegate their powers of inspection of aircraft to certain engineers who, by their integrity, experience, and knowledge, had proved that they could shoulder this heavy responsibility. Such engineers, after serving the industry in that capacity for a qualifying period and passing the stiff examination, become Licensed Aircraft Engineers. They are then competent to inspect aircraft and certify as to their safety on the appropriate form, within the terms of their licences.

There are five classes of licence issued, each granting certain powers to its holder. The A-licence covers the duties of certification of safety for flight of airframes and certain minor repairs. The A-licensed engineer, then, is normally in charge of the airframe section of the maintenance detachment at transit stations, where the work is not likely to involve major repairs. When an aeroplane arrives at his station it

ALMOST HIDDEN *by the mass of equipment surrounding it, this P.A.A. Clipper Constellation is undergoing a comprehensive overhaul, including an undercarriage retraction test*

SERVICEABILITY LOG *records the state of airworthiness; defects are reported by the captain in the left-hand column and those responsible for the repairs sign on the right.*

is refuelled and has a Check-R or Check-D carried out on it under the supervision of the A-licensee. When he is satisfied with the work done, he will certify the aeroplane safe for flight. During the course of his inspection he may find certain repairs are necessary. If these repairs are minor repairs within the definition of the A.R.B., he may undertake them himself; but if outside, he must call upon the holder of a superior licence, the B-category.

B-category Licence

This licence authorizes the holder to certify as to the overhaul of airframes, the performance of certain approved major repairs and modifications, the construction and replacement of parts, and the materials used. The tenure of this licence obviously confers considerable powers and responsibility, and is much harder to obtain. An engineer holding it is a very valuable man. He is most likely to be found at a major-overhaul base, where he superintends the airframe work carried out on annual inspections and structural repairs. When assured that the work has been properly completed, he is entitled to sign the Certificate of Safety for Flight, certifying that such major work has been inspected by him, and is in conformity with the standards required by safety.

The A- and B-licences refer entirely to work on airframes; that is, work dealing with nearly everything up to engine-installation, but excluding the engines themselves. The engines are inspected and certified by engineers licensed in categories

C and D. The responsibilities of the holders of C- and D-licences are identical in degree to those of A- and B-licences, but extend to engines only.

Radio and radar equipment is serviced by holders of a Radio Maintenance Engineer's Licence, issued to experienced candidates who pass the appropriate examination of the Ministry of Civil Aviation.

A further licence, the X-licence, empowers the holder to certify various items of equipment not covered by the other licences. These items include propellers, instruments and electrical equipment.

Certificate of Airworthiness

The licensed engineer thus plays a very important part in the running of an airline. Its safety and reliability depend largely upon him. His powers are autonomous, and no superior can direct him to certify an aeroplane as airworthy if it is against his judgment to do so.

A permanent record of every detail of an air-liner is contained in its Certificate of Airworthiness, which includes a picture of the aeroplane for which it is issued, its registration letters, type and number of engines, brief performance data, maximum loads under various conditions, the limits of the range of its centre of gravity, whether smoking is allowed, and, in general, all conditions pertaining to its safe operation. Current agreement in I.C.A.O. is leading to a revision of the Certificate of Airworthiness, which will become merely a certificate of validity, giving the briefest particulars of the aeroplane. It will be compulsory to carry a Flight Operating Manual, which will set out, in much more detail than the existing C. of A., all operating data.

Log books are kept for certain components which have a flying-time limit of operation. These components, as already stated, include engines, propellers, and power plants. In these log books, the flying time of the aeroplane whilst using each

SERVICING *a DC–3 at a New Guinea airport. Every detail of an air-liner is recorded in its Certificate of Airworthiness or in the power-plant and propeller log books.*

REFUELLING *a B.O.A.C. Constellation. The captain must sign the Serviceability Log to* *the effect that there is sufficient fuel, oil and liquid coolant aboard.*

individual component fitted is recorded, together with a record of any adjustments made during that time and minor parts changed, so that the complete history of the unit is available. None of these log books may be carried on the aeroplane to which the relevant item is fitted; in the event of failure of a unit, its record may be inspected immediately at the base.

Serviceability Log

Probably the most important form in use is the Serviceability Log, for in this are recorded changes of airworthiness. All defects, major or trivial, are shown, and also particulars of any inspections carried out on the aeroplane. Before the aeroplane may be certified by the licensed engineer as safe for flight there must be, against each report of unserviceability, a corres-

ponding note of the rectifying action taken.

In addition, the Serviceability Log bears the Certificate of Safety for Flight (which must be signed by the engineers licensed for engines and for airframes) and also details of the total weight and the position of the centre of gravity of the aeroplane for the particular flight it is about to undertake. Finally, there is a declaration by the captain that he has ensured that there is sufficient fuel, oil and radiator coolant on board for the proposed flight.

The Serviceability Log is the official means of liaison between the flying and engineering staff, serving as a log of all defects and their rectification and a summary of all details relevant to a proposed flight. It offers a further example of the system adopted by civil aviation to make absolutely sure that safety comes first.

219

CHAPTER 8

AIR-TRAFFIC CONTROL

THE duty of the air-traffic control officer is to help the pilot on his way. In some respects he may be likened to the policeman on point duty, who regulates the traffic to ensure a smooth, safe flow with the minimum of delays; or to the railway signalman, who sees that the line is clear before accepting a train into his particular section of the track and passing it on to the next.

The air-traffic controller, however, is dealing with traffic moving at very high speeds, in three instead of two dimensions, and incapable of stopping or even slowing down to any appreciable extent. He must, therefore, keep the traffic moving and see that the pilot is able to reach land safely before his fuel supply is exhausted.

Rules of the Air

There are rules of the air just as there are rules of the road, but these alone, as in the case of road transport, are not sufficient when traffic is heavy and visibility is bad. It is the responsibility of the air-traffic control organization, in such circumstances, to keep a constant check on the relative positions of all aircraft, in space and time, so that no risk of collision arises, and to see that the pilots are cleared to take off and land in correct sequence. The normal rule is "first come first served"; but there are exceptions. An aeroplane which is approaching to land, for example, has right of way over one ready to take off; while if there are several

aircraft waiting to land and one is short of fuel or otherwise in trouble, the aeroplane in distress takes priority over all the rest and must be brought in safely without delay.

It will be apparent that a simple rule such as "Keep left," as applied to road traffic in the United Kingdom, is not good enough for aircraft which can fly in all directions and at different height levels. The rules of the air relating to crossing and overtaking are, however, simple to follow and understand. But, in general, they obviously apply only in good visibility when pilots are able to see each other's aircraft and take appropriate avoiding action.

When a pilot is following some well-defined landmark on the ground, such as a railway line or a main road, the rule is to keep to the right. In most aircraft the pilot sits on the left side of the cockpit and it is therefore most convenient for him to keep the railway line, or whatever landmark he is following, on his left side. From this follows the rule relating to aircraft which are approaching head-on at any time, above or below cloud, and over land or sea: both pilots must alter course to the right so that they pass to the left of each other, just as though they were following some visible landmark over the surface of the earth.

When one aeroplane is overtaking another and both are flying in the same direction, the aeroplane ahead has right of

AT PRESTWICK AIRPORT *air traffic is controlled from the building shown above. The control room, built almost entirely of glass, commands a view of the airport and its approaches. The aerials mounted on the control tower are for radio communication and direction-finding.*

INSIDE THE CONTROL TOWER *at Northolt. The control officers are in R/T or Aldis-lamp contact with aircraft using the airport, whether they are on the ground or in the air.*

GROUND-TO-AIR *communication by R/T. This picture shows a controller in voice (R* *communication with an approaching aeroplane at Prestwick Airport.*

way and the one behind must overtake by turning to the right and passing well clear of the one ahead. Overtaking by diving underneath or climbing over the top of the other aeroplane is not permitted.

There is one other rule of the air which, though applied to road traffic in some countries, is not familiar to the majority of motorists in the United Kingdom: when aircraft at the same height-level are flying on collision courses—courses which, if maintained, would lead to a collision—it is the duty of the pilot who has the other aeroplane on his right to give way.

It will now be realized that one of the first things any pilot has to learn is to keep a very careful look-out for other aircraft.

This is all the more important as sp increase. If, for example, two aircraft six miles apart and approaching head there are only 30 seconds in which to t avoiding action if both are travelling 360 m.p.h. It is, however, not so diff. as it might appear to tell whether or two aircraft are on collision courses. risk of collision exists only if the rela bearing of one from the other remains changed, and this can easily be dete by noting whether the other aircraft pears to remain at precisely the same s on the windscreen.

There is one other simple rule wh should be mentioned: the Quadran height Rule. Unlike those alre mentioned, it applies in bad visibility only, and provides a measure of safety automatically, even when pilots are flying "blind." The principle of this rule is that pilots fly at different heights according to their direction of flight. The rule does not apply to aircraft flying at very low levels. For the purpose of this rule, the compass is divided into four quadrants, the north-east, south-east, south-west and north-west, and the pilot selects his height according to the quadrant within which his course lies.

If his course lies in the N.E. quadrant, for example, he will fly at a height in odd thousands of feet: 3,000, 5,000, 7,000 and so on. If it lies in the opposing, S.W., quadrant his available heights are the even thousands: 4,000, 6,000, 8,000 and so on. In the S.E. quadrant, "odds plus 500" are used (3,500 ft., 5,500 ft., for example). "Evens plus 500" are used in the N.W.

quadrant. This rule ensures that aircraft approaching head-on will invariably pass with at least 1,000 ft. vertical separation.

Control of Aircraft Movements

The rules of the air thus provide a considerable degree of safety in good weather and an adequate margin in bad weather in areas where traffic density is not great and the risk of collision is negligible. But where traffic is heavy—as, for example, in the vicinity of busy aerodromes and along the major civil air routes—it is necessary, in the interests of safety and speed, to control the movement of all aircraft from some central point where all movements are known.

There are four different types of air-traffic control service, and these will be dealt with individually; but, to quote from the official publications on the subject: "The primary object of the Air Traffic

CONTROL-TOWER RADIO *equipment at Southend Airport includes remote-control unit on the left, and the direction-finding aerial control and V.H.F. receiver on the right.*

Control Service is to promote the safe, orderly and expeditious movement of air traffic." Under this general heading is included responsibility for advising such organizations as fire and lifeboat services when any aeroplane is known or believed to be in any danger, and for giving any help possible to such distress organizations.

The four types of control service mentioned are Aerodrome Control, Approach Control, Area Control and Flight Information. Together they make up the air-traffic control service, but each has a specific function to perform.

The first two are concerned only with aircraft in the immediate vicinity of an aerodrome, whether taxi-ing in or out, taking off or preparing to land; the last two, the area-control and flight-information services, are provided for the benefit of aircraft in flight from one place to another, that is, for those aircraft which are generally referred to by the term aircraft *en route*, or *en route* traffic.

Aerodrome and approach controllers, dealing as they do with aircraft on and in the immediate vicinity of an aerodrome, occupy certain rooms in the control tower. Area Control and Flight Information, however, are provided from an air-traffic control centre which is usually located in the business quarter of a large town where good communications facilities exist.

Functions of Aerodrome Controller

To deal first with the Aerodrome Controller, he is responsible for the movement of all aircraft which are in visual contact with the aerodrome, whether on the ground or in the air. Before the pilot taxies out to take off, he finds out from the Aerodrome Controller which runway is in use, when it is safe to start taxi-ing and when to turn on to the runway and start his take-off run.

Similarly, with landing aircraft, the Aerodrome Controller, from his glass-walled control room at the top of the con-

CONTROL ROOM *at Uxbridge is designed to provide control for the South-east Flight Information Region of England by W/T or by continuous voice communication.*

trol tower watches all aircraft in the circuit, sees that they follow one another in in correct order and gives them instructions as to where to turn off the runway and how to reach the unloading bays. He must make sure that aircraft do not follow one another in too closely and that no risk of collision arises between landing and departing aircraft. In official terms, his duty is " to provide adequate supervision of all traffic on the movement area and aircraft flying in visual reference to the ground in the immediate vicinity of an aerodrome." Thus he has, in addition, to control all vehicles on the movement area, such as maintenance vans, tractors, lorries used by contractors engaged on building or repair work—and, of course, aircraft which may be under tow to and from the maintenance areas.

The controller, however, is as a rule not responsible for movements on the apron, or the loading and unloading bays; here, at any rate at the more important aerodromes, a separate marshalling staff takes over.

He has, indeed, the major responsibility of seeing that the runways are kept constantly in use, but must be always on the alert to see that each individual aircraft has the runway to itself for the critical periods of take-off and descent.

Approach Control

Most people are familiar with the control tower, or at any rate with the aerodrome-control room on its roof. It is not so generally known, however, that at the busier terminals there may be a second control room, usually on the floor immediately beneath. At many aerodromes, aerodrome control and approach control are both exercised from the same room, but at busy aerodromes, in some countries at any rate, it is considered desirable to separate the two. The Aerodrome Controller must have a good view over the entire aerodrome and its approaches so

ALL AIRCRAFT MOVEMENTS *are recorded on the blackboards around the Movement Control Room at Northolt. An air-liner is followed from start to finish of its flight.*

that the size of his control room should not be great, nor house more than two or three people at the most. The Approach Controller, on the other hand, does not need to see the aircraft, and as he is dealing with aircraft flying blind, in or above cloud, he needs a fairly large room to house his staff and the equipment used.

The Approach Controller, in fact, handles aircraft arriving and departing in bad weather when pilots are unable to fly by visual reference to the ground and unable to see each other as they come in to land or climb away outbound with their passengers or cargo. If the cloud base is not too low, and the visibility beneath it is good, the Approach Controller will hand over inbound aircraft to the Aerodrome Controller as soon as the pilots report contact; that is, as soon as they are able to see the aerodrome and complete a normal visual landing. In worse conditions, the pilot will make his entire approach by instruments and will remain under approach control until he has completed his landing run and is ready to turn off the runway to the arrival bay.

Aircraft Stacking

When all is going smoothly, it should be possible for arriving aircraft to land with little or no delay, even in the worst weather; but often, owing perhaps to aircraft arriving off schedule due to adverse winds, a number of aircraft may arrive in a peak hour at a greater rate than it is possible for them to land. In such circumstances they must be "held" or "stacked," one above the other, the latest arrivals joining the stack at the top and working their way down in turn.

Aircraft waiting to land in this way are required to fly to and fro across a radio beacon or along a radio beam in accordance with a set holding pattern, and it is the duty of the Approach Controller to feed them into the stack at a safe height and tell the pilots when it is safe for them to descend from one level to another. He must also pass them all the information they need regarding local weather conditions and the landing aids available at the aerodrome for their use, and, if necessary, assist them to locate the aerodrome by passing homing bearings.

Control by Radar

The development of radar devices has done much to reduce the amount of stacking, as the controller, using radar, is given a visual picture of the positions of all aircraft from one instant to the next. It is then no longer essential to rely so much on height separation. Further, he can guide the aircraft readily and achieve a higher rate of flow than is possible when his sole means of information as to the positions of his aircraft is the individual pilots' reports of their own positions. This regulation of arriving traffic by means of radar is at present the duty of the Ground Controlled Approach (G.C.A.) Director, referred to in the following chapter; but before long, it will become part of the Approach Controller's normal work.

The Approach Controller is not, as his name implies, concerned only with aircraft arriving at the aerodrome. He is responsible for all aircraft flying blind within a radius of 10, 20, 30 or more miles from the centre of his aerodrome, and for seeing that outbound aircraft, on whatever route they are flying, do not conflict with each other or with inbound traffic arriving, holding, or making their final approach. As a general rule, outbound aircraft leave the approach-control zone at the lower levels, and inbound aircraft enter above; but this is not always possible, nor is it desirable when, for instance, there is risk of icing at the higher levels or when an inbound aircraft has engine trouble and needs to be brought in with the least possible delay.

The main function of aerodrome and approach controllers, then, is to look after

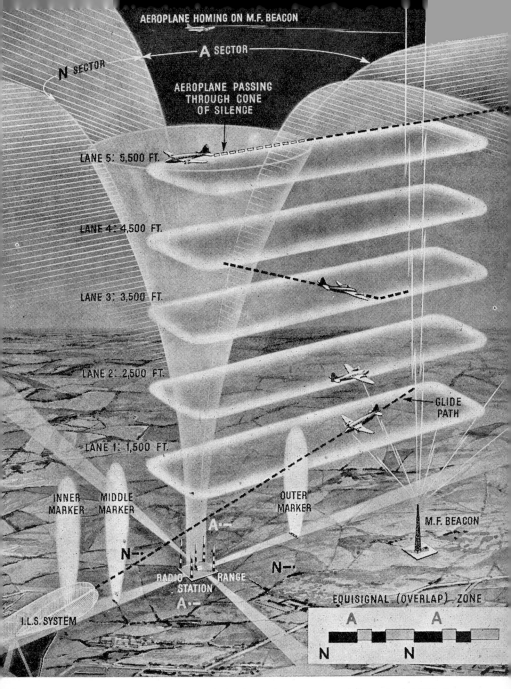

STACKING *ensures that aircraft waiting to land are always separated by at least 1,000 ft. No two aircraft may occupy the same lane; each must fly around the holding pattern until instructed to move down one lane. The radio range provides audible signals which inform the pilot that he is on one of the "legs," or in one of four "A" or "N" sectors. An M.F. beacon is sometimes used to mark the farther end of the pattern and as a homing aid.*

227

RADIO COMMUNICATION STATION 3

RADIO COMMUNICATION STATION 2

AIRPORT J

AIRPORT E

AIR-TRAFFIC CONTROL CENTRE 3

AIR-TRAFFIC CONTROL CENTRE 2

AIRPORT K

AIRPORT D

RADIO BEACON

AIRPORT L

D.F. STATION

RADIO COMM. & D.F. FIXER STN

SIGNALS CENTRE

PASSENGER STATION

RADIO BEACON

RADIO

AIRPORT A
- APPROACH CONTROL (COMMUNICATIONS, D.F., G.C.A)
- AERODROME CONTROL
- RUNWAY CONTROLLERS
- BRIEFING & CLEARANCE
- FLIGHT INFORMATION
- MET. FORECASTERS
- MARSHALLERS
- LOCAL D.F. STATION
- ACCIDENT / FIRE
- OPERATORS' OFFICES
- PUBLIC TEL. EXCHANGE
- ADMINISTRATION

CONTROL CENTRE

MET. H.Q.

RADIO

AIR-TRAFFIC CONTROL CENTRE 1.
- AREA CONTROLLERS
- FLIGHT INFORMATION
- AIRPORTS AND BASES
- OTHER CENTRES (HOME)
- OTHER CENTRES (OVERSEAS)
- MET. H.Q.
- SEARCH AND RESCUE
- OPERATORS' OFFICES
- D.F. FIXER STATIONS
- NAVIGATION AIDS
- PUBLIC TEL. EXCHANGE
- ADMINISTRATION

LANDLINE

AIR-TRAFFIC CONTROL COMMUNICATIONS. *Three imaginary control areas are shown in this drawing, each with an air-traffic control centre which is linked to airports, aircraft, and search and rescue, meteorological and direction-finding services, by radio or landline. Air-traffic Control Centre 2, for example, is linked to Airport E by landline.*

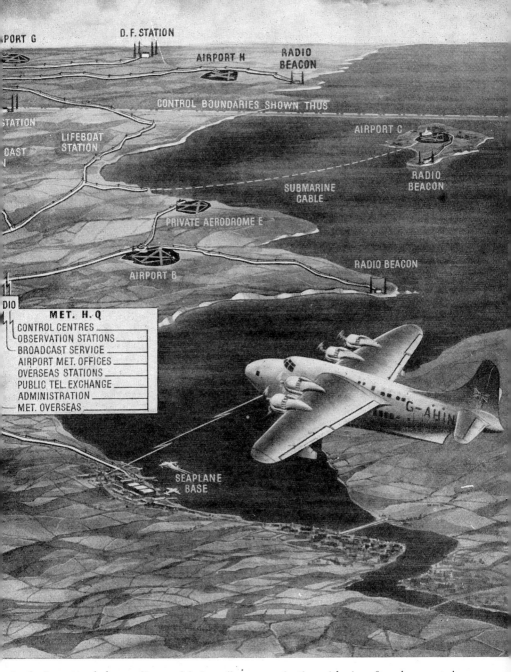

As the inset panel shows, Airport A is in radio communication with aircraft and connected by landline to Control Centre A and Meteorological H.Q. All the services listed in the inset are interconnected within the airport. Communications play an indispensable part in controlling the movements of aircraft and ensuring co-ordination of all ground services.

aircraft during the first and last stages of flight. What happens in between? In areas where there is little or no traffic there is no need for any form of air-traffic control to supplement the safety provisions of the rules of the air; but where traffic is appreciable, area-control service or flight-information service is provided, depending on the traffic density. The former takes care of aircraft in what are termed Control Areas, and the latter in Flight Information Regions, which will be explained.

Flight Corridors

Control areas are established where the density of traffic is sufficiently great to warrant close control of the movements of aircraft—that is, broadly speaking, in areas where the protection afforded by the quadrantal-height rule is not adequate. Naturally, such areas are generally to be found along the main civil air routes; thus control areas usually take the form of corridors or "airways" some ten miles wide and varying in depth according to requirements. They may extend from 2,000 to 10,000 ft. or so above sea-level; but, over high ground, the lower limit is raised to ensure that there is always at the very least 1,000 ft. between the aircraft and the ground itself, whilst the upper limit will largely depend on the number of aircraft likely to be using the airway at any one time.

The Area Controller is thus, as a rule, responsible for the safety of aircraft following a well-defined route, and his task is to keep a constant check on the positions of all aircraft on the route, to allot to each a safe height at which to fly and to provide a clear path for aircraft wishing to ascend or descend *en route*. Here, again, radar is likely to play a big part when a large number of aircraft has to

CONTROL TOWER *at a Chinese civil airport. In airports such as this, where the volume of traffic is low, simple speech-communication equipment suffices.*

be dealt with, as it can present to the controller a continuous picture of the exact positions of all aircraft. This alone, of course, is not sufficient; if delays are to be avoided, and a smooth flow of traffic ensured, the controller must be always looking ahead and taking necessary action soon enough to prevent congestion at any point.

When radar cover is not available, the controller is dependent on "position reports" from the pilots themselves in order to build up a picture of the traffic situation. These reports are usually passed to the control centre by radio as each aeroplane passes over specific check points along the route. Check points are usually marked by a radio beacon of some kind to assist the pilot in sending accurate information; but however accurate his navigation may be, delays due to transmission of messages and to their interpretation on the ground obviously make it impossible to provide the controller with so reliable and up-to-date a picture as the radar display.

Finally, we come to the Flight Information Region, in which flight-information service is provided. The sole purpose of this service is to render assistance to pilots; and, in such regions, the decision as to whether or not any suggested alteration in course, height or speed is to be made rests entirely with the pilot himself.

Flight Information

When flying within a flight-information region, the pilot is able at any time to contact the appropriate air-traffic control centre by radio and from it obtain information of, for example, visibility and cloud-base at any aerodrome within the region, and other meteorological information provided by the meteorological staff at the control centre.

Also passed to the pilot by this means are navigation warnings: these inform the

FLYING-BOATS *landing at Bangkok are controlled from a launch. The controllers contact the aircraft by R/T or by Aldis lamp.*

pilot that certain radio navigation aids are temporarily off the air for maintenance or repair, that certain aerodromes are temporarily out of action, or give other information of a similar nature which may help the pilot in one way or another.

In some flight-information regions, what is termed Informative Control is also available on request. This service is available to pilots who wish to be advised of the approximate positions of other aircraft known to be flying on or near their particular routes.

It will be apparent that, in order to carry out his tasks efficiently, the air-traffic control officer must know a great deal about each individual aeroplane

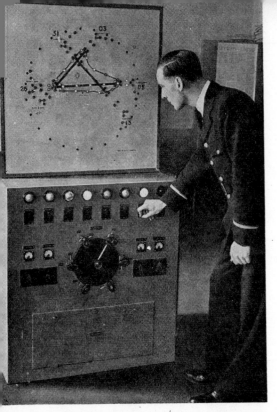

under his care. He must know before it takes off just where and when it is going, the height at which it is to fly and its approximate speed, otherwise he cannot fit it in to the traffic pattern. Further, once the machine has taken off, he must be informed at fairly frequent intervals of its progress if he is not able to check this for himself by radar.

The Flight Plan

There are thus two main types of information required: first, details of proposed flight is to be conducted in a flight-information. When the whole of a proposed flight is to be conducted in a flight-information region, it is not necessary for the pilot to complete and submit a flight plan unless his course takes him over dangerous terrain or over the sea—although many pilots make a flight plan invariably. Similarly, no flight plan is required if the entire flight will take place in good weather. But in all other cases, a flight plan is prepared and passed by hand, teleprinter or telephone to the air-traffic control authorities.

LANDING-LIGHT CONSOLE *at Duns-fold Aerodrome is shown above, while the corresponding London Airport equipment is illustrated below. The landing lights are operated by remote control from the control tower.*

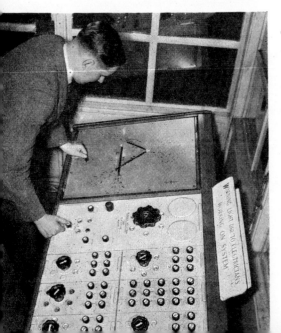

The plan contains all the details which the controller needs, such as the route, destination, proposed cruising altitude or altitudes and speeds, and the radio call sign of the aeroplane. The intended time of departure is also included, together with the estimated time of arrival at the destination or first point of landing. Other information which is included in case of need is the endurance of the aeroplane in terms of hours and the alternative aerodromes which the pilot will head for if, owing to bad weather or for any other reason, he is prevented from landing at the aerodrome indicated in the flight plan.

On receipt of this flight plan, the controller will examine it in relation to other flights covering the same period of time and, if no conflict exists, he will approve the plan and advise the pilot accordingly.

232

INTERNAL COMMUNICATION *within the control building is often dependent upon pneumatic message-delivery tubes, as shown, which convey written messages at great speed.*

Assuming that the pilot is ready to taxi out at the intended time, he will then contact the Aerodrome Controller by radio and will be given clearance to take off as soon as the runway is clear. Should there be some delay in moving off and the pilot not be ready within five minutes or so of his stated time of departure, his flight plan will be revised and fresh approval obtained.

If, however, the controller finds that the proposed flight will conflict with one previously submitted, the pilot will be informed accordingly and will possibly be requested to delay his departure for ten minutes or so, to accept an alternative cruising height or perhaps to follow a slightly different route. So far as air-line traffic is concerned, of course, the schedules are so arranged that delays of this kind seldom occur.

In order to help the air-traffic controller to carry out his duties satisfactorily, there are many different kinds of special equipment provided for his use.

First there is display equipment, from which he can see at a glance the traffic situation in his area; and, second, communications equipment, with which he is able to send and receive messages to and from the aircraft and other aerodromes or control centres.

Displayed Information

The types of display equipment which have been devised are many and various and no attempt will be made to describe them all here. Some are peculiar to certain countries, while others will depend on the type of control service being provided. In the aerodrome-control room, for example, the controller needs little display equipment, as he is dealing all the time with aircraft which he can see from his position at the top of the control tower.

The Approach Controller, however, is working, so to speak, in the dark, and must have a form of "totalisator" display showing essential details of all inbound and outbound traffic expected over a period of about half an hour, so that he can readily plan in advance his traffic patterns and deal rapidly with all movements.

In the air-traffic control centre, the equipment needed is more elaborate still; some of the controllers in the centre may be dealing with control areas such as the "airways" found in the United States and in many other countries, whilst others are responsible for providing flight-information service to aircraft flying off the airways in the less densely occupied portions of the airspace. Some of these aircraft may, of course, wish to enter or pass through the airways, so a very close liaison is necessary.

The equipment most commonly used for controlling aircraft along airways is known as a flight progress board, built in the form of a desk in front of which the controller sits with details of his aeroplanes recorded in symbolic form on slips of paper held in metal clips. These clips can be made to slide up and down two vertical rods so that the information displayed can be kept always in a definite order.

A controller may have, perhaps, five columns to deal with, each column referring to a specific check point. The slips may be inserted so that the aeroplane flying at the highest altitude is shown at the top and the others in appropriate sequence from the top downwards. The system is, however, flexible, and an Approach Controller at an aerodrome, using the same type of progress board, may find it more convenient to use one column for departing aircraft and to insert the slips in time sequence rather than height.

The controller in charge of a flight-information region will usually find it

INSIDE THE D.F. ROOM *at Northolt Airport. A ground radio D.F. operator is passing a bearing in morse code by means of medium-frequency radio.*

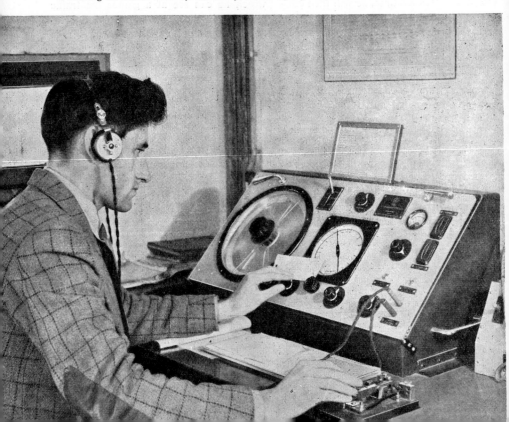

CONTROL OFFICERS *on duty at London Airport. On the left is a cathode-ray direction-finding console; the face of the tube is calibrated in degrees of the compass.*

more convenient to have traffic displayed in plan on a plotting table or screen on which the various aerodromes and main geographical features are shown. Aircraft may be indicated by small plaques, moved across the table as the aircraft proceed on their way, with a colour code to indicate height and an arrow to show the direction of travel. Each plaque will probably bear the flight-plan number, and full details of each individual aeroplane may be recorded on a "tote" display board against each number.

The high speeds of modern aircraft and the introduction of the jet-powered aeroplane, with its very high-altitude flight involving long periods of climb and des-

cent, have added considerably to the Area Controller's problems; the ideal form of traffic presentation or display has yet to be devised. It is possible that, before long, the main display will consist of a large projected image of a radar picture but, as mentioned before, this alone is not enough.

Automatic computors must be perfected so that the controllers can tell from one minute to the next whether the traffic flow is satisfactory or whether action needs to be taken to delay some aircraft, move them in height or change their direction in order to prevent a dangerous situation from arising or undue congestion from taking place. Also, of course, a pilot may wish to change his flight plan whilst in flight, possibly to avoid a thunderstorm or a turbulent layer, and the controller must be able to tell without delay whether or not, having regard to other traffic, it is safe for him to do so.

Apart from displays of the kind mentioned, on which are recorded flight details, the controllers must also have reliable and up-to-date weather information readily available so that pilots can be warned of, say, icing conditions on the route, and advised of the most suitable diversion aerodromes to head for should their destination aerodrome be unable to accept them.

Weather displays may take any of a number of different forms, from the complex illuminated panel, remotely controlled from the local meteorological office, to a simple reproduction of the weather map pinned up on a notice board. The Aerodrome and Approach Controllers, of course, need very accurate information as to the surface wind's speed and direction and height of cloudbase and, ideally, this is presented to them on meters let in to the control desk. The current barometric pressure must also be displayed, as pilots need this information to set their altimeters correctly.

Efficient Communications

So much for display equipment. But the communications equipment is probably the most important used by the entire control service. Without fast and accurate communications between the pilot and the controller and from one control room to another, it would be impossible for air-traffic control to function. On the efficiency of the communications system depends the efficiency of the entire control service; and as flying speeds increase, so the need for ever more rapid means of communication becomes all the more important.

Communications may be divided into two general classes, ground-to-ground and air-to-ground. Fixed and mobile communications, as they are sometimes respectively termed.

The first, ground-to-ground communications, are used to pass flight-plan and other information from the pilot or other representative of the aircraft operator, to the air-traffic controller concerned, and also to supply relevant details of flights to be passed from one control room to another when, for example, the proposed flight will take the aeroplane through more than one control area or flight-information region. Control centres and destination aerodromes must be warned of approaching traffic and, of course, distress organizations must be alerted immediately if any aeroplane is known or thought to be in trouble.

Telephone and Teleprinter

Air-traffic control messages from one ground station to another are normally passed by telephone, teleprinter or radio, depending on the circumstances. The air-traffic control organization usually has a private telephone system for its exclusive use.

The teleprinter may be described as a two-way typewriter by means of which messages typed on a keyboard at the place of transmission are automatically reproduced at the receiving end in typescript on a continuous strip or roll of paper.

Radio communications, or point-to-point communications as they are usually known in this connexion, are used mainly for very long-distance messages; but radio is also sometimes employed as a stand-by should the ground link fail, and may even be used across short sea crossings if submarine cables become overloaded or defective.

As might be expected, the tendency today is to make increasing use of direct telephone or speech lines in order to

RUNWAY CONTROLLER *uses an Aldis lamp from his mobile cabin to give clearance and other signals, especially to small aircraft not fitted with radio. Coloured screens are used: a steady red signal, for instance, tells the airborne pilot to give way to other traffic.*

reduce transit delays to the absolute minimum. Records of messages must, of course, be made for a variety of purposes, including accident investigation in the event of a mishap; and there is likely to be an ever-increasing number of automatic speech recorders installed on traffic-control networks. These enable the control and communications staffs to concentrate on their work without having to log all messages sent and received.

Long-distance, point-to-point communications are almost invariably transmitted in morse; speech is sometimes used, but it is a fact that an experienced radio operator can read a morse-code message through static and other forms of interference which would make a spoken message quite incomprehensible. The future, however, may well see the introduction of a form of radio teleprinter as the standard method of point-to-point communication for air-traffic control.

The brief details which have been given of the task of air-traffic control make it clear that communications between air and ground are also vital; and here, although numerous scientific advances have been made since man first flew, one of the most ancient forms of communication is still to be found. By no means all aircraft, even today, are fitted with radio equipment, and the pilot of a small aeroplane is often dependent on flashing light signals from the controller.

Signals to Aircraft

The Aldis lamp, with coloured screens, is commonly used. A steady green light, directed at the pilot, means "all clear to land." A steady red tells the airborne pilot to give way to other traffic. A series of red flashes indicates that the aerodrome is unsafe and the pilot must land elsewhere.

To the pilot on the ground the lights have similar meanings. A steady green, for example, means "all clear to take off," a steady red means "stop" and a series of red flashes warns the pilot that he is obstructing the landing area and must move clear. Other messages are passed in a similar way: a flashing white light, for example, tells the pilot taxi-ing out that he must return to the apron and not proceed on his journey.

There are two forms of radio communication used between ground and air: radio telephony (R/T), in which speech is used as on the telephone; and radio telegraphy, or wireless telegraphy (W/T). R/T is rapidly becoming universal

HOW GERMISTON, *the Rand airport, looks to the pilot of an aeroplane. The control buildings and tower are at the right of the picture, overlooking the aerodrome.*

FLYING-BOATS *using marine bases are controlled in much the same way as landplanes. This picture shows a part of the marine base at Darrell's Island, Bermuda.*

as the means of communication between Aerodrome and Approach Controllers and aircraft taking off or landing. The controller talks direct to the pilot, so there is no time lost in the passing of an instruction and the aeroplane's response. The most efficient form of R/T for the purpose is transmitted by radio waves of Very High Frequencies (V.H.F.) The range of such waves is not great, being similar to that of television, but is sufficient for the purpose. V.H.F. has the advantages that interference from static is negligible.

One difficulty with R/T is, of course, that of language. Although most of to-day's air-line pilots are English-speaking, most of the larger aerodromes offer W/T facilities which may be used by foreign operators. When W/T is used, there is generally a radio operator in the air in addition to one on the ground, although sometimes the pilot himself sends and receives morse messages whilst flying the aeroplane. Some delay, however, is bound to result as messages have to be encoded and the direct contact between controller and pilot is broken. Most messages between controller and pilot can be passed quite satisfactorily

by W/T, but it is not possible to use the Ground Controlled Approach (G.C.A.) system, described elsewhere in this book, without direct R/T between the Talk-down Controller and the pilot.

International Code

Although R/T, on medium or high frequencies, is in some places used for long-range communications, W/T is the main form of communication in control areas and flight-information regions in most countries. Speed, though important, is not quite so vital as in the immediate vicinity of an aerodrome and W/T has the advantage, already mentioned, that, with skilled operators, it is readable through heavy interference. Added to this, standard messages can be passed by W/T, in the Q-code, with great rapidity.

The Q-code is used throughout the world. Groups of three letters, each group starting with the letter Q, are used to convey definite meanings. The Q-code is thus an international language.

There is still one link in the communications channels to be described. It has been explained that, when W/T is used, the controller passes his messages to the pilot and receives the pilot's replies

239

through the medium of a radio operator, who may be stationed in a communications room adjacent to the control room —or even in an entirely separate building. Messages between the control room and the communications room may be passed in a variety of ways, but one of the most common is the pneumatic-tube system found in many large shops.

This chapter would not be complete without some reference to pyrotechnics, which still have their uses as a means of conveying information from ground to air. A green pyrotechnic signal, for instance, has the same meaning as the steady green from an Aldis or similar type of lamp: "all clear to land." A red signal indicates to the pilot that, in spite of any previous clearance he may have received, he is not to land for the time being. This signal is most commonly used in an emergency when it appears to the controller that the pilot has not understood a previous message or when something unexpected happens, such as an aeroplane landing out of turn or preparing to land down-wind by mistake.

Rockets, also, are still sometimes put to good use, their main purpose being to assist aircraft without radio to locate an aerodrome when the ground is obscured by a layer of mist or haze and the air is clear a few hundred feet up. In such conditions a rocket can be seen for many miles, even by daylight, and many aircraft have been brought safely home by this simple means.

It is well known that aircraft can take off and land at a much higher rate in good weather than in bad, and one of the aims of air-traffic control is to increase the safe bad-weather movement rate. But air-traffic control on its own cannot achieve the ideal of bringing the bad-weather rate up to the good-weather rate, either for take-offs or for landings; the aircraft designer, the engine and instrument designers, the communications experts, the airport designer and the meteorologist all have vital parts to play.

MARSHALLER FLAGS IN *a K.L.M. Convair-Liner. At night, lighted wands are used. The position of the flags in this picture tells the pilot that he must stop.*

CHAPTER 9

AIRCRAFT
LANDING SYSTEMS

I N the early days which marked the entry of the aeroplane as a serious competitor in the field of public transport, air-line operators were faced with the task of achieving a high standard of operation in three fundamental requirements : safety, punctuality and regularity.

As one might expect, from the very nature of its operational medium, civil aviation has found its biggest enemy in the battle to attain these ideals to be the weather. The development of blind-flying instruments, radio navigational aids and de-icing systems were logical steps taken in an effort to improve the safety of aircraft operation and, to a certain extent, the regularity and punctuality of the services. It was soon realized, however, that unless some kind of assistance could be given to the pilot whereby he could effect a landing under the worst possible weather conditions the regularity of the services would suffer to such an extent that air transport would cease to be regarded as a competitor to be taken seriously.

The safety factor had also to be considered. It was clearly uneconomic for the aeroplane to be forced to carry additional fuel in order to be able to reach a clear aerodrome if the weather should happen to close in at the destination. Yet, clearly, this sacrifice of payload was essential if a high standard of safety was to be maintained.

We are all familiar with the delays incurred by surface transport in conditions of poor visibility or fog. And this type of weather, unfortunately, is not the only one likely to affect the regularity and punctuality of air services. The presence of a layer of low cloud over the airport has similar, if not quite so serious, consequences as fog—which, in the past, almost always caused cancellation of the flight.

Instrument Runway

The development of radio and other aids to landing in bad weather was therefore allotted a high priority. At first, these aids consisted of simple direction-finding equipments which would enable the pilot to descend over the top of the aerodrome, break cloud and make a visual circuit and landing. Later, it was realized that these were ineffective in poor visibility and that something in the nature of a radio beam directed along the approach path to a runway was an urgent requirement. This led to the development of the modern systems in use today which not only guide the pilot on to the approach line, but also in his descent along this line.

Each international airport now has at least one runway which is designated the instrument runway. This is so called because it is the runway on which landings are made in adverse weather conditions requiring the pilot to carry out an approach on instruments.

Several factors determine the choice of the instrument runway. The most important one is the nature of the terrain and artificial obstructions on the approach path. The ideal approach path is one which is free from upstanding obstructions, such as high ground or tall chimneys, for a distance of three or four miles. The direction of the instrument runway should be as close as possible to that of the prevailing wind. It should also be long enough to cater for the fact that, in poor visibility or fog, the wind is usually calm and, as a result, the aeroplane must make a longer landing run than would be the case if it landed into a strong wind.

The ground transmitters of certain of the radio and radar landing devices used by the aeroplane are usually permanently installed in line with the instrument runway. If, however, there is a strong, gusty wind blowing across the instrument runway it may be necessary to use another runway for landing, in which case there will usually be a mobile system such as Ground Controlled Approach (G.C.A.) which can readily be made available. Alternatively, if the cloud base is not too low and the visibility underneath the cloud is good enough, the pilot may use one of the permanent systems to break cloud and then carry out a visual circuit and landing.

The Pilot's Needs

There are a number of different landing aids in use throughout the world at the present time. None, however, can be considered as landing aids in the true sense of the word "landing." Before seeking an explanation of why this should be so, let us first enquire into the real nature of a pilot's requirements of a landing aid.

First, he requires guidance on to and along an approach path in line with the runway. Second, he requires guidance during his descent along this path which will ensure a safe clearance over any obstacles and, third, he needs assistance to enable him to make a safe and gentle landing soon after crossing the runway threshold. All the so-called approach and landing systems provide for the first of these needs and, to a limited extent, for the second. Two systems provide a high degree of accuracy for both the first and second. None makes any provision for the third.

Ideal Glide Path

The need for a solution to this difficult problem is, of course, well recognized. With present equipment and aircraft instrumentation, however, blind landings are out of the question. The accuracy of the aircraft altimeter, which works on a system of barometric pressure, cannot be guaranteed better than plus or minus 50 ft. The radio glide path of the Instrument Landing System (I.L.S.) being a straight line with a slope of 1 in 20, ends abruptly at the touch-down point. What is required here, of course, is a path which, from a height of 100 ft., is a smooth curve becoming tangential to the runway at the point of touch-down.

The normal technique employed by a pilot during the landing is to level off a foot or so above the ground and hold the aeroplane in that position until flying speed is lost, when the craft drops gently on to the runway. Until such time, therefore, as an aid has been developed which will enable the pilot to use his normal technique under completely blind conditions, the instrument approach must always be broken off at some point before the touch-down. This point, known as the critical height, depends on a number of factors, the most important being the nature of the surrounding terrain and obstructions, the landing aid used, and the characteristics of the particular aircraft at low speed with the undercarriage and flaps lowered. If, when the pilot reaches the

THE RUNWAY AT FILTON *Aerodrome as seen from the air. The huge buildings in which the Brabazon was constructed can be seen to the left of the runway.*

critical height, he cannot complete the landing by visual means, he must climb away to a safe height and divert his aeroplane to another aerodrome where weather conditions are better.

To assist the pilot in determining whether or not an instrument approach is a practicable proposition in given weather conditions, critical heights are laid down for each particular approach aid at all aerodromes the pilot is likely to visit and these are listed in the operations manual. Against the critical height, a figure is given for the meteorological visibility which would be needed to complete a landing from this height under visual conditions. Let us suppose that, at a certain aerodrome, the critical height and visibility required for the selected landing aid were specified as 200 ft. and 1,100 yd. If the weather report gave the height of the base of the low cloud as 300 ft. and the visibility as 2,000 yd., the pilot would know that a landing was feasible. If, however, the visibility were 2,000 yd. but the cloud-base only 100 ft., a landing would be impracticable and the pilot would immediately divert to another aerodrome where conditions were more suitable. Again, if there were no cloud at all, but the visibility were 500 yd., a landing would not be attempted.

Types of Approach Aid

Systems providing aid to approach and landing are basically of two types, those controlled by the pilot and those controlled by ground personnel. Both have their advantages and disadvantages, but at the present time the type operated by the pilot is generally accepted as being the more

243

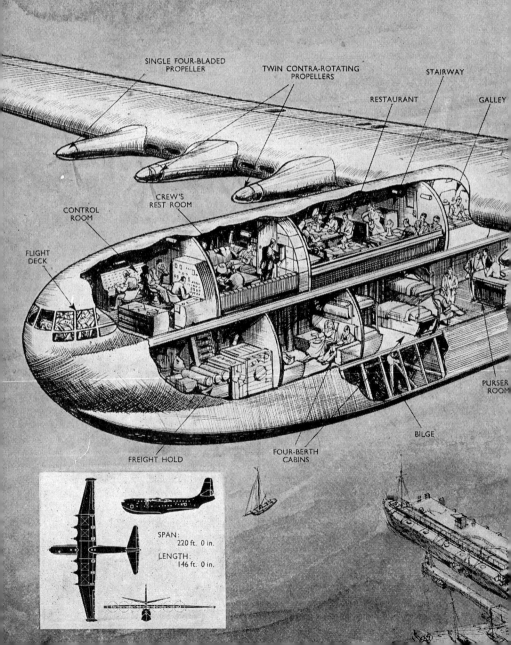

SAUNDERS-ROE PRINCESS
AN INTERIOR DESIGN SCHEME

SINGLE FOUR-BLADED PROPELLER

TWIN CONTRA-ROTATING PROPELLERS

STAIRWAY

RESTAURANT

GALLEY

CREW'S REST ROOM

CONTROL ROOM

FLIGHT DECK

PURSER ROOM

BILGE

FREIGHT HOLD

FOUR-BERTH CABINS

SPAN: 220 ft. 0 in.

LENGTH: 146 ft. 0 in.

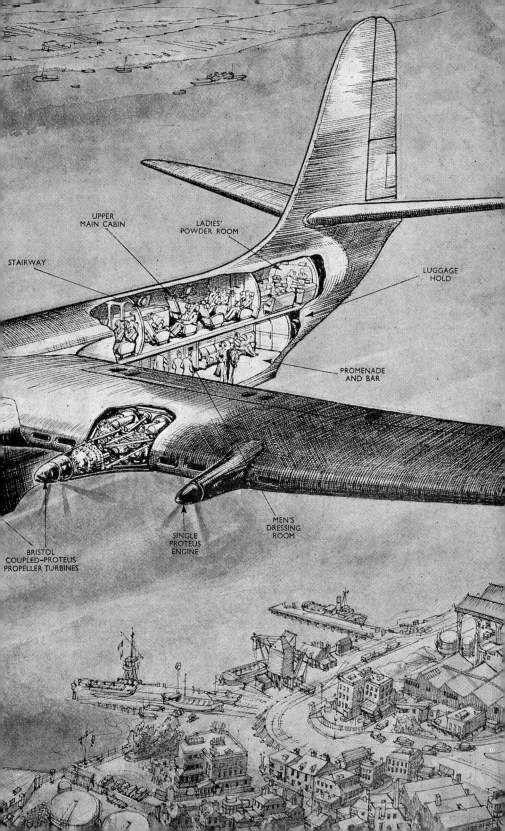

UPPER
MAIN CABIN

LADIES'
POWDER ROOM

STAIRWAY

LUGGAGE
HOLD

PROMENADE
AND BAR

BRISTOL
COUPLED-PROTEUS
PROPELLER TURBINES

SINGLE
PROTEUS
ENGINE

MEN'S
DRESSING
ROOM

CONSTELLATION, *safely brought down by G.C.A., taxies past the G.C.A. trucks. The search and height-finding aerials are seen projecting from the roof of the control vehicle.*

desirable of the two. Under this system, of course, the pilot's work is considerably increased. He has, in addition to his normal blind-flying instruments, to watch the special instrument used in conjunction with the automatic ground transmitters, interpret his position from the readings, and alter the aeroplane's attitude accordingly. On the other hand, he has the satisfaction of knowing that provided the ground equipment is functioning satisfactorily (and often he is enabled to check that this is so) the safety of the aeroplane and its passengers, for which he is ultimately responsible, is in his own hands and not in those of someone on the ground.

The ground-controlled system, whilst relieving the pilot of the additional burden of interpreting the readings of his landing instrument, is psychologically unsatisfactory as the pilot has no way of determining whether or not the ground controller has made a mistake, but must rely on instructions passed by the controller.

Modern air-line practice is tending towards a combination of the two types of aid, wherein one system is used as a monitor of the other. This method will be explained more fully later when the landing aids are described in detail.

Of the various landing systems now in use the more precise ones are the Instrument Landing System (I.L.S.), Standard Beam Approach (S.B.A.), Beam Approach Beacon System (B.A.B.S.), and Ground Controlled Approach (G.C.A.). The first three of these are pilot-controlled, whilst the last is operated by ground personnel.

Standard Aids

This multiplicity of aids, useful as it might appear to be at first sight, has considerable disadvantages. The cost of installing more than one system on all major airports is, in most countries, prohibitive. Carrying several types of airborne radio equipment in aircraft results in a loss of payload. The cost, too, of training pilots in the use of several aids and of maintaining them in flying practice is very heavy. It will be seen, therefore, that the need for standardization on one type of landing aid is an urgent one.

Agreement has lately been reached on an international basis that I.L.S. shall be the standard aid at all major international airports, and that G.C.A. shall be available as a standby for use in emergency. An important feature of G.C.A. as regards emergency operation is that no special radio equipment need be carried in the aircraft.

In I.L.S., guidance on to the approach path in line with the runway is provided by a radio transmitter called a localizer beacon. The signals received by an aircraft radio receiver from the localizer are applied to the vertical pointer of a crossed-pointer meter in such a way that if the aeroplane is off track, the needle deflects to the left or right, indicating which way the pilot must turn the aeroplane in order to regain track. The needle will remain vertical provided that the aeroplane tracks correctly in line with the runway. It will be seen that the aeroplane in this case must be somewhere in a vertical plane which passes through the localizer beacon and the extended centre-line of the runway; this plane is called the localizer plane.

Guidance during the descent is provided by a second radio transmitter called the glide-path beacon. As before, the signals received by the aircraft radio equipment are applied to the crossed-pointer meter so that if the aircraft is below or above the correct approach path the horizontal needle is deflected up or down. The needle remains horizontal as long as the aeroplane remains on the glide-path. As the craft may be descending along a correct slope and yet not be tracking correctly in the right direction, the aeroplane's position, in this instance, may be anywhere in a sloping plane which passes through the glide-path beacon. This plane is called the glide plane.

From Euclid we learned that a straight line was defined as the shortest distance between two points. Later on a new definition was given to us, namely, that a straight line is formed by the intersection of two planes. It is the latter definition which gives us the ideal approach path in space: the intersection of the localizer plane and the glide plane.

To ensure that the aeroplane flies down the correct approach path, the pilot must manoeuvre his aeroplane so that the two needles cross in the centre of the meter. In practice, in order to avoid having to carry out a series of minor adjustments to the aeroplane's attitude, the approach is considered to be safe so long as the needles intersect inside a small circle marked in the centre of the dial.

The localizer beacon of the I.L.S. is located at the up-wind end of the runway—

that is, the end opposite to that at which the aeroplane touches down. The glide-path transmitter is located to one side of the runway in line with the touch-down point. Although the localizer and glide-path beacons form a complete system in themselves, it has been found desirable in practice to incorporate three additional low-powered beacons called markers.

I.L.S. Marker Beacons

These marker beacons are separately named outer marker, middle marker and boundary marker, and are dispersed along the approach path at distances of approximately twenty- four- and one-thousand feet respectively from the glide-path beacon. Their function is to provide the pilot during the approach with an indication of his distance from touch-down. In addition, they can be used to check the alignment of the glide path. With the gradient of the path set at 1 in 20, the aeroplane passing over the outer marker should be at an altitude of 1,000 ft., and, similarly, when

INSIDE A G.C.A. TRAILER, *the crew can follow the movements of approaching aircraft by means of meters and radar displays, and are in speech (R/T) contact with the pilot.*

247

passing over the middle marker his height should be 200 ft. The boundary marker was originally designed as a warning for the pilot to look ahead for a visual landing. Present-day practice, however, usually decrees, that an approach under instrument-flight conditions shall be discontinued before the aeroplane has descended to as low as 50 ft. and the use of the boundary marker is likely to be confined to emergency landings.

In the control cabin, passage of the marker beacons is indicated to the pilot visually by means of three lights, purple for the outer marker, amber for the middle marker and green for the boundary marker.

Navigational Beacons

All radio aids used for final approach have a range of reception limited to a few miles' radius of the airport. As a result, there are usually one or more navigational beacons located in its vicinity which may be used in conjunction with the aircraft radio compass for homing to the aerodrome. Suitably positioned, they can also serve to hold, or stack, the aeroplane in a restricted air space while it waits its turn to land, as illustrated. It will be seen that the radio-range station is located between the I.L.S. middle and outer markers in line with the runway. The M.F. beacon, however, is about seven miles from the aerodrome and offset from the line of the runway. This lay-out enables the pilot to maintain a "race-track" holding pattern by first homing to the radio-range station, and then turning left to home to the M.F. beacon.

Let us now join our aeroplane which is awaiting its turn to land and accompany the pilot through the successive stages of the approach which will culminate in a landing. We are number two to land, and the pilot has been instructed to fly at 2,500 ft.

The pilot, before entering the aerodrome control zone, has received the weather report and satisfied himself that the cloud base and visibility are such as to permit him to descend safely to his critical height and complete the landing under visual conditions.

As soon as the pilot who is number one to land has reported to control that he has reached the outer marker of the I.L.S. (and is therefore four miles from touchdown), the pilot of our aeroplane will be given turn one and "cleared to final."

Whatever his position in the holding pattern, he will immediately fly towards the M.F. beacon and at the same time descend to 1,500 ft. Arriving over the beacon he maintains this altitude and turns left to join the localizer beam of the I.L.S.

At this point he carries out his cockpit check for landing: wheels down and locked, engine r.p.m. increased, some landing flap lowered, fuel contents noted, brake pressures checked and so on. Flying level at 1,500 ft., our pilot starts to eliminate drift—that is, if there is any drift due to a cross-wind, he will determine a course to steer which will keep the localizer needle vertical. As the aeroplane comes up to the glide path the glide path needle will gradually lower to the horizontal position. With the needle horizontal, the pilot knows that he has intercepted the glide path and so reduces engine power, lowers more landing flap and starts the descent.

Crossing the outer marker beacon at 1,000 ft., he reports his position to Approach Control, receives his clearance to land and continues his descent.

Critical Height for Approach

Let us suppose now that the critical height for this approach is 200 ft. In other words, when the aeroplane crosses the middle marker beacon, the pilot should be able to look up from his instruments, see the runway ahead, and land by his normal visual technique. As the aeroplane approaches this altitude, the pilot prepares

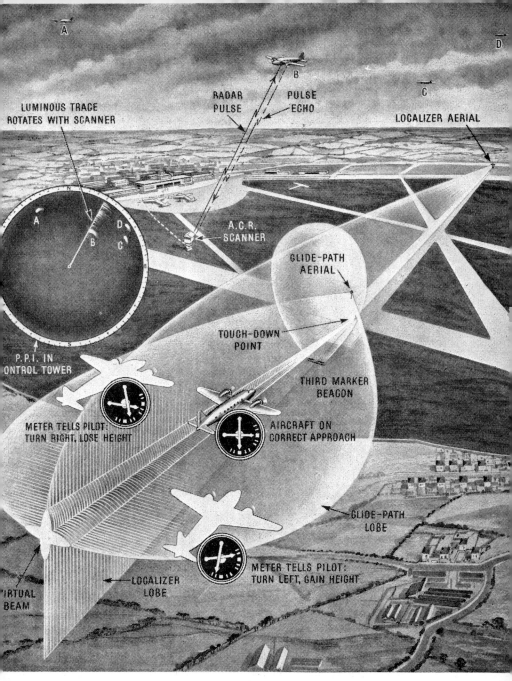

BLIND APPROACH BY I.L.S. *The correct landing path lies along the intersection of the planes formed by the horizontal and vertical radio beams or lobes; deviations are shown to the pilot by a crossed-pointer meter. Three marker beacons, of which the third is shown, tell the pilot how close he is to the runway. Meanwhile, the air-traffic controller knows the position of all aircraft within his area from the P.P.I. screen on his Airfield Control Radar (A.C.R.).*

249

himself for a possible overshoot; this means that if the visibility and cloud height are below the minimum requirements, he will lose no time in opening the throttles and climbing away. Present-day meteorological reporting systems unfortunately cannot be adapted realistically to the pilot's needs. The visibility reported at the meteorological office may not be the same as that obtaining from the cockpit looking slightly downwards. Similarly, the cloud base at the critical break-off point may be lower than that over the aerodrome itself. But in our case, the weather is kind, the second pilot shouts "contact" as we pass over the middle marker and we go straight in to make our landing.

Counteracting Drift

Some explanation should be made at this stage of the phrase "eliminate drift." The success of an instrument approach depends primarily on the skill of the pilot in determining a heading or course to steer which will keep the aeroplane on the localizer beam. In conditions of no wind, or when the wind is blowing directly down the runway, his task is simple and consists only of steering along the direction of the

beam. In other words, if the direction of the beam is due west, he steers 270 deg.

But, if the wind blows from the side— say from the south-west at 20 m.p.h.— and the pilot continues to steer 270 deg., his track over the ground will be 280 deg. and the needle of his cross-pointer meter will move over to the left, indicating that he must turn left to regain the beam. The aeroplane is then said to have drifted over to the right and the angle between heading and track (10 deg.) is called the drift angle. To counteract the effect of the wind, the pilot will head the aeroplane slightly into wind and steer 261 deg. On this heading there will be 9 deg. of drift and consequently the aeroplane will track correctly on 270 deg.

In practice, of course, the process consists of making allowance for drift rather than eliminating it. A series of S-turns are made on each side of the beam, the angle through which the aeroplane is turned being gradually diminished until a point is reached where the localizer pointer remains steady. The heading at this point is the one which will keep the aeroplane on the beam. If it happened that the aeroplane were off track at the

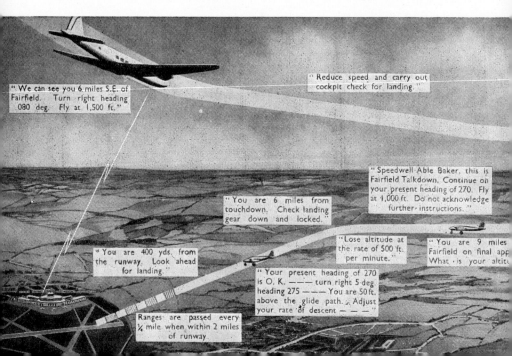

" We can see you 6 miles S.E. of Fairfield. Turn right heading 080 deg. Fly at 1,500 ft."

" Reduce speed and carry out cockpit check for landing."

" Speedwell-Able-Baker, this is Fairfield Talkdown. Continue on your present heading of 270. Fly at 1,000 ft. Do not acknowledge further instructions."

" You are 6 miles from touchdown. Check landing gear down and locked."

" Lose altitude at the rate of 500 ft. per minute."

" You are 9 miles Fairfield on final app What is your altitu

" You are 400 yds. from the runway. Look ahead for landing."

" Your present heading of 270 is O. K. —— turn right 5 deg. heading 275 —— You are 50 ft. above the glide path. Adjust your rate of descent —— "

Ranges are passed every ¼ mile when within 2 miles of runway.

time the correct heading was found, another small S-turn would be required to position it on the beam.

Unfortunately, it has been found that on many occasions the wind, and therefore the drift, changes as the aeroplane approaches the runway because of the effect of surface friction. In addition, the beam becomes narrower and the localizer needle more sensitive, so that it becomes increasingly difficult to stay on the correct course.

We have only to consider the formidable list of instruments used by the pilot to understand how this comes about. Information on the progress of the flight is presented to the pilot through the medium of the I.L.S. cross-pointer meter, directional indicator, air speed indicator, altimeter, artificial horizon and the vertical movement indicator. This information is obtained by "sampling" each instrument in turn, a process which takes between three and five seconds.

Suppose, then, that the aeroplane is flying steadily down the approach path, but that immediately after sampling the I.L.S. meter an error in track is acquired through a gust or change of wind. A period of possibly five seconds therefore elapses before the pilot detects the error and a further delay occurs between the pilot's reaction to this information and the aeroplane's response to his corrective action. In the latter stages of the approach the pilot is presented with error information faster than he can deal with it, larger, and larger heading corrections become necessary, and finally the chain of action described above breaks down. The approach has become unstable and there is nothing the pilot can do but initiate overshoot procedure and make a fresh start.

The defects in the existing method of presenting the information from the I.L.S. and the difficulties ensuing from the necessity of using so many blind-flying instruments have long been recognized. These, however, are now in process of being rectified and resolved.

The Zero Reader

A new method of I.L.S. presentation called the Zero Reader has been evolved which obviates the use of all the conventional instruments with the exception of the air-speed indicator and the altimeter, and pilots who have flown using the prototype

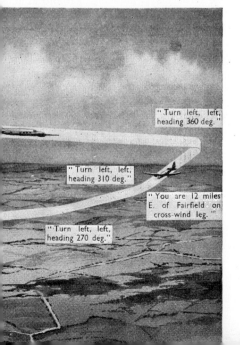

"Turn left, left, heading 360 deg."

"Turn left, left, heading 310 deg."

"You are 12 miles E. of Fairfield on cross-wind leg."

"Turn left, left, heading 270 deg."

R/T TALK-DOWN. Typical phraseology used in talking-down a pilot on G.C.A. Thirty miles from the airport the pilot receives and acknowledges instructions, which bring him in line with the runway, from a director who knows the position of the aeroplane but not its height. The talk-down controller takes over for the last stage: meters and P.P.I.s in front of him indicate the aeroplane's position in three dimensions. The pilot has merely to obey instructions, without acknowledging them, until he sees the runway ahead of him. As with all systems in general use, instrument approach is broken off at a certain point before touch-down, and the actual landing is made by normal visual means, with the pilot in full control of the aeroplane.

251

instrument are enthusiastic about the results achieved. In addition to facilitating I.L.S. approaches, it can be used for normal route flying with or without radio aids.

The Zero Reader comprises several components, the pilot's instruments being the indicator, the heading selector and the selector switch. As illustrated, the indicator is a simple two-element meter in which two mutually perpendicular pointers move relatively to each other over the face of the instrument. The vertical pointer moves from left to right whilst the horizontal one moves up and down. In the centre of the face is a small aeroplane which represents the zero mark.

The deflection of the vertical pointer is controlled by bank, compass heading and localizer signal in such a way that when the vertical pointer moves over to the right, due, say, to an off-track signal from the localizer, the pilot merely has to move his wheel slightly to the right as if he were following it. By so doing the pointer returns to zero with no overshoot and with no anticipation being required of the pilot.

The deflection of the horizontal pointer is controlled by pitch and altitude if in level flight, or by the glide-path signal if making an I.L.S. approach, in such a way that if the horizontal pointer moves upward due to, say, the aeroplane being below the glide-path—the pilot pulls back slightly on the control column and the pointer returns to zero. In practice, the pilot concentrates on the intersection of the pointers rather than on the individual pointers themselves and then moves his controls, without delay or anticipation, in such a direction that the miniature aeroplane appears to fly to the intersection.

The Zero Reader works in conjunction with the Gyrosyn compass (Gyroscope-synchronized) in which the reading of the compass master-unit is transmitted electrically to several repeaters fitted at the various crew stations. The Heading Selector consists of one of these repeaters, plus a

concentric course setter. Rotation of the knob which selects a given heading causes the appropriate compass signal to be sent to the indicator.

The selector switch enables the pilot to select the particular function he wishes the equipment to perform. There is a main control-selector switch in the centre and an altitude-control switch to the right.

Using the Zero Reader

Let us see how the pilot uses the Zero Reader to facilitate an I.L.S. approach. First, he joins the beam at 1,500 ft., using the normal I.L.S. crossed-pointer meter. Then he turns the control-selector switch to the position marked LOC (localizer), switches the altitude-control switch to ON, and rotates the course setter of the heading selector to the heading of the localizer beam (270 deg. in our case). Thereafter he concentrates on keeping the indicator pointers on zero.

Drift due to cross-wind is quickly detected by observing the heading selector. Suppose that a position has been reached where no more movements are required to "zero" the pointers and that the compass pointer reads 260 deg. This means that the aeroplane is "crabbing" left into wind, the drift angle being 10 deg. It also means that the aeroplane is slightly off the beam to the right by an amount equivalent to 10 deg. of compass signal. The pilot thus moves the course setter to coincide with the compass pointer, and in so doing the pointer deflects to the left. A slight application of left bank will return the pointer to zero.

By controlling bank to keep the indicator continually on zero, the aeroplane is thus made to fly in a smooth curve to arrive close to the centre of the beam.

As the I.L.S. meter indicates our approach to the glide-path, the pilot moves his switch to the approach position. The altitude control is automatically switched off and the glide-path signal inserted into

THE ZERO READER *overcomes delays caused by the necessity for reading several instruments while approaching by I.L.S. Information is presented to the pilot by two indicators: the indicator (centre) shows position in elevation and azimuth in relation to the correct flight path, while the heading selector (right) is pre-set to the required course, and in case of any deviation from it, sends a corrective signal to the indicator unit. The selector switch (left) sets the apparatus to the function it is to perform.*

the pitch indication. The pilot then adjusts his power settings to give the required rate of descent and once more brings both pointers to zero. The increase in sensitivity of the localizer beam as the aeroplane approaches nearer to the runway is barely noticeable and approach failure due to instability is thus obviated.

The Zero Reader is undoubtedly a great step forward in aircraft instrumentation and also towards the goal of flight under the worst weather conditions.

Ground Controlled Approach

Ground Controlled Approach (G.C.A.), a wartime development employing radar techniques, is one of the most successful forms of landing aid yet devised. It has acquired a large following amongst pilots because of its high degree of accuracy and because of the ease with which a pilot, with little or even no experience of the system, can successfully accomplish a let-down. The controller passes instructions to the pilot by R/T and the pilot has merely to fly the aeroplane on instruments as accurately as he can and at the same time carry out the orders received implicitly.

G.C.A. comprises two distinct radar systems called, respectively, the Search System and the Precision System. The search system employs a vertical rotating aerial which produces a narrow, fan-shaped beam sweeping an area of radius 30 miles. Information is presented in the form of a radar map on a P.P.I. (Plan Position Indicator), aircraft appearing as bright yellow traces or blips against a dark green background. Permanent obstructions such as buildings are also shown on the screen, but the brightness of these is reduced to provide the necessary contrast with the aircraft blips. The indicator is provided with a rotatable compass rose and heading lines, and these, in conjunction with electronic range (or distance) circles, enable the distance and bearing of the aircraft blip from the aerodrome to be read off immediately. The P.P.I. operator is thus able to pass courses to steer which will bring the aeroplane into a position between four and ten miles away in line with the runway, where the precision system takes over for the final descent.

At large international airports, where the race-track type of holding is employed, the G.C.A. search system is normally only used for monitoring purposes and for guiding aircraft whose navigational radio equipment is unserviceable, or in an emergency situation when a landing must be effected without delay.

Before describing the precision system of G.C.A. in detail it is necessary to emphasize the radical difference between the principles of G.C.A. and the I.L.S. In the I.L.S., the correct approach path is formed by the intersection of two planes, the vertical localizer plane and the sloping glide plane. In G.C.A., however, the approach path is an imaginary one. The position of the aeroplane in terms of distance, bearing and elevation relative to the G.C.A. unit is determined by radar beams. This position in space is then related to an ideal approach path and translated by the controller into corrections to the heading and rate of descent.

Siting the G.C.A. Unit

The G.C.A. unit is usually sited some 500 ft. to the right of the runway looking towards the approach path, and some 4,000 ft. from the runway threshold, so that aircraft can be followed up to the very moment of touch-down. An accompanying illustration shows the rotating beam of the search system and the two narrow fan beams used in the precision system. These latter beams together sweep an area 20 deg. wide in azimuth (horizontally) and 7 deg. in elevation (vertically), the movement being known as scanning.

During the searching process, the elevation beam scans vertically from an angle 1 deg. below the horizontal to 6 deg. above the horizontal, and at the same time the aerial is moved from side to side throughout a sector of 20 deg. Similarly, the azimuth beam scans horizontally through an angle from 5 deg. to the right up to 15 deg. to the left of a line parallel to the runway, while its aerial is moved up and down so as to sweep through an angle of 7 deg.

The process of searching for the aeroplane is simplified if the height of the approaching aeroplane is known in advance. At ten miles range an aeroplane flying at 1,500 ft. will subtend an angle of $1\frac{3}{4}$ deg. in elevation. Thus, if the azimuth aerial is set at this angle the aeroplane should appear somewhere within the scan. When it does so the bearing is taken and set on the elevation aerial so that both beams can hold the aircraft at the same time. Once the aeroplane has been located the process becomes automatic, and minor adjustments to the aerial positions are made continuously throughout the period of its descent.

The information from the azimuth beam is displayed on a partial P.P.I., the aeroplane appearing as a bright blip. The indicator is viewed indirectly through a half-silvered mirror so that the display is superimposed on a plate on which is drawn a line representing the direction of the approach path. Range is measured from touch-down, and range markers (at right angles to the approach line) are provided every half-mile up to three miles, and every mile from three to ten miles. In addition, through the movement of a cursor which is made to follow the aircraft blip, the lateral deviations from the approach line are presented to the talk-down controller on a centre-zero meter, the zero mark representing the approach line. The controller, making allowance for any wind drift, transmits by R/T any alterations to the aeroplane's heading which are necessary in order to bring the aeroplane back on to the correct approach line.

Displaying the Elevation Beam

A similar arrangement is provided for the display of the information given by the elevation beam. In this case an artificial glide path together with range markers are seen superimposed on the P.P.I. and the deviations from the ideal path presented on a centre-zero meter. The controller informs the pilot of the exact amount of

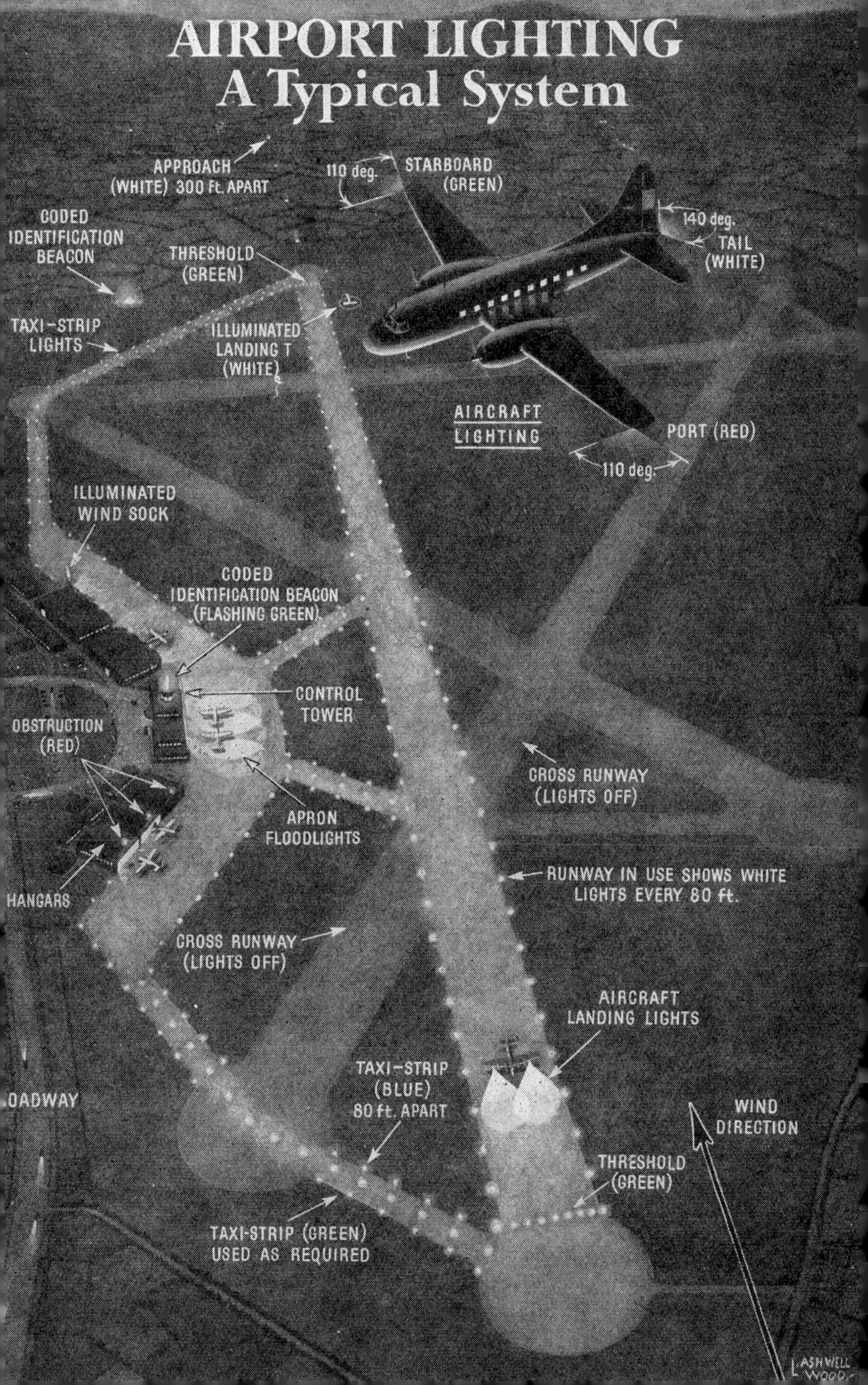

AIRPORT LIGHTING
A Typical System

APPROACH (WHITE) 300 Ft. APART

110 deg.

STARBOARD (GREEN)

140 deg. TAIL (WHITE)

CODED IDENTIFICATION BEACON

THRESHOLD (GREEN)

TAXI-STRIP LIGHTS

ILLUMINATED LANDING T (WHITE)

AIRCRAFT LIGHTING

PORT (RED)

110 deg.

ILLUMINATED WIND SOCK

CODED IDENTIFICATION BEACON (FLASHING GREEN)

CONTROL TOWER

CROSS RUNWAY (LIGHTS OFF)

OBSTRUCTION (RED)

APRON FLOODLIGHTS

HANGARS

RUNWAY IN USE SHOWS WHITE LIGHTS EVERY 80 ft.

CROSS RUNWAY (LIGHTS OFF)

AIRCRAFT LANDING LIGHTS

ROADWAY

TAXI-STRIP (BLUE) 80 ft. APART

WIND DIRECTION

THRESHOLD (GREEN)

TAXI-STRIP (GREEN) USED AS REQUIRED

L. ASHWELL WOOD

GROUND CONTROLLED APPROAC
(G.C.A.) Talk-down System
(NOT TO SCALE)

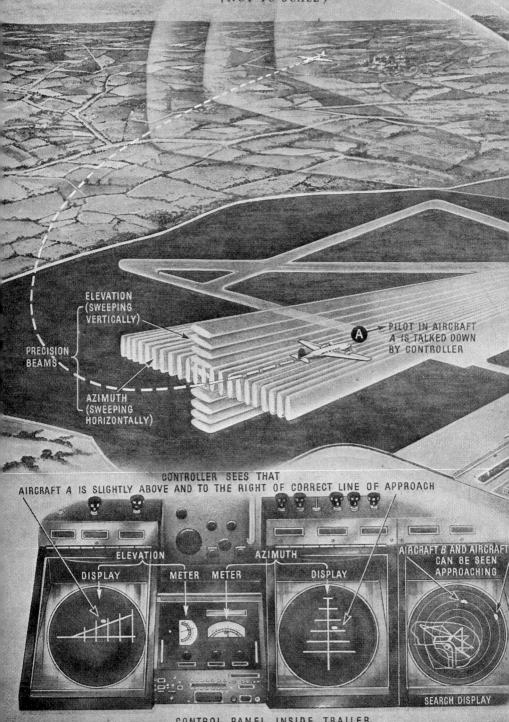

ELEVATION
(SWEEPING
VERTICALLY)

PRECISION
BEAMS

AZIMUTH
(SWEEPING
HORIZONTALLY)

A   PILOT IN AIRCRAFT A IS TALKED DOWN BY CONTROLLER

CONTROLLER SEES THAT
AIRCRAFT A IS SLIGHTLY ABOVE AND TO THE RIGHT OF CORRECT LINE OF APPROACH

ELEVATION

DISPLAY

METER   METER

AZIMUTH

DISPLAY

AIRCRAFT B AND AIRCRAFT
CAN BE SEEN
APPROACHING

SEARCH DISPLAY

CONTROL PANEL INSIDE TRAILER

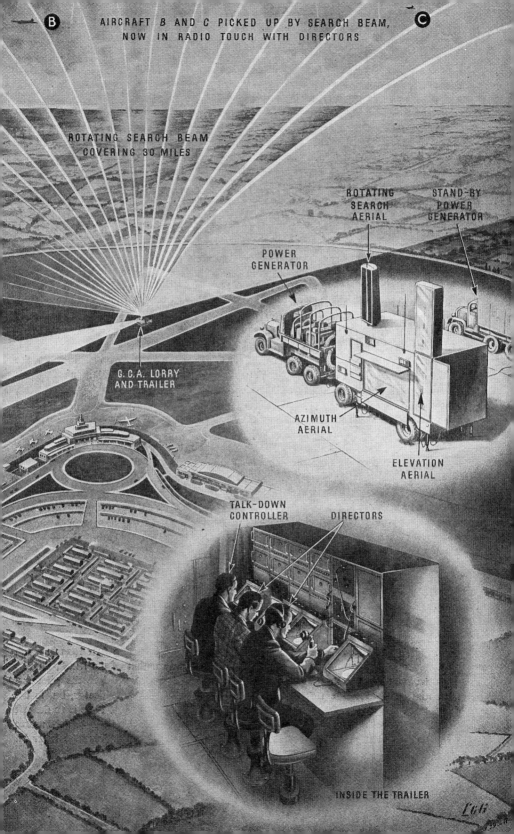

AIRCRAFT *B* AND *C* PICKED UP BY SEARCH BEAM, NOW IN RADIO TOUCH WITH DIRECTORS

ROTATING SEARCH BEAM COVERING 30 MILES

POWER GENERATOR

ROTATING SEARCH AERIAL

STAND-BY POWER GENERATOR

G.C.A. LORRY AND TRAILER

AZIMUTH AERIAL

ELEVATION AERIAL

TALK-DOWN CONTROLLER

DIRECTORS

INSIDE THE TRAILER

deviation and instructs him to adjust his rate of descent. For the last part of the descent, two other P.P.I.s, having an expanded scale of two miles instead of ten, are used. The illustrations show a typical approach pattern together with the R/T patter used by the Talk-down Controller in contact with a pilot.

For and Against G.C.A.

The advantages of G.C.A. as a monitor of, and supplement to, the pilot-operated aids are becoming increasingly recognized. The procedure followed in this method is a relatively straightforward one. Before starting the final descent, the captain requests the G.C.A. controller to monitor his approach. This means that throughout the descent the G.C.A. controller will follow the path of the aeroplane and at intervals give advice to the pilot in such terms as: "You are 50 ft. above the glide path," "You are 200 ft. to the left," "You are three miles from touch-down," and so on.

No attempt is made to instruct the pilot as to how he shall translate the information into necessary alterations to the aeroplane's heading and rate of descent; the purpose of monitoring is essentially one of checking that the I.L.S. (or other system in use) is functioning satisfactorily, and at the same time ensuring that, if an emergency arises due to failure of the ground equipment, the G.C.A. controller is in a position to take over and guide the aeroplane throughout the remainder of the descent.

The merits of G.C.A. are manifold. The fact that no special equipment is needed in the aeroplane makes it of unquestionable value in emergency. The unit is mobile, so that a precision approach is possible on a variety of runways, and not only on the instrument runway. Range information is continuously available throughout the descent and the pilot can be warned if there are other aircraft or obstacles in the vicinity. Also, the pilot can concentrate solely on his normal blind-flying instruments to the exclusion of additional special instruments such as crossed-pointer meters.

The high cost of operation, especially as regards man-power, and the language problem are factors which weigh heavily against the system, but which future development will no doubt eliminate. The biggest drawback, however, so far as the pilot is concerned, is inherent in the system itself. Many air-line captains are extremely reluctant to place themselves entirely in the hands of controllers on the ground. They assert that this practice virtually amounts to the relinquishment of the captain's responsibility for the safety of his aeroplane in one of the most critical periods of the flight, and that the system should be confined to use in emergency and as a monitor in conjunction with a pilot-operated aid.

How far this opinion will affect the trend of development of landing aids it is difficult to forecast. For the time being, at any rate, it is safe to say that G.C.A. has made a very significant contribution to the level of safety in civil aviation and that the system will be retained in some form or other for many years to come.

The Instrument Landing System has been described in detail mainly because it is representative of all the pilot-operated aids. Mention must be made, however, of two other pilot-operated systems which are in wide use at the present time.

S.B.A. and B.A.B.S.

S.B.A. (Standard Beam Approach) consists of a localizer beacon together with two marker beacons, called the inner and outer markers.

The localizer beacon functions in much the same way as that of the I.L.S., but the information is presented to the pilot not by means of a visual indicator, but in the form of audible signals. If he is to the left of the localizer plane he will hear the morse letter A and if to the right, the letter N.

WITH FLAPS DOWN, *a Hermes IV approaches to land. Radar, radio and visual aids have made safe landings possible even in conditions of near-zero visibility.*

The signals combine to form a steady note when the pilot is flying on the beam—in the plane of the localizer.

The inner marker is located a few hundred yards from the end of the runway and the outer marker about two miles away. To facilitate the approach, a non-directional beacon is usually installed four miles away in line with the runway. The pilot descends to 1,000 ft. whilst homing to this beacon and positions himself on the beam. When over the beacon he starts his final approach and loses height at 500 ft. per minute to a height of 600 ft. If, on reaching this altitude, he has not passed over the outer marker beacon, he will fly level until he has done so and then resume his normal rate of descent to the critical altitude.

This type of let-down, where no glide path is employed, is called a step-down approach. The principle is used to much greater effect in the Beam Approach Beacon System.

B.A.B.S. is a radar talk-down system employing a radar transmitter on the ground and a combined transmitter and receiver in the aeroplane. The radio operator interprets the position of the craft from the signals on his radar screen and passes to the pilot courses to steer which will bring the aeroplane on to the beam. The system also provides continuous range indication, which is equivalent, of course, to an infinite number of marker beacons.

Approaching on the beam at a distance of six miles at a height of 1,500 ft., the radio operator instructs the pilot to descend to 1,250 ft., at five miles to 1,000 ft., at four miles to 750 ft. and so on down to the critical height.

Later models of the airborne equipment are fitted with a pilot's indicator similar to the crossed-pointer meter.

High-intensity Approach Lighting

The drawback in all the landing systems mentioned so far is, of course, the failure to provide the pilot with the help he needs to bridge the gap between the critical height and the touch-down point.

One solution to the problem has been produced, however, in the form of a system of high-intensity approach lighting. Such a system must provide the pilot with all the indications he receives in normal day

259

HIGH-INTENSITY APPROACH LIGHTING. *The system shown provides the pilot with indications of direction, horizon and position in relation to the glide path. The approach line is marked by triple, double and single white lights and is crossed by seven bars of sodium lights indicating horizon. These bars are progressively narrowed to converge on the touch-down point on the runway: thus, if the pilot flies so that a portion of his windscreen is filled by each successive bar at regular intervals, he knows that he is making a correct approach.*

flying in good weather conditions. He will need directional guidance, some sort of artificial horizon which will tell him whether his aeroplane is banked or flying level, and information as to whether or not he is adhering to his correct glide path. If he can also be told his distance from the end of the runway, so much the better.

Modern Lighting System

A system complying with all these requirements has recently been developed and is shown in an accompanying illustration. The approach line is marked by a line of incandescent white lamps, each of 100,000 candle-power, arranged at 100-ft. intervals and extending for a distance of 3,500 ft. from the runway threshold. The first 1,000 ft. consist of single lights, the next 1,000 ft. of double lights and the outermost 1,500 ft. of triple lights, thus providing an indication of distance.

Seven bars of sodium lights, each light of 8,000 candle-power, are arranged across the centre line at 500-ft. intervals and act as artificial horizons. These sodium lights are yellow-orange in colour and are capable of shining through fog. The length of each bar is proportional to its distance from the touch-down point, which is assumed to be 1,000 ft. from the end of the runway.

A pilot passing over the first bar would note its apparent length, probably measuring it against a part of his windscreen as shown, and if succeeding bars appeared to be the same he would know he was on the correct approach path to the point. If the succeeding bars appeared longer, however, he would realize that he was undershooting the touch-down point; and, conversely, if they appeared shorter he would know he was overshooting. Thereafter he would regulate his rate of descent accordingly.

The system can be used in visibilities as low as 100 yd. by night and 200 yd. by day (the increased brightness of the background makes it less effective by day).

Under these conditions, the centre-line lights can be seen at distances of 400 yd., and the bars at 300 yd. For a pilot at a height of 150 ft. these distances would be approximately halved owing to restricted downward visibility from the cockpit. He would thus see seven white lights, and one bar would always be visible except for a very short period.

Used in conjunction with G.C.A. or I.L.S., the system may well prove to be the answer to the bad-weather landing problem for many years to come. Fortunately, the number of occasions when visibility is nil are rare as compared to the number when the visibility is of the order of a few hundred yards. As a result, the regularity of air-line operations can be relied upon to attain the same high standard as that enjoyed by surface transport at the present time.

Overcoming Fog

Owing to the critical nature of its formation, the forecasting of fog has always been and will continue to be one of the most difficult aspects of a meteorologist's work. Although high-intensity lighting systems will cope with visibilities down to as little as one or two hundred yards, the problem of landing in conditions of zero visibility as a matter of routine has yet to be solved. In these conditions, of course, civil air operations are normally at a standstill.

However, if there has been a sudden and unexpected widespread deterioration in the weather, pilots may find themselves in a fog-affected area with insufficient fuel left to enable them to divert their aircraft to suitable aerodromes outside the area. To cater for this emergency, there is available to the pilot a system called FIDO, the letters of the name being derived from the phrase—Fog Intensive Dispersal Of.

The system is based on the principle of evaporation of fog water droplets by direct heating of the atmosphere. Petrol which is vaporized and under pressure is ignited and the heat generated raises the temperature of the atmosphere in the vicinity of the runway. Burner lines extend along each side of the runway for about two-thirds of its length; in addition, three more burners are arranged at the approach end in the form of an open rectangle, the transverse burner being about three-hundred yards from the runway threshold. This ensures a clear area for the final stage of the approach. The touch-down point is marked by two short burner lines adjoining the main runway burners and at right-angles to them.

FIDO Approach Procedure

The glare from the installation is such as to make reading of the flying instruments by the captain difficult during the final approach, and it is usual for the second pilot to call out the readings of the airspeed indicator and altimeter. Approaches are made some 10 m.p.h. faster than normal in order to counteract the effect of turbulence when entering the cleared area.

FIDO consumes fuel at the rate of some sixty-thousand gallons per hour. A period of 15 minutes for warming up costs approximately £500 and thereafter £125 a minute. In view of this extremely high cost of operation the system can only be called into use by the Senior Air Traffic Controller for the area or by the captain of an aeroplane who requests an emergency landing.

Fully Automatic Flight

What of the future? One school of thought contends that eventually the human pilot will cease to have any control over the flight of his machine from the time it enters the aerodrome control zone to the time it touches down on the runway. Whether or not this will happen in the foreseeable future is a matter for speculation. It is certain, however, that the years to come will see great advances in auto-

ARTIST'S IMPRESSION of a landing in fog by the aid of FIDO. Two rows of pipes flank the runway; petrol is forced through jets in them and ignited. The fog is dispersed by the heat. Operating expenses of the system prohibit its use except in emergency.

NIGHT LANDING *at London Airport. A Constellation flies over one of the seven bars of sodium lights which form part of the high-intensity system illustrated on page* 260.

matic flight. Today, the ability of the electric automatic pilot to carry out an I.L.S. approach is accepted without question as a logical and natural development. Who can doubt that, given a suitable landing system, completely automatic operation will eventually follow?

A glide path, leading in a gentle curve to the runway, and derived from an elec-

tronic computor fed by signals from a radio altimeter and a radar distance-measuring equipment, is not outside the bounds of possibility.

Whatever the methods employed, safety allied with service will be uppermost in the minds of all who are striving to make civil aviation the most highly efficient system of public transport in the world.

CHAPTER 10

AIR-LINES
AND THE WEATHER

THE vagaries of the weather are certainly well known by experience to everyone in the British Isles. In fact, the weather is one of Britain's standing national jokes, and it makes headline news only too frequently.

In the air the weather is generally quite as capricious as on the ground, and frequently more unpleasant in its effects. Weather can even be dangerous unless adequate precautions are taken.

In modern civil aviation the accent is on speed, comfort, regularity and safety—especially safety. A very high proportion of the accidents which have occurred through-

out the history of aviation has been attributable either directly or indirectly to the weather. Today, as a result of experience and progress, many devices for countering the weather are available. But even so, the air-line captain still treats it with great respect, and never embarks on a flight without first consulting the meteorologist. Forewarned is forearmed; and on the basis of the information provided by the forecaster, the captain plans his flight and is prepared either to avoid or deal with any weather hazards that are expected.

Thus, the forecaster's job is to warn the captain of the weather conditions which he

DC-4 AIR-LINER of Australian National Airways taxies towards the tarmac below a sky of "fair-weather" cumulus—the soft, fleecy clouds often seen on a warm day.

WEATHER EQUIPMENT *at Dunsfold aerodrome. The Stevenson screen holding thermometers and other instruments is on the left, while the mast is surmounted by anemometer gear.*

will encounter on his route, and will have to contend with on landing. Every effort is made to ensure that the captain is provided with forecasts and warnings of the highest order of accuracy. Moreover, the captain requires much more information in his forecast than does the man in the street. He requires details of the visibility, heights of cloud bases and tops, heights at which icing will occur, heights at which strong up or down currents are likely, the direction and speeds of the winds at different levels, as well as the regions in which rain, hail, thunderstorms, snow or fog is expected.

Making Rain

Since it is human nature to blame somebody for everything that occurs, the forecaster is usually blamed for the weather which actually exists, and is jokingly asked why he cannot produce anything better. To provide the kind of weather that would suit everybody is rather beyond his scope, though attempts have, in fact, already been made to produce particular types of weather.

Experiments in the United States, in particular, have produced results which were hardly dreamed of as recently as a few years ago. By scattering "dry ice" (solidified carbon dioxide) into certain types of cloud, under certain temperature conditions, showers of much-needed rain have been produced in regions where drought was threatening serious losses to the farming community.

Layers of low cloud have been cleared over small areas to enable aeroplanes to descend more safely (though to the consternation of the people on the ground beneath, who unexpectedly suffered a slight fall of snow, even in the summer) and it has even been claimed that the hurricane or tornado, which too frequently has taken its toll of life and property, can be reduced in intensity under certain conditions. In the British Isles, too, during the war, thick fog on aerodromes was successfully dispersed over the runways, so that aircraft returning from night operations could land safely.

All these attempts to control the weather are, however, very limited at the present. In any case, the desirability of control of a more general nature is a very debatable point.

The importance of weather information to aerial warfare resulted in big expansions in the meteorological organization throughout the world, and today the civil air-lines are able to reap the benefit of some of the wartime developments. These include better communications facilities for transmitting weather reports, the use of radar methods for obtaining data about the upper atmosphere, improved designs in instruments for making meteorological observations, and new forecasting techniques.

The supply of weather information to the modern air-line captain presents, however, a very different series of problems to the meteorologists from the problems with which he had to contend in wartime. For example, a Bomber Command operation usually involved the forecasting of conditions for one particular route and one particular target. The forecaster at a modern airport, however, has to be prepared to provide information to a variety of captains, each flying a different route and bound for a different destination. In order to do this, it is essential that a continuous supply of weather data, covering a large area, should be available at the airport with the least possible delay.

Met. Instruments and Codes

By international agreement, each state meteorological authority is responsible for collecting and distributing weather data from its observing stations. Observations are made at least every three hours, and at some stations near main air routes and at main airports they are made every hour or half-hour.

These weather reports are based on readings of the instruments shown on the facing page. Most of the instruments will be familiar, but some deserve description. The anemometer translates wind suction and pressure into movement of a float within the cylinder forming the base of the instrument ; the float movement is made to record wind speed on a graph. Wind direction is also marked on the same graph by a pen which is moved mechanically via the wind vane. Another form of anemometer employs three cups which are rotated by the wind. The rate of rotation is displayed in terms of wind speed.

The alidade is used at night along with a cloud searchlight (not shown) to measure the angle of elevation of the base of the cloud where the vertical beam of the searchlight strikes it. Knowing the angle and the distance of the observer from the searchlight the cloud height is easily calculated.

Humidity is computed by comparing the reading of a wet-bulb thermometer (whose bulb is kept in a saturated muslin cap) with the reading of an ordinary thermometer. The latent heat of evaporation from the water which surrounds the wet bulb causes its temperature to fall. In conditions of 100 per cent humidity, of course, both thermometers will give the same reading. The hygrograph gives a permanent and continuous, although not so accurate, record of humidity.

The apparent duplication of such instruments as the wet- and dry-bulb thermometers and the hygrograph; the barometer and the barograph; and the maximum and minimum thermometers and the thermograph (which gives a continuous record of temperature), is easily explained. The recording instruments supply a permanent and continuous record of the variations over a period of certain conditions. The record supplied, however, is not precise enough for direct measurement of the values of the elements involved. Barometer readings, for example, are reported to three places of decimals if read in inches—after corrections for errors caused by variations

266

METEOROLOGICAL-STATION EQUIPMENT. *A link in the international chain, this meteorological office sends hourly reports to the Central Office. The reports are based on the readings of the instruments shown, which give minutely accurate data of temperature, pressure, upper-air conditions, cloud, humidity, and so on. Data from all stations are re-distributed.*

in temperature, height above sea-level and so on have been applied.

The readings of all instruments, together with certain other data, are then coded for dispatch. The code, which is used throughout the world, makes it possible to report the wind speed and direction, the visibility, the types, amount and heights of the clouds, the barometric pressure, the temperature, the relative humidity or dew point, and give a description of the salient features of the present and past weather. All this information, when coded, requires only five or six groups of five figures each.

Area and National Centres

Each country is usually divided into areas, each area having a communications centre known as the Area Collecting Centre. The stations within that area send their coded observations to the collecting centre by teleprinter, telephone or radio.

Each Area Collecting Centre is then responsible for transmitting all the observations from its own area to the country's National Collecting Centre.

At the National Collecting Centre, the reports are edited for retransmission; generally, one broadcast gives an extensive coverage for internal use; while another, for external use, gives a less detailed selection which is yet sufficient to provide an adequate coverage.

What is known as the internal collective is then broadcast (either by teleprinter or radio) from the national centre for the benefit of all the forecasting centres in that country, and the collective for external use is also broadcast—again by teleprinter or radio—for the benefit of all other countries capable of intercepting the broadcast.

There are, in addition, a number of high-powered radio receivers and transmitters all over the world which are used for

AT BROMMA AIRPORT, *near Stockholm, an observer plots the latest weather data. The weather charts facing him are marked with the hours at which full reports are sent in.*

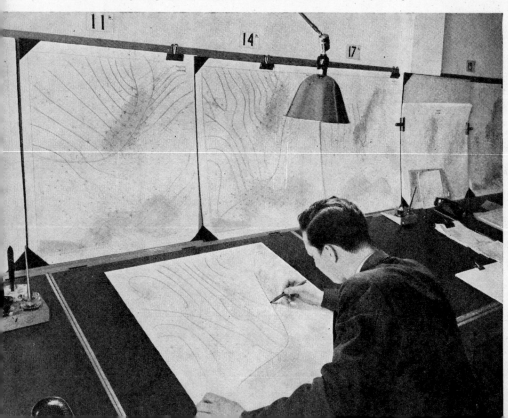

collecting broadcasts from national centres over a wide area. These reports, after editing, are rebroadcast for the benefit of more distant countries or continents. In the same way, these special centres intercept reports from other distant countries and continents, and then retransmit them for the benefit of their adjacent countries.

So, day and night, every day of the year, a continuous interchange of weather reports is taking place over the whole world, and the time of each broadcast has been so carefully worked out and dovetailed that an absolute minimum of delay occurs. Thus, reports from the main airports in Europe are received at London Airport within half an hour or so of the observation being made; and even reports from North America are available within two hours.

In addition, reports from ships at sea, from aircraft, and from soundings into the upper atmosphere made at special stations, are flashed round the world by means of this great communications network.

As this information is received in the meteorological office at the airport, it is plotted on outline maps embracing the whole area over which aircraft departing from that airport are likely to fly. These outline maps have all the main reporting stations marked by small circles, and the report for each station is plotted in a special "shorthand" of symbols around

RAYS OF THE SUN *are focused by the crystal ball of the sunshine recorder to burn a record of the duration of sunshine on a crescent-shaped card marked in hours.*

RECORDING RAIN-GAUGE. *Water is admitted to the metal chamber behind the clock drum holding the graph, and is siphoned away when the chamber fills. The graph shows the amount and time of rainfall.*

WIND SPEEDS AND DI-
RECTIONS *in the upper
air may be obtained by
meteorological flights, radio-
sonde balloons, or by direct
observation by means of a
theodolite of a balloon rising
at a known rate, as shown
here. Azimuth and elevation
are read off every minute
to a second observer, who
works out the height and
bearing of the balloon on
the spot, using a special
slide-rule. As the theodolite
is telescopic, readings may
be taken to very great
heights. On days of low
cloud the balloon is soon
out of sight, and tracking by
radar methods is necessary.*

the weather map, showing areas of high pressure, or anticyclones, and areas of low pressure, or depress-

that circle. The forecaster and the plotters are as familiar with the code and symbols as they are with their own native tongue, and can immediately translate these hieroglyphics into a statement of the weather conditions in any particular area.

Forecasting Techniques

These charts are prepared every three hours; and, in some cases, maps covering a smaller area may be compiled as frequently as every hour. As each chart is plotted, the forecaster proceeds to analyse it by carefully examining the characteristics of the air in the regions covered by the chart. He inserts boundary lines called fronts between currents of air of different properties or of different origin, and then goes on to draw the lines (isobars) joining places with the same barometric pressure. This gives

ions. From the three-hourly sequence of charts, the forecaster is able to keep a continuous check on all the developments of the weather situation, and estimate the characteristics of the weather over any particular region for a given time ahead.

There is considerably more to forecasting than merely tracking the movements of, say, areas of rain as reported from ground stations. The intensity of rain belts, areas of fog—in fact, of all weather phenomena—is constantly changing. A particular weather situation over Britain may give very different conditions by the time it reaches Scandinavia. The forecaster therefore has to be able to foresee such developments, and so must have more information than the surface charts alone provide.

Soundings of the upper atmosphere by

means of a radio sonde provide much of this information. The radio-sonde set is carried up into the atmosphere by means of a balloon about six feet in diameter, which is filled with hydrogen. The set contains miniature instruments which record minute changes in pressure, temperature and humidity as the balloon ascends. Each of the instruments is attached to a radio transmitter, and changes in the characteristics of the upper air are noted by a change in frequency in the transmitted signal. The different frequencies are noted by the observers on the ground, who, by means of a chart, are able to interpret them in terms of actual values of pressure, temperature and humidity.

Radar "Targets"

Also attached to the balloon is a radar "target," which makes it possible to follow the track of the balloon by radar from the ground. By plotting the track of the balloon, wind speeds at different heights in the atmosphere can be computed.

Ascents to heights of forty or fifty thousand feet are made in this way from a network of stations every six or twelve hours.

Similar upper-air data are also obtained by special reconnaissance flights, and the winds and temperatures as observed by air-line aircraft are also a valuable contribution towards obtaining sufficient information about the upper levels of the atmosphere to enable the forecaster to provide the accurate details which are demanded of him.

The upper-air information is plotted in special graphical form and from it cloud thickness, intensity of rain, height of freezing level, probability of thunderstorms, and other important details of the weather can be deduced. The height contours of

METEOROLOGICAL ORGANIZATION *is truly world-wide. Here is a met. office operated by Chinese personnel using the methods and special codes which are internationally agreed.*

different pressure levels are also calculated and drawn on maps, and provide essential information concerning upper winds, and the movements of pressure centres.

Exchanging Weather Data

For the main longer-distance air routes a procedure exists whereby the terminal airports on these routes are provided with special communications facilities, and can easily exchange weather information with each other. As a typical example, in the case of the North Atlantic route, Prestwick in Scotland and Montreal are two such communications centres. Prestwick receives, directly, weather reports from Iceland, from shipping in the eastern half of the North Atlantic, and from weather reconnaissance flights from bases in the British Isles. Moreover, all captains of transatlantic aircraft landing at Prestwick give the forecaster there all the details of the

weather encountered and of the winds throughout the flight. Similar information for the western half of the Atlantic pours into Montreal.

Thus the forecaster at Prestwick is better provided with information about the eastern half of the route, and the conditions for landing at Prestwick, than is his counterpart at Montreal; who, similarly, can be regarded as the authority on the western half of the route. Consequently, each forecaster prepares coded messages and transmits them to his counterpart at regular intervals, indicating the features of the weather maps and upper-air charts for his area, and giving his forecast for the route and for the landing conditions at the main airports in his area. This system ensures that both terminals possess the best possible information to supply to the captains of aircraft.

In some regions, such interchange of information is even achieved by telephone; the forecasters can actually talk to each other about the conditions to be expected on their respective portions of the route, and so benefit from each other's more detailed knowledge of his own area.

One to two hours prior to departure the captain visits the meteorological office, where he is provided with a number of documents, according to the

TELEPRINTERS convey weather data from 200 reporting stations in Britain to the Central Met. Office shown, where the reports are collated and rebroadcast automatically. The system used employs teleprinters which code messages by perforating a paper tape.

REPORTS FROM OVERSEAS *and from reconnaissance flights and shipping are received by radio and simultaneously typed at one of Britain's Area Collecting Centres.*

WEATHER INFORMATION *is given to the captain of a B.E.A. air-liner by a senior forecaster prior to take-off. Additional weather data is later passed by radio.*

CHIEF FORECASTER *marks the fronts and areas of high and low pressure. Cold fronts are indicated by blue crayon, warm fronts by red. Curved lines join places of equal pressure, and are called isobars.*

type of flight which he is planning to make. For long-distance flights documentation includes an outline weather map covering the area of flight and a chart showing the anticipated form of the map, say, some six or twelve hours later, according to the duration of the flight. The contours of one or more upper-air pressure levels are also provided, and these show pictorially the pattern of the winds at these levels and their expected development.

In addition, a detailed forecast is provided, which shows the route divided into zones and depicts the weather conditions to be expected in each zone. This forecast gives a pictorial cross-section of the cloud forms and their vertical extents, as well as statements of the visibility, significant weather, intensity and limits of icing in cloud, intensity of turbulence, and upper winds of each zone.

Finally, a form is provided which gives details of the landing conditions (surface wind, cloud amount and cloud base, surface visibility and weather) anticipated at the destination at the time of arrival, and also at a number of selected alternative aerodromes, in case it should for any reason be necessary for the captain to divert from his original destination.

As well as this written information, the forecaster personally gives a full explanation of the weather situation and its developments to the captain, and is also able to illustrate exactly what is happening by means of his working charts.

Flight Plan

On the basis of all this information the captain, in conjunction with his navigator, proceeds to prepare his flight plan. The sort of problem he has to consider is that of choosing the best route and operating height (compatible with the height of the terrain in the vicinity of his track) to enable him to avoid the worst flying weather, and also to obtain the greatest possible help from the winds. Again, if it appears doubtful whether he will be able to land at his scheduled destination because of unfavourable weather, he has to prepare plans for alternative routes to one or more alternative terminals.

From this planning he calculates the amount of fuel he must carry in order to be sure of being able to make his flight safely, and have sufficient fuel in reserve to enable him to reach any diversion aerodrome as may be necessary. The amount of fuel to be carried is, of course, directly related to the strengths of the head-winds likely to be encountered, and also determines the weight of passengers and freight which can be carried.

Thus the information provided prior to departure is largely for the purposes of planning the flight and for drawing the

274

captain's attention to any hazards which may be met, so that he is prepared to take the necessary action to counter them.

The information provided at the aerodrome before departure is the most up-to-date available at the time of briefing. If the flight is a long one, however, unforeseen developments or changes may occur —and, in any case, even if everything goes according to plan, additional information to confirm this is welcome to the captain. Consequently, arrangements are made to pass the latest weather reports to the aeroplane during flight. In some cases, these are obtained by direct request from the aeroplane to the air-traffic control centres en route (who, in turn, obtain the information from the meteorological office serving them).

In case of long flights over oceans or sparsely populated regions, the aerodrome of departure remains in constant radio communication with the aeroplane until it reaches the mid-point of its flight, and so passes notification of any significant weather changes; thereafter, the aerodrome of destination undertakes the responsibility of providing such information.

Aviation Broadcasts

On routes of heavy air traffic, such as those operated over Europe, a network of special meteorological broadcasts for aviation has been set up. This consists of a series of transmissions from the main aerodromes every half-hour, at fixed times and on fixed frequencies, and the information is comprised of actual station weather reports from a selection of aerodromes together with the forecast landing conditions for the next few hours. The information is given in a special numerical code.

By intercepting these broadcasts, the aeroplane's captain obtains a complete series of reports of the latest weather prevailing at the places on his route, and also

AIRSPEED AMBASSADOR *flies above some moderately developed cumulus cloud. The generic name cumulus is applied to all clouds of rounded form, whatever their height.*

CLOUD AND COLLISION RADAR *indicates the proximity of thundercloud and high ground. Radar pulses beamed from the aeroplane are reflected back by obstructions, making a trace on the circular fluorescent screen facing the pilot. The curved lines on the screen indicate range. A photograph of the screen (above, left) shows how the pilot is warned of the cloud formation pictured at a distance of 20 miles, while that on the right shows responses at 15 miles.*

the latest opinions regarding the conditions for landing at his destination.

Airmet Broadcast

Warnings of any hazardous weather, such as thunderstorms, areas of severe icing or turbulence or fog and very low cloud are also broadcast at frequent intervals, so that the captain is fully aware at all times of any dangerous phenomena.

In the British Isles in particular there is also an almost continuous speech broad-

cast of weather reports and forecasts transmitted from the British Central Forecasting Office. This broadcast includes a talk by the forecaster on the prevailing weather over the British Isles and its expected development in the immediate future. It is known as the Airmet broadcast and can be heard on most household radio receivers on a wavelength of 1,221 metres.

In the earlier days of air-lines, flights were often made under what are known as contact conditions. That is, the pilot flew within sight of the ground as far as possible and navigated largely by map-reading.

Under such a system, the requirements for the flight were adequate surface visibility over the route, and a cloud base sufficiently high to ensure that any high ground would not be obscured. Stories are still told of veteran pilots who operated for so long on a particular route that they could complete their flight in conditions of amazingly low visibility, so well did they know the landmarks of the country below them. It must be remembered, however, that in many instances the aircraft which they flew were very much smaller, and that their speed was, with some exceptions, only half that of the modern air-liner, so that they were consequently much more manoeuvrable. A visibility of 1,000 yd. for example is virtually twice as useful to a pilot travelling at 100 knots as to the pilot travelling at 200 knots.

Flying above the Weather

With the faster aircraft of today and the accuracy of navigation under blind-flying conditions, contact flying is a thing of the past. The captain can select an altitude for his flight which will be most advantageous from the weather aspect, and which will also ensure maximum comfort for his passengers. If there is fog and very low cloud obscuring the ground along the route, the captain will climb after take-off to a height which will, as far as is possible, keep him above such unpleasant conditions. Many a passenger has been amazed to find himself in bright sunshine and clear air with the top of a sheet of cloud below him, only a few minutes after taking off in gloomy, foggy weather.

It is very often possible to find a level, at which good flying conditions exist, somewhere in the lowest 8,000 ft. or so of the atmosphere. But there are occasions on which solid walls of thick cloud bar the route, and flying conditions in the cloud would be, at least, unpleasant. The tops of these cloudbanks may extend to 30,000 ft. or more above the earth's surface.

Now the properties of the atmosphere steadily change with height. The air becomes progressively less dense, pressure decreases, and the amount of oxygen in the air also decreases. Up to heights of about 10,000 ft. the effect on most people is negligible; but above this the lack of oxygen is more and more detrimental.

Consequently, without any special measures it would not be possible to fly over cloud masses of this type. Each passenger could be provided with an oxygen mask, but this imposes an inconvenience. Many aeroplanes are now equipped with a far better solution to the problem: pressurized cabins. In aircraft so equipped, the atmosphere inside the fuselage is maintained at a pressure and in conditions similar to those experienced at lower altitudes, so that the

SCANNER *of the cloud and collision radar set is a parabolic reflector, gyro-stabilized. The aerial which transmits and receives the radar pulses projects from the centre of the scanner. With this equipment, warning of cumulonimbus may be received up to 40 miles.*

aeroplane may be flown at very high altitudes without any discomfort being experienced by the passengers. In this way, such flights can be made above the weather over the whole route.

However, on many of the world's air routes at the present time, it is not feasible for a variety of reasons to operate at such altitudes, and although the worst weather can generally be avoided by judicious pre-flight planning, it is sometimes necessary to fly through clouds and conditions which demand particular alertness.

Thunder and Lightning

Thundery cloud and thunderstorms are at all times unpleasant to fly in. Thunder clouds always tower to great heights and may be so extensive that it is impracticable to circumnavigate them completely. In such cases, the height and track of the aeroplane is modified so that it flies through the most innocuous portion of the cloud. Flying conditions are invariably bumpy or turbulent in such clouds, and the captain will always try to fly at a height where turbulence is likely to be least in order to minimize the unpleasant sensations that such conditions cause.

Lightning, in itself, is not usually dangerous, but is at least as disconcerting in the air as it is on the ground. The precaution of winding in the trailing radio aerial has to be taken whenever the aeroplane is in the vicinity of thunder cloud, and the interference (atmospherics) due to the proximity of lightning interferes seriously with the reception of radio messages and upsets normal working of some of the navigational aids; this applies to both the airborne and ground equipment.

Static Discharge

In recent years, owing to the increased size and speed of aircraft, a common cause of interference to aircraft radio has become apparent. This interference, which may predominate for lengthy periods during flight and in different types of weather conditions, is called precipitation static, and is directly due to electrical charging and discharging of the aeroplane during flight in strong electrical fields such as may exist in the vicinity of charged clouds of thundery type, or in an atmosphere laden with particles of ice, snow, rain, dust or smoke.

Aircraft meeting these conditions become electrically charged at a very high rate, and electrical discharges break out at places such as wing tips, propeller tips and aerials. The principle of the method employed to combat this is to prevent the building up

CUMULUS IN THE FIRST STAGE. *These little puffs of cloud are more developed over land than over sea, suggesting that the picture was taken early in the morning, in summer.*

LARGE CUMULUS *and cumulo-nimbus clouds such as this are avoided by the wise pilot. Strong convection within the formation seen in the centre has extruded a turret of cloud.*

of such big electrical charges by fitting either bunches of long-fibre cotton strings or tufts of brass bristles near the wing tips and on the tail section, in order to induce discharge. The risk of encountering such conditions can be assessed by study of the meteorological situation and forecasts.

Icing Hazards

Ice formation on aircraft is another hazard which may be encountered on the flight, and when flying in cloud with temperatures near freezing point, the captain has to maintain a particularly sharp look-out for any symptoms. There are a number of methods of ice formation, and the rapidity with which it forms on the aeroplane varies according to conditions. As far as the formation of ice in clouds is concerned, the rate of formation is generally much less in layer clouds than in the heaped shower cloud or thunder cloud (cumulus or cumulo-nimbus).

Without delving into the technicalities of ice formation on aircraft, it is sufficient to say that the larger the water-drops in the cloud, the more rapid is the rate of ice accretion. Rapid ice formation on aircraft in cloud can always be avoided either by flying below the freezing level, or by flying at a height well above the freezing level where the cloud is composed of dry ice particles, which do not adhere to the machine to any great extent and which are less densely distributed.

Ice can also form rapidly, however, when the aeroplane is not flying in cloud. The conditions for such formation are rather special, and fortunately do not occur very often. They are usually encountered in continental areas after a cold spell when warmer air is spreading across at higher levels. In such a situation, the aeroplane may be flying in temperatures below freezing point, with rain falling on it from cloud in the warmer air above. On striking the aeroplane, the rain will immediately freeze, and if the rain is sufficiently heavy, the wings and fuselage will quickly be covered with a sheet of clear ice.

The effect of all types of ice accretion on aircraft is detrimental to their aerodynamics and consequent performance. Ice on the propeller upsets the balance and pitch, apart from the fact that if any appreciable quantity accumulates there is always the danger that the lumps which are hurled off by the spin of the propeller might cause structural damage by striking the airframe. The weight of the ice itself on the aeroplane is considerable if icing is rapid, and, coupled with the decreased aircraft performance, it may make it impossible for the aeroplane to climb.

Combating Icing

Most air-liners are equipped to combat airframe icing. The rate of formation is checked by application of de-icing fluid to those parts most favourable to the building up of ice, and ice which has already formed can be removed from the leading edges of the wings to some extent by a mechanical process.

Although the types of icing discussed so far do not occur when the temperatures are above freezing, one cannot disregard icing completely at these temperatures. Ice may form and choke the carburettor at temperatures as high as several degrees above freezing. This is due to the fact that after passing through the air-intake, the air expands, and the expansion is accompanied by a reduction in temperature. The reduction may be sufficient to freeze the water droplets contained in the air which is being drawn into the carburettor, if the air is damp. This form of icing is now quite readily overcome by electric heaters, which can be switched on if such dangers are at all likely.

Some idea has been given of the dangers that may be encountered during flight. In all cases, though, it is seen that precautions or preventive measures can be taken to ensure safety. In order to take such measures it is clearly essential that the captain be provided with adequate and accurate information concerning the weather conditions over his route, and this is precisely why it is necessary to issue such detailed forecasts to him, and why such elaborate communications arrangements have been made to supply him with information while he is in flight.

Landing Problems

The meteorological problems confronting the pilot on landing are different from those encountered during flight. Whereas fog and low cloud no longer impede the safe and accurate navigation of aircraft today, these elements still restrict landings.

Much has been done, and is still being done, to develop instrument-landing aids to enable the largest and fastest of air-liners to land in conditions of low visibility and low cloud ceiling. But despite this, the captain must know what order of visibility and cloud height to expect at his destination aerodrome, and in the event of conditions being poor, information must be readily available to tell him what the conditions are at other aerodromes suitable for landing, so that he may proceed without any delay to an alternative aerodrome if the one where he intends to land is subject to conditions below the minimum necessary for safety.

In this last respect, most air-line companies prescribe weather minima (that is, lowest visibility and lowest cloud base) for every aerodrome to which they operate, taking into consideration the nature of the surrounding terrain, obstructions such as buildings and chimneys, the type of aircraft and the landing aids available. This stating of weather minima is just another of the many precautions taken to ensure maximum safety, and if conditions are below these limits, the captain will not attempt his landing but will proceed to one of the alternative aerodromes prescribed for him.

Strong cross-winds—that is, strong winds

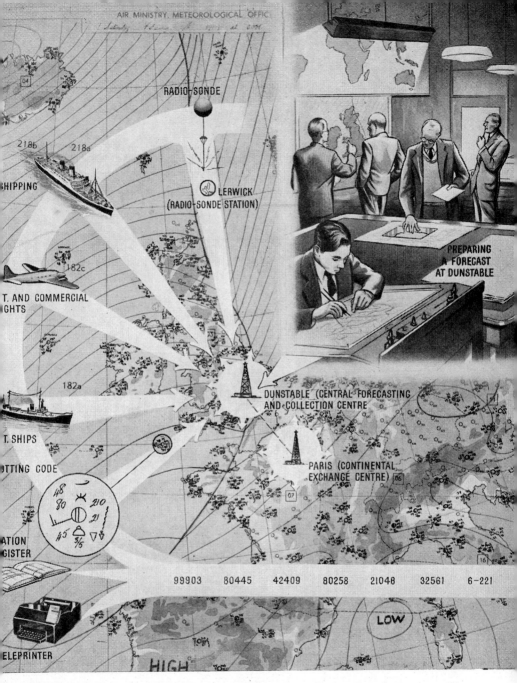

METEOROLOGICAL ORGANIZATION. *Weather information is plotted in a special code on charts similar to that forming the background to this illustration. A typical "plot" is enlarged in the small circle. Weather data are passed between stations and recorded in the station register by a number code. Collated data from the sources shown form the basis of the forecasts which are broadcast by radio, teleprinter and telephone.*

blowing across the direction of the landing runway—can also imperil a safe landing, though cross-wind components of up to about 18 knots (21 m.p.h.) are not considered a hazard. Again, much depends upon the type of aircraft, and the strong, gusty cross-wind is much more of a menace than the steadier wind, on account of the turbulent conditions associated with it. The more modern aerodromes have runways orientated so that the frequency with which it is necessary to land with a strong cross-wind is reduced to a minimum, and with three runways at approximately sixty degrees to each other, the frequency of such conditions in most cases becomes very small.

Sudden changes in wind direction, such as are experienced with banks of thick, thundery type of cloud, and with line-squalls, are, of course, dangerous to landing aircraft, and the meteorological officer at the airport has to be sure to warn the control officer whenever such conditions are likely, so that precautions can be taken to ensure that no aeroplane is making a landing when such a wind-shift occurs.

Close liaison between the airport meteorologist and the aerodrome controller is necessary at all times, so that the controller is always prepared for changes in the weather and can communicate appropriate instructions to the aeroplane's captain.

The preceding pages have described the general meteorological organization and how the air-liner captain is supplied with up-to-date information of the weather conditions he may expect on his flight. There is, however, one particular aspect of the weather which plays a fundamental part when the economics of air-line flying is considered: the wind.

Pressure-pattern Flying

Winds at different heights over a given place vary both in speed and direction. In temperate latitudes, winds at high altitudes are in general from a westerly direction and increase with height. This is due to the distribution of temperature over the earth's surface, with cold air over the polar regions and warm air in the equatorial belt giving rise to what is called a thermal wind whose strength is directly related to the temperature variation.

Winds at low altitudes, below about six-thousand feet, may blow from any direction but as one ascends the tendency is always for the wind speed to increase with height and to blow from a westerly direction.

Knowledge of the wind speeds and directions at various levels is most important in planning a flight. A very striking example of the part played by the winds is given by the North Atlantic route between London and New York. The winds at high

ANVIL-SHAPED CLOUD *behind these buildings at Aberdeen Airport is caused by the spreading out of the top of a cumulo-nimbus cloud, which indicates thundery conditions.*

AVRO TUDOR *flies between a layer of cirrus above, and small cumulus developing beneath it. Cirrus clouds, which are composed of ice crystals, occur at heights of 25-35,000 ft.*

levels generally being strong westerlies, it is obvious that the most helpful wind for the crossing from New York to London would be found by flying as high as possible. The most advantageous wind in flying from London to New York, on the other hand, would generally be found at lower altitudes, for even if the winds were westerly at all levels, the lighter ones, which offer the least opposition, usually occur in the lower layers.

The greater the head-wind, the longer does it take to make the flight, and so, in turn, more fuel has to be carried; on a long flight, such as the Atlantic crossing, the difference in time of flight between conditions of strong head-wind and conditions of strong tail-wind is a matter of several hours.

The flying of the North Atlantic, and other long flights over oceans, has led in recent years to a new technique in flight planning and navigation. It is known as pressure-pattern flying, and is, in fact, a practical solution of the problem of finding the flight-path which will take the shortest time and which will be the most efficient at the cruising speed of the aeroplane.

Routes and Meteorology

The theoretical treatment is complex, but it is based on the fact that the wind direction is related to the pressure system obtaining. (Air is known to rotate anti-clockwise round an area of low pressure and clockwise round high-pressure areas, for example.)

The pilot flies not at a constant altitude, but at the constant atmospheric pressure level which will give him the greatest advantage of helping winds. This involves selecting the optimum track from the meteorological upper-air chart giving the wind-flow pattern at the particular pressure

FLYING ABOVE CLOUD. *The layer of cloud beneath the wing is strato-cumulus which has become merged into a blanket formation. Broken alto-stratus (sheet cloud at a higher level) and cirrus (high cloud) is seen above.*

level selected. During the flight, calculations of drift and readings of pressure and radio altimeters enable the navigator to keep check on the situation and amend the course of the aircraft.

Some amazingly large savings in time of flight can be made by such planning and navigating in certain circumstances, and by flying a path of much greater distance than the Great Circle (or shortest-distance) track. For example, the shortest time track from London to New York may, in some meteorological situations, be found to be a route going as far north as the vicinity of Iceland and Greenland.

The necessity for using a radio altimeter in pressure-pattern flying in order to determine precisely the altitude of the aeroplane above sea-level restricts this form of navigation largely to flights over sea areas. The North Atlantic route is the one on which the technique is most generally and most successfully used, for one of the essentials for efficient application of pressure-pattern flying is a good supply of accurate upper-air information. The ocean weather ships set up in the Atlantic during recent years play an invaluable part in providing this information.

Weather Ships

By international agreement, the United States, Canada, France, Norway, Sweden, Holland, Belgium and the United Kingdom agreed to co-operate in a project to equip and supply some ten weather-reporting ships on the North Atlantic, to be located in a pattern designed to provide observations of weather conditions for air routes throughout the region.

While their duties are primarily meteorological, the ships also serve as search and rescue vessels for both shipping and aircraft in distress. They also provide navigational aids for aircraft in flight.

The weather information is sent by radio at regular intervals to meteorological services on both sides of the Atlantic, and aircraft in flight may, of course, listen in to the broadcast of these messages if so desired.

Met. Analyses and Planning

Some idea has been given of the function of meteorology from the aspect of everyday flying. There is another aspect of meteorology which is probably not so generally well realized, and that is the part which it plays in planning the air-line programmes.

A vast amount of meteorological data exists in the form of analyses and summaries of weather conditions at particular places and over regions. Such data are used when new routes are planned, in order to choose routes which avoid, as far as possible, areas of particularly persistent bad weather. They are also used to resolve such problems as whether it is possible to operate with greater regularity, from the point of weather conditions, into airport A than into airport B, so that the air-line can take this into consideration in its endeavour to provide the public with a service which is of the highest standard from the point of regularity.

Met. and Research

The time-tables which are issued to the public take into consideration the mean effect of the winds on each route, and this information, again, comes from the meteorological records. Temperature data, wind analyses and other records are required by the engineering experts in connexion with the performance of aircraft in different regions.

These are all examples of the many contributions which are made by the weather services in this particular field.

And meteorology also plays its part in planning for the future. The International Air Transport Association (I.A.T.A.) is an organization of representatives of all the main air-lines, and one of its activities is to formulate the common meteorological requirements of its members. The standardization of the form in which meteorological information is provided to air-line captains, the evolution of new codes for transmitting weather messages to aircraft in flight, and the institution of a special network of meteorological broadcasts to aircraft in certain regions, are some examples of the problems which it has considered in conjunction with International Civil Aviation Organization (I.C.A.O.) and the International Meteorological Organization. The work of these international organizations will continue in the fields of research, development and organization towards their common goal of complete safety in air travel.

EVENING SKY *over the B.O.A.C. flying-boat base at Victoria Falls, Southern Rhodesia, as passengers embark at the jetty. The cloud is cumulus and alto-cumulus, at two levels; it is well broken and is dissipating. A clear night sky usually follows such conditions.*

CHAPTER 11

TODAY'S AIR-LINERS

To talk of the present-day air-liner is, at any time, inclined to be misleading, for the aircraft in service at any period represent the products of a span of, perhaps, 15 years. Three stages of development usually exist at any one time; they are represented by: the latest air-liners to become standard equipment on the air-lines; the older types which are still in service, perhaps with modifications, and probably not fulfilling their original role; and the future air-liner which is only beginning to come into service, or is still undergoing test and development.

A transport aeroplane is a very expensive piece of equipment whose useful life is normally reckoned as about seven years. This means that, as a new type takes about three or four years to design, construct and test, the replacement aircraft is being considered at a point halfway through the useful life of the earlier type.

Although an aeroplane is a comparatively delicate vehicle, history has shown that many designs of air-liner have been employed for two or three times the normally accepted duration. One outstanding example is the Douglas DC–3, which first saw service in 1934 and which is today in service in larger numbers than any other

FIRST PRODUCED IN 1934, *the de Havilland Dragon Rapide has given reliable service all over the world and is still in wide use. The Rapide can carry up to eight passengers.*

SUPER DC-3 *is fitted with more powerful engines, and also wings, tail and airframe of more modern design. The passengers' stairway, when raised, becomes an integral part of the fuselage.*

single type of air-liner. Under an I.C.A.O. ruling its international air-line life is scheduled to terminate in 1952, but it may well be in service in various countries, on domestic or internal routes, for a further period which will give this type a life of over 20 years. There are over a thousand of these aircraft in service on scheduled air-lines and there are many of the original 1934 and 1935 airframes still in use.

Two attempts to prolong the life of the DC-3 have been made. The first, in the U.S.A., was the development by the Douglas Aircraft Company of the Super DC-3. In this, the development of the existing DC-3 was brought up to date by modifications to the fuselage and under-carriage, the fitting of more powerful engines and new wings and tail unit.

In Britain, two DC-3s have been fitted experimentally with gas turbines driving propellers. The gas turbines fitted have been Rolls-Royce Darts in one aircraft and Armstrong Siddeley Mambas in the other.

The Douglas DC-3, designed and built by the Douglas Aircraft Company at Santa

PANAIR DO BRASIL DC-3 *at Barraras. The DC-3 is still the most widely used air-liner in the world. It is powered by two Pratt & Whitney Twin Wasp motors, each of 1,200 h.p.*

Monica in California, is a low-wing two-engined, all-metal monoplane. A logical development of the DC-2 and the earlier Boeing 247, the DC-3 was designed as a 21-passenger type and, together with the 14-passenger DC-2, it was one of the first of the all-metal two-engined monoplane air-liners to go into large-scale service throughout the world. In fact, it is the aeroplane on which many of the world's air-lines have been built and developed successfully.

Britain's Postwar Needs

Following the war period, in which few new transport aeroplanes had been produced outside the United States, the DC-3 continued in service, and its military counterpart, of which thousands had been built, was converted to civil use. The British R.A.F. name for this military type is Dakota, and this name has now been adopted widely.

Although in most cases the DC-3 still accommodates 21 passengers, versions have been produced with seating for as many as 36. The DC-3 is normally powered by two 1,200-h.p. Pratt and Whitney Twin Wasp engines, weighs loaded 28,000 lb., has a span of 95 ft. and cruises at 185 m.p.h.

A number of DC-3s was obtained for British air-lines, but a shortage of dollars for these aircraft and their spare parts, together with the need to earn currency by exporting, made it desirable that Britain should produce a suitable medium-range air-liner of similar dimensions and capacity to the DC-3. As the DC-3 was already an old aeroplane it was reasonable to expect the new type to have a superior performance.

This new aeroplane appeared as the Vickers-Armstrongs Viking, an all-metal mid-wing monoplane accommodating 21-27 passengers, powered by two 1,690-h.p. Bristol Hercules engines and cruising at over 200 m.p.h. This new type was adopted as the standard type of air-liner to operate the main routes of the then newly formed British European Airways Corporation. Over 40 of these Vikings were commissioned by the Corporation, and since their introduction in 1946 they have gone into service in Africa, the Argentine, Denmark, Egypt, Eire, India, Iraq and the British West Indies. The King's Flight is composed of Vikings, while a number of British charter companies use this type.

Jet Air-liner

An interesting experimental version of this air-liner is the Nene-Viking, in which the two reciprocating engines have been replaced by two Rolls-Royce Nene pure-jet gas turbines. This aeroplane, in the course

AVRO TUDOR 4. *This air-liner, powered by four Rolls-Royce Merlin engines of 1,740 h.p., was produced soon after the war, and was in service with British South American Airways.*

FIRST TRANSPORT-TYPE AEROPLANE *to be powered by four jet engines, the Tudor 8 has provided valuable research data. Its Nene gas turbines are mounted two in each nacelle.*

PRESENT-DAY AIR-LINERS *offer passengers great comfort. Shown here is the interior of a B.E.A. Viking, with the passengers enjoying luncheon. There is a tendency today, however, to reduce the luxuries of air travel in order to effect a cut in costs and, therefore, fares.*

A MODERN FRENCH AIR-LINER, *the Bretagne can accommodate* 30 *passengers and has a cruising speed of just under* 260 *m.p.h. It is powered by two* 1,620-*h.p. engines.*

of its experimental flying, flew from London to Paris in 34 minutes.

In France, the DC–3 was put into service with Air France and a number of charter companies following the war, but, as in Britain, the desire to introduce a national product was achieved. As a result Air France now has among its fleet about 40 Languedoc 161 monoplanes. Although these are not modern aeroplanes, this type being designed prior to the war, they should give good service until such time as a new French type is available.

Languedoc and Bretagne

The Languedoc, powered by four 1,450-h.p. Twin Wasp engines and having accommodation for 33 passengers, obviously does not compare well economically with the two-engined Viking, which can carry 27 passengers. The Polish Air Line also flies some Languedoc aircraft, but these have Gnome Rhone engines. The Languedoc is built by the Société Nationale de Constructions Aéronautiques du Sud-Est and has a span of 95 ft. 5 in. and a cruising speed of 217 m.p.h.

The air-liner likely to replace the Languedoc is the S.N.C.A.S.O. S.O.30P Bretagne now on order for Air France. This is a mid-wing two-engined monoplane with retractable nose-wheel type of under-carriage, and twin fins and rudders. The two 1,620-h.p. Pratt and Whitney engines give the 30-passenger Bretagne a cruising speed of 258 m.p.h. The loaded weight of this air-liner is just under 40,000 lb.

American four-engined Types

During the war the United States produced two extremely successful four-engined transport aircraft. These were the Douglas Skymaster, known civilly as the DC–4, and the Lockheed Constellation. Both appeared first in military colours. The Constellation was designed originally for the United States air-line Trans-World Airline, so it is not surprising to find that today T.W.A. is the biggest operator of this type, which is one of the most successful high-performance long-range transport aeroplanes ever built.

Over 200 Constellations are now flying with world air-lines. In the U.S.A. American Overseas Airlines, Capital Airlines, Chicago and Southern Air Lines, Eastern Air Lines and Pan American Airways fly Constellations in addition to T.W.A. B.O.A.C., K.L.M., Air France, Air-India International, South African Airways and Qantas Empire Airways all have fleets of Constellations, while in South

America Panair do Brasil and the Venezuelan air-line L.A.V. fly this type.

The Constellation, spanning 123 ft. and having four 2,500-h.p. Wright Cyclone engines, has already undergone much development. Originally its maximum weight was 86,250 lb. This has now been increased to 107,000 lb. with a consequent increase in payload and range. The Constellation, which has a pressurized cabin normally seating 40–44 passengers, cruises at 320 m.p.h. and has a maximum range without fuel reserves of about 5,000 miles.

"Air-coach" Travel

The Douglas DC–4 or Skymaster is, like its smaller stable-mate, the DC–3, in wide service. It has proved itself a reliable aircraft, but by modern standards it is rather slow, cruising at only a little over 200 m.p.h. The DC–4 has four 1,100-h.p. Twin Wasp engines and, with a wing span of 117 ft., weighs 65,000 lb. The normal accommodation is for 40–44 passengers, but high-density seating is installed in some of these aircraft. In the United States, so-called air-coach travel has recently been introduced by some of the air-lines, and many DC–4s are used on these services in which no luxury is offered but on which cheaper fares are charged. The reduction in comfort has made possible the carrying of more passengers per aircraft.

From the DC–4 have been developed two air-liners, both similar in concept and in size. These are the Douglas DC–6, which is the peacetime successor to the DC–4, and the DC–4M or Canadair Four, which is a Canadian-built development of the DC–4, and powered by British Rolls-Royce Merlin engines.

The DC–6, which is the Douglas counterpart of the Lockheed Constellation, is used widely in the United States and by a number of the world's major air-lines, including the British Commonwealth Pacific Airlines, which uses DC–6s on its trans-Pacific route. The DC–6 is very much like the DC–4, but it has a larger fuselage and more powerful engines which provide, respectively, better accommodation and improved performance. The DC–6, unlike the DC–4, is pressurized. The main forward cabin and the smaller aft cabin provide extremely comfortable accommodation for up to 52 passengers. The engines are 2,100-h.p. Double Wasps, which give the DC–6 a cruising speed of up to 325 m.p.h.

IN WIDE USE *throughout the air-lines of the world, the Douglas DC-4 is somewhat smaller than the later DC-6. The DC-4 has four engines, each of 1,100 h.p.*

In some versions there is a club lounge in the rear of the aft cabin.

In 1947 Trans-Canada Air Lines began to operate Canadair Four air-liners on its North Atlantic services. These first Canadairs were 36-passenger unpressurized aircraft and they built up a good reputation for reliability. This first batch of aircraft was made available to TCA by the Royal Canadian Air Force until the air-line received its own fleet of pressurized 40-passenger aircraft. These 300-m.p.h. air-liners, weighing 78,000 lb. loaded, were delivered and put into service in 1948. They now work on all the main trunk routes of the company.

Since the introduction of this type by TCA, which company calls them North Star Skyliners, B.O.A.C. has commissioned a fleet of 22 Canadairs under the class name of Argonaut. The Argonauts are used on the England–Japan and other services. A third operator of this type is Canadian Pacific Air Lines, which has four of these aircraft flying its trans-Pacific routes from Vancouver.

British Overseas Airways used a collection of converted war aircraft, mainly consisting of Avro Lancastrian (converted bombers), Avro York (converted military transports), and Short Hythes (converted military flying-boats), immediately after the war. A number of Constellations was added and now the Canadairs are also in service.

Similar in general appearance to the Canadair is the British Handley Page Hermes 4. This is a low-wing monoplane powered by four Bristol Hercules engines and capable of carrying 40 passengers at about 300 m.p.h. at 25,000 ft. for up to 2,000 miles. Twenty-five of these are to serve B.O.A.C.'s Empire routes. An experimental development, the Hermes 5, has four Bristol Theseus gas turbines driving airscrews. A military version of the Hermes is the Hastings, which is one of the standard Royal Air Force transport aeroplanes.

British Flying-boats

Following the withdrawal of the older types of flying-boats B.O.A.C. standardized on one type of flying-boat—the Solent.

The Solents, built by Short Brothers at Rochester and subsequently by Short and Harland at Belfast, are double-deck four-engined deep-hulled flying-boats having a high-set wing and thereby offering their passengers a splendid view of the terrain over which they are flying.

The Solent has a wing span of 112 ft. and weighs 33 tons. The four 1,675-h.p. Bristol Hercules engines give these flying-boats a cruising speed of 213 m.p.h. Thirty-four

DISTINCTIVE TAIL FIN *of a Saab Scandia is well shown in this photograph. This air-liner is less powerful than the Martin 2-0-2, which it somewhat resembles, and carries 32 passengers.*

HANDLEY PAGE HASTINGS *is the military version of the Hermes. The Hastings is powered by four* 1,675-*h.p. Bristol Hercules engines, giving it a maximum speed of some* 300 *m.p.h.*

passengers are accommodated in a number of cabins arranged on both upper and lower decks. Tasman Empire Airways has a fleet of these flying-boats working on its Australian–New Zealand route.

The Short Sandringham is of very similar appearance but somewhat inferior performance to the Solent and it is used by Norwegian Air Lines on its routes from Stavanger, Bergen and Oslo to the Arctic north of Norway. These flying-boats are also used in South America and were for a time in service with B.O.A.C., when they were known as the Plymouth class.

Replacing the DC–3

When civil air-lines began their return to peace-time operation it soon became apparent that a DC–3 replacement was an urgent necessity. In Britain the Viking was produced and in the United States two new short-range air-liners were designed and built; these were the Convair-Liner and the Martin 2–0–2. They are both 36–40-passenger low-wing monoplanes powered by two 2,400-h.p. Pratt and Whitney Double Wasp engines. The two types are of similar appearance and almost the same size, the Convair having a span of 91 ft. 9 in. and the Martin a span of 93 ft. 3 in. The Convair

weighs 40,500 lb. loaded and cruises at up to 288 m.p.h., or nearly 20 m.p.h. more than the Martin.

The Martin 2–0–2 is in service in the United States with Northwest Airlines and also in Chile and Venezuela, but the Convair-Liner has been more widely adopted, having been commissioned in the U.S.A., Holland, Belgium, Switzerland, Pakistan, China, Australia and the Argentine. The Convair has a remarkably short take-off and steep climb, and a very short landing run with the use of braking propellers.

In Sweden, another DC–3 replacement type has been produced: this is the Saab Scandia. The Scandia is a lower-powered air-liner than the Convair-Liner and the Martin 2–0–2, but it is a very efficient aeroplane which has undergone extensive trials in many parts of the world; it is to go into service with Swedish Air Lines. Capable of carrying 24–32 passengers and having two 1,450-h.p. Twin Wasp engines, the Scandia can cruise at 228–278 m.p.h. With a loaded weight of 32,408 lb. and a wing span of 91 ft. 10 in. the Scandia possesses the same good take-off characteristics as the Convair-Liner. The Scandia is also extremely manoeuvrable, which is an asset for landing

AIRSPEED CONSUL *is a short-stage or feeder-line transport carrying five passengers at a maximum speed of* 192 *m.p.h. It is powered by two* 395*-h.p. Armstrong Siddeley Cheetah engines.*

at airports situated close to mountains.

In the Soviet Union a DC-3 replacement has been produced and put into large-scale service on the routes of Aeroflot—the Soviet Air Line. This type is the IL-12 two-engined monoplane designed by Sergei Iliuchin. The IL-12 is a well-designed airliner in a class similar to the Viking. It seats 28 passengers and can, with adjustments to the position of the front cabin wall, accommodate an extra four passengers.

Two 1,630-h.p. AM 82FN radial engines supply the power and give this type a cruising speed of a little over 200 m.p.h. The IL-12 has a retractable nose-wheel-type undercarriage and a hot-air de-icing system. A number of IL-12s is in service with both Czechoslovak Air Lines and Polish Air Lines.

Two larger Soviet air-liners about which little is known outside the U.S.S.R. are the four-engined TU-70, designed by Tupolev, and the IL-18. The latter is known to be in service on some of the Soviet trunk air routes and it will probably be put into service by Czechoslovak Air Lines.

The air-liners described here have all been in the medium and long-range categories. In addition, many of the world's short-distance air routes, particularly domestic services, are flown by small two-engined aeroplanes seating six to ten passengers. Probably the best known and most used of these aeroplanes is the de Havilland Dragon Rapide. This is a small wood-and-fabric biplane seating six to eight passengers and powered by two 200-h.p. Gipsy Six engines. The span is 48 ft. and the cruising speed 120 to 130 m.p.h. The Rapide was first produced in 1934 and it has played a very great part in building up short-haul services.

Miniature Air-liner

Soon after the war the de Havilland Aircraft Company built a new monoplane called the Dove. This has become a popular type and is used in many countries. The Dove, although having a span of only 57 ft. and weighing only 8,500 lb., is in reality a miniature modern air-liner having all-metal construction, retractable nose-wheel-type undercarriage and braking air-

RUSSIAN-DESIGNED AIR-LINER. *The IL-12 shown above accommodates 28 to 32 passengers. It is of all-metal construction and modern design and cruises at over 200 m.p.h.*

screws. The two 340-h.p. Gipsy Queen engines give the Dove a cruising speed of 179 m.p.h.; it can accommodate up to 11 passengers. There is also an ambulance version, and a military transport version which is known as the Devon.

The Dove, although having an excellent performance, cannot operate into and out of some of the small aerodromes used by the Rapide and so, largely for this reason, the British European Airways Corporation has put out a specification for an aeroplane to replace the Rapide.

Light Amphibian

Two other British land aeroplanes and one amphibian have also appeared in this light class. These are the two-engined Percival Prince, the four-engined Handley Page-Miles Marathon and the two-engined Short Sealand amphibian.

The Marathon is a high-wing monoplane with four Gipsy Queen engines, and the Prince, which is also a high-wing monoplane, has two Alvis Leonides engines. Neither of these aeroplanes is yet in air-line service. An experimental version of the Marathon is flying with two Armstrong Siddeley Mamba gas turbines driving airscrews.

The Short Sealand is a five- to eight-passenger monoplane amphibian with a boat hull and retractable-wheel under-carriage. Available with either two Gipsy Queen in-line or two Leonides radial engines, this type has been adopted for service with British West Indian Airways.

Australia has built a new light transport aeroplane: the Australian de Havilland Company's three-engined Drover. This is a robust little aeroplane designed for the same tough sort of work as that at which the Rapide has for so long excelled. The Drover is a low-wing all-metal monoplane with a fixed-tail-wheel type of under-carriage. The three 145-h.p. Gipsy Major engines are mounted one in the nose and one each side, forward of the wing. The Drover can carry seven passengers at a cruising speed of 135 m.p.h.

A United States aeroplane in the small air-liner class is the Beech 18. This is a small two-engined monoplane which is in service on short routes in a number of countries, including India and Egypt. France has placed a small air-liner on the market in the form of the S.N.C.A.S.O. S.O.95 Corse II, an all-metal two-engined monoplane which has gone into service with Air Services of India. The Corse II seats ten to thirteen passengers, has a span of 59 ft. 2 in., a weight of 12,300 lb. loaded, is powered by two 440-h.p. Renault engines and cruises at 217 m.p.h.

Single-engined Aircraft

In an even smaller class than these two-engined types are the single-engined aeroplanes used for short-stage air-line and charter work. The best known and most used of these is probably the Canadian Noorduyn Norseman, a rugged high-wing monoplane powered by a single Wasp engine of 600 h.p. and carrying up to eight passengers. The Norseman, which is used in fair numbers in Canada and Scandinavia, can operate on wheels, floats or skis. The latest successful aeroplane in this class is the Beaver, designed and built by the Canadian branch of the de Havilland Aircraft Company. The Beaver is powered by a 450-h.p. Pratt and Whitney Wasp Junior engine. It is of similar lay-out to the Norseman and carries a pilot and six passengers. The Beaver is all-metal and was specially designed for hard work in fairly remote areas. It is already in service in Canada and, like the Norseman, it can also use wheels, floats or skis. The Beaver has a span of 48 ft., weighs 4,820 lb. as a seaplane and in that form cruises at up to 137 m.p.h. This aeroplane has a very short take-off run and can operate from very small lakes or clearings.

Long-range Air-liners

During 1949 the largest air-liner to go into regular service was commissioned when Pan American Airways began using the large Boeing Stratocruisers on both Atlantic and Pacific routes. Shortly afterwards, American Overseas Airlines also placed Stratocruisers on its North Atlantic services. United Air Lines brought this type into service between the U.S. west coast and Honolulu and Northwest Airlines put Stratocruisers both on its transcontinental and trans-Pacific routes.

B.O.A.C. also uses Stratocruisers over the North Atlantic. These B.O.A.C. Strato-

UPPER DECK *of a Stratocruiser. The pressurized figure-8-section fuselage of the Stratocruiser is separated into two decks which can accommodate over one hundred passengers.*

BOEING STRATOFREIGHTER *is similar to the Stratocruiser outwardly, but the interior is arranged to take 43,000 lb. of cargo. A military version can carry 141 fully-equipped troops.*

cruisers bear names made famous during the 1930s by the Short Empire flying-boats.

The Stratocruiser is a large double-deck monoplane, its pressurized fuselage having a figure-8 section. The crew and main passenger cabins are on the top deck and the freight holds and a bar and lounge are on the lower deck. Normally it accommodates up to 75 passengers. It has a span of 141 ft. and a loaded weight of over 60 tons. The four 3,500-h.p. Wasp Major engines drive braking airscrews and give

the Stratocruiser a cruising speed of 340 m.p.h. at 25,000 ft. and a maximum range of over 4,000 miles. The fin and rudder is made to fold down sideways so that the Stratocruiser may be serviced in a hangar.

France has also built an aeroplane in the same class as the Stratocruiser. This is the S.N.C.A.S.E. S.E.2010 Armagnac, of which 25 are on order for service with Air France.

The Armagnac is a very clean-looking mid-wing monoplane with a large single fin

DE HAVILLAND BEAVER *is a particularly neat all-metal feeder-line aeroplane carrying six passengers. The wing span is 48 ft. and the cruising speed 137 m.p.h.*

BRISTOL 170 FREIGHTER *is loaded at the nose, which is separated down the centre to form two doors which fold right back. The Wayfarer passenger version carries up to 48 passengers.*

and rudder. Four 3,500-h.p. Pratt and Whitney Wasp Majors supply the power and drive braking airscrews to reduce the landing run. This pressurized air-liner will carry up to 80 passengers, has a wing span of 160 ft., weighs 160,000 lb. and has a cruising speed of 276 m.p.h. at 19,000 ft. at 50 per cent power.

In France, large freight-carrying aircraft have received a lot of attention and the most successful of these so far produced is the double-deck Breguet 76 Deux-Ponts. This is a large mid-wing monoplane with retractable nose-wheel type of under-carriage and twin fins and rudders. The very deep fuselage can accommodate 100 passengers or a payload of up to 40,000 lb. Four 2,000-h.p. Gnome Rhone engines power this 40-ton aircraft, which cruises at 223 m.p.h. It has a span of 141 ft.

Britain has given some attention to the freight transport. Soon after the Second World War the Bristol Aeroplane Company built its type 170, which was produced as a freighter with front loading doors, a passenger aeroplane with normal entrance, or as a combined passenger and freight aeroplane. The 170, known as the Way-farer in its passenger version, is a high-wing two-engined monoplane with a fixed

INCREASING INTEREST *in aircraft as a means of cargo transport has led to such designs as the 162-ft.-span Universal Transport, of which a scale development model is shown here.*

ITALIAN AIR-LINER. *This Savoia S.M.95 monoplane, developed from a wartime type, is a four-engined aeroplane which flies across the Alps on the London-Rome route.*

undercarriage and a deep snub-nosed fuselage.

The largest British freight aeroplane is the Blackburn and General Aircraft Universal. This is a large high-wing monoplane powered by four 1,950-h.p. Bristol Hercules engines and is capable of carrying a payload of 24,640 lb. of freight or up to 90 passengers. The span is 162 ft. and the total weight 87,300 lb.

As well as the countries mentioned so far, Italy builds many of its own transport aeroplanes and, additionally, has exported some air-liners to Egypt and Turkey. These are the three-engined Fiat G.12 and G.212 and the four-engined Savoia S.M.95. These are all either wartime aeroplanes or developments of wartime types.

A large Italian air-liner, designed as such, is the Breda Zappata BZ-308. This aeroplane is of about the same size and weight as a Lockheed Constellation, but at present its future is rather vague.

Gas-turbine Air-liners

Having surveyed, as fully as space will permit, the present generation of air-liners, some idea of the next generation can be gathered. Almost certainly these will be composed mainly of gas-turbine-powered

types, although air-liners such as the Constellation, DC-6 and Stratocruiser will remain in service for a considerable time. All the gas-turbine-powered air-liners, both pure jet and gas turbine driving propellers, are in Britain and Canada.

In Britain, Vickers-Armstrongs have produced a successor to the Viking: the Viscount, driven by four turbo-propellers. This type was the world's first propeller-turbine air-liner and it has been chosen for service with British European Airways and British West Indian Airways. The Viscount and the Armstrong Whitworth Apollo of similar lay-out have attracted world-wide attention.

The Viscount has a span of 94 ft. and an all-up weight of 48,000 lb. Powered by Rolls-Royce Dart turbo-propellers, it has a cruising speed of up to 322 m.p.h. and accommodation for 40-44 passengers. By comparison, the Apollo is powered by four Armstrong Siddeley Mamba turbo-propellers, weighs 39,500 lb., and has a span of 92 ft. It can cruise at speeds up to 305 m.p.h. with a complement of 24-31 passengers.

Perhaps the most exciting new aeroplane is the de Havilland Comet—the world's first pure-jet air-liner. It is a beautiful

CIERVA AIR HORSE *is Britain's first transport helicopter, carrying 24 passengers at a speed of over 120 m.p.h. The advantages of the helicopter type of aircraft are obvious, but the payload and speed are not yet so high as in machines of orthodox design.*

MODEL OF THE BRISTOL TYPE 175 *reveals an interior seating plan. Other interior schemes envisaged include 38- and 60-passenger designs. This type, which has four piston engines, has been ordered for service with the British Overseas Airways Corporation.*

AVRO JETLINER. *Powered by four Rolls-Royce Derwent gas turbines, the Jetliner can carry 50 passengers at 427 m.p.h. The Jetliner typifies the modern practice (which the pressurized cabin made possible) of flying high and fast. It is built in Canada.*

monoplane with swept-back wings spanning 115 ft., and four Ghost gas turbines in them. It accommodates 36 passengers and cruises at nearly 500 m.p.h. at about 40,000 ft. Fourteen Comets are to go into service with B.O.A.C. in about 1952.

The graceful Airspeed Ambassador has been ordered for British European Airways and may be the last British piston-engined air-liner to go into service. The Ambassador has a sleek fuselage and long tapering wings. It is powered by two 2,700-h.p. Bristol Centaurus engines. It can cruise at 312 m.p.h., weighs 52,000 lb., and will accommodate 49 passengers in its pressurized cabin.

The Canadian jet-propelled air-liner mentioned earlier is the 50-passenger Jetliner designed and built by A. V. Roe Canada, Limited, at Malton, Ontario. The Jetliner is a low-wing monoplane with four Rolls-Royce Derwent gas turbines. It weighs 60,000 lb. loaded and has an estimated maximum cruising speed of 427 m.p.h.

Following a period of mail flying with Trans-Canada Air Lines, it is likely that this type will be put into service by TCA as a passenger air-liner. The span is 98 ft. 1 in.

Much development work has to be undertaken on the prototype Brabazon now flying, and if this type does go into service on B.O.A.C.'s North Atlantic routes it will not be until well into the 1950s.

Three of the large Saunders-Roe Princess flying-boats are being built at Cowes in the Isle of Wight and the first is expected to fly in 1951.

B.O.A.C. has ordered 25 new air-liners from the Bristol Aeroplane Company. These are the Bristol Type 175, a low-wing monoplane announced as being powered by four 2,810-h.p. Bristol Centaurus engines. As this type is not expected to go into service until 1953 or 1954, it may well have Bristol Proteus gas turbines driving propellers. The Bristol Type 175 will have a span of 140 ft. and a payload of 17,610 lb. Accommodation will be provided for 50 passengers in the B.O.A.C. version.

HULL OF THE PRINCESS FLYING-BOAT *is moved across the erection shop. The domed figure-of-8 structure at the rear of the hull is the pressure bulkhead. The Princess is designed for long-range trans-ocean air service; the first is expected in 1951.*

CHAPTER 12

AIRCRAFT
OF THE FUTURE

T HE conflict between the stern realities of the technicians and the dreams of over-zealous visionaries is probably never more acute than in the realm of aeronautics and its offspring, the science of astronautics.

Indeed, nothing is easier than to relax and let the imagination play with thoughts of air-line leviathans, or, from the comfort of an armchair, predict the day when we shall fly round the moon and even venture beyond.

Unfortunately, perhaps, the technician will have his say; so the present remarks will be confined to a more sober and practical assessment of future aircraft: an assessment based on knowledge of present technical attainment and experimental work in hand.

But even the most sober expert will agree that we are on the threshold of developments which will oust previous notions as completely as the powered biplane, itself replaced by the monoplane, ousted the balloon.

Why should this be particularly true today? The answer lies in the sources of power available. Until recently, the aircraft designer was always hampered by the limitation of the power at his command. Now, the position is entirely reversed.

Using present units—let alone those which are under development—in one modern research aeroplane which is a modified transport air-liner (the Tudor 8 which has four Rolls-Royce Nene gas turbines) the total maximum power developed is a thrust equivalent to that of 24,000 h.p.

Nothing approaching this power was available to most of the aircraft whose names have become household words. The Boeing Stratocruiser's four piston engines, for example, develop a maximum of 14,000 h.p.

With this revolutionary increase in power available, there are more designs on the drawing boards than ever before in the history of aeronautics. Designers have been given a new freedom; their use of it is one of the most fascinating speculations of the future.

Nevertheless, certain basic truths, the foundations of key problems, must be appreciated and understood before the picture comes into proper focus.

Limitations on Size

At first assessment, it would seem that with virtually unlimited power all the designer has to do is to make a rapid calculation of the weight of the projected aeroplane and then equip it with units powerful enough to drive it through the air. But it is not as simple as that.

One limitation on aircraft size, for

ROCKETS THRUST *a Lockheed Constitution into the air after a very short take-off run. Experiments are being made to apply this take-off technique to air-liners ; if successful, a considerable gain in payload would result, and shorter runways could be used for taking off.*

ENGINES OF THE BRABAZON *are run up before take-off. With piston engines installed, a maximum of 20,000 h.p. is developed ; the propeller-turbine installations increase this figure considerably. Modern sources of power are revolutionizing aircraft design.*

STAIRWAY connects the two decks of the Lockheed Constitution. Wing span is 189 ft. and the aeroplane is 156 ft. long. In spite of its great size, the Constitution can be landed so lightly that a special indicator has been fitted in the cockpit to inform the pilot that his wheels have contacted the ground.

example, is the aerodrome itself. There are few big aerodromes in the world and not one of them can accept, on their runways and taxi tracks, a weight of 500 tons. Another limitation is the strength of the wings; no air-liner has yet been built to exceed the speed of sound, not so much because of the inability to produce enough power to drive the aeroplane at that speed but because the structure would not stand the strain.

But, of course, future aircraft will not necessarily be giants—they may be pygmies—although the natural inclination is to regard future aircraft as being necessarily bigger than those of today.

Range and Speed

Just as there are weight limitations, so there are range and speed limitations. Although today we have aircraft capable on flight-refuelling methods of more than 10,000 miles non-stop flight, and an aeroplane has made a 23,452-mile flight around the world without alighting, there is obviously a rational limit to range. Few stages in the world economically exceed the 3,550 miles of the air route from New York across the Atlantic, and most modern trunk-route stages are within the range of 1,000-2,500 miles non-stop.

Speed limitations at present are governed by what is known as the compressibility barrier. In non-technical language this may be explained as follows.

The atmosphere is made up of a number of molecules. When a sound is made, these molecules vibrate at the frequency of the sound source, and the sound is transmitted by them at about 760 m.p.h. at sea-level. But the speed of sound decreases with increasing altitude, because of the reduced temperature and density of the atmosphere; at 30,000 ft., for example, sound travels at only about 660 m.p.h.

At speeds below the speed of sound, an aeroplane passes through the air slowly enough to allow the molecules time to be pushed aside. As the speed of sound is approached, however, the molecules have less time to be moved aside. And in the region of the speed of sound, and also within a certain limit above it, the molecules jostle with a cumulative force, resisting the passage of the aeroplane.

One eminent scientist has graphically described this as being equivalent to cycling blindfold against the flood tide of

G-AGPW

LOUNGE AND
COCKTAIL BAR

CENTRE SALOON
(38 SEATS)

REAR SALOON
AND CINEMA
(23 SEATS)

BRISTOL
COUPLED PROTEUS
ENGINES

TWIN CONTRA-ROTATING
PROPELLERS

MEN'S
TOILET
ROOM

SPAN:
230 ft. 0 in.

LENGTH:
177 ft. 0 in.

BRISTOL BRABAZON

AN INTERIOR DESIGN SCHEME

MAIN KITCHEN
AND PANTRY

100 PASSENGERS

LADIES'
TOILET ROOM
(PORT SIDE)

BERTHS

ENGINEER'S
STATION

NAVIGATOR'S
STATION

SEATING
FOR 39

CABIN
SEATING 6
(DAY)

CREW'S
REST
ROOM

RADIO
OPERATOR'S
STATION

FLIGHT
DECK

UP TO 180 PASSENGERS *may be carried on the U.S. Navy Lockheed Constitution. The aircraft weighs 92 tons and could carry 92 passengers in air-line service.*

spectators issuing from a large football ground: a description which gives a colourful impression, but which grossly understates the number of molecules resisting the aeroplane.

Research scientists are today studying the effects of this compressibility barrier. There is ample evidence that, in some mysterious way, after the barrier is passed the airflow becomes smooth again.

Passing the Barrier

The effects of entering the sound barrier are extraordinary and surprising. First, the buffeting is very severe. Secondly, one of the most famous test pilots described the noise as equivalent to ten underground trains going into a tunnel. At the same time the enormous pressure set up causes a rapid rise in temperature (just as heat is generated in a bicycle pump). To give an example of this, in an experimental flight to 50,000 ft. where a speed of 700 m.p.h. was attained the temperature in the cockpit rose by 98 deg. F. But it should be added that this was offset considerably by the atmospheric temperature at that altitude: 65 deg. F. below ground temperature.

American technicians have probed even further; and whilst their knowledge is entirely theoretical, they estimate that at 400,000 ft. the air temperature is 215 deg. F. —that is, higher than the boiling point of water on earth. At this height, at night only (when free of the sun's direct influence) the skin temperature of a body moving through space is 340 deg. F., or considerably higher. But that is only provided that the body or missile is not askew in flight; any such deviation would cause the temperature to rise to double, treble or even more. At 75 miles altitude, say the American theorists, the temperature "in the sun" is 900 deg. F., but if it is any consolation to the would-be aerial voyager in the upper atmosphere, the temperature at a height of 190 miles is reduced to 700 deg. F.

It is thus obvious that the heating and cooling problems of high-altitude flight are formidable. Likewise, in extreme conditions such as these, the present instruments would be unsatisfactory. According to calculations on the V.2 rocket-bomb which passed on its journey at approximately 3,500 m.p.h., the difference in temperature between the nose and the tail was some 800 deg. C.

To read of such speeds is tempting to the crystal-gazers. There is, of course, no reason at all why they should not be far exceeded. The highest speed gauged so far is that of light: 186,325 miles per second. As this is regarded as a transmission rather than material movement, however, we may perhaps turn to a meteorite as the fastest known thing associated with the earth.

The meteorite attains such a speed in the void beyond our atmosphere that on frictional contact with the resistant air enveloping the earth it attains white heat and is burnt out. Clearly, such a speed would be a limiting one to passenger aircraft!

Nevertheless, some idea of the target already in sight—or perhaps in the foreseeable future—may be gained from the following information. The U.S. Army Air Force is reliably reported to be pondering no fewer than sixty design studies by the world-famous Douglas Company concerning the X-3 supersonic research aircraft project. This machine will have a Mach number of 3 (that is, its speed will be three times that of sound) and will operate at heights of the order of 300,000 ft.

It is only fair to comment that the design studies put forward range from "blunt, stubby-nosed designs to long slender fuselages with sharp, bullet-like nose and tail." Of course, this is also a military project, not a civil one.

Opposing Views

Despite many assertions to the contrary, it can well be argued that it is the curse of air-liners that aviation has been picked upon from its infancy in the balloon era for military exploitation. The achievements of the pioneers were rapidly adapted for the military benefit of countries. By some this has been hailed as a benefit; since governments, having more money to spend than individuals, were able to finance great developments and spur on progress.

Others have been equally convinced that such progress is false progress; and they have pointed out, with chapter and verse, the stultifying and braking action which military intervention has.

Two clear examples of this latter view are found in the story of engine development: the First World War was won, in the air, by the rotary engine although the Rolls-Royce and other reciprocating en-

FLYING-WING DESIGN. *The A.W.52 shown here is a twin-jet, tailless, experimental aeroplane which may well be a pointer to the appearance of future air-liners.*

gines came in at the concluding stages, and in the Second World War it was the reciprocating engine which brought victory in the air, although the jet engine was already far advanced even before the Second World War broke out.

Advantage of Propeller-turbine

Those examples, which might seem to be red herrings concerning airways and airliners, give particular point to the views of Mr. Peter Masefield, while Director-General of Long-Term Planning, Ministry of Civil Aviation, who had this to say in a lecture at the Royal Aeronautical Society:

"The propeller-turbine engine is, at present, most suitable for medium-range operations at moderate speeds and heights —up to about 425 m.p.h. and 35,000 ft. When more fully developed for civil purposes, eventually, in conjunction with improved air-traffic control, the propeller-turbine is likely to show advantage over the piston engine for all but very short- or very long-range operations and—in the largest sizes—for all operations.

"The chief difficulty with the propeller-turbine engine today is that, because of the small amount of interest in it for military purposes, almost all the development costs have to be spread over relatively few civil orders. The propeller-turbine is, in consequence, not receiving the amount of effort which it deserves and only a fraction of the development which is being concentrated on the turbo-jet. The establishment of a strong Air Transport Command in parallel with civil air-lines will greatly assist the development of new power plants."

Whilst, however, most of the experimental work concerns military aircraft or missiles in the realm of high speed and altitude, the air-liners of the future are taking shape on the drawing boards on the information gleaned from military sources. It is safe to say that as technical knowledge advances, many of today's projects will be stillborn; the subject of the future

must thus be approached with caution.

Experience to date has made it increasingly clear that tomorrow's world airways must cater for two distinct categories: freight and passenger aircraft. In the former, conditions which would be insupportable to human cargo can in some cases be accepted freely; in the latter, numerous factors such as the pressurized cabin (in which the atmosphere inside the aircraft is maintained at a pressure equivalent to that at much lower altitude than the aircraft is actually flying at) have to be taken into account.

Clearly, the ultra-high speeds can be attained in the non-human-cargo aircraft, but they will only be attained if it is an economic proposition to do so. After all, most of the world's freight moves slowly; to give an example, green bananas ripen on the ship journey to Europe, and there would be no especial advantage in flying green bananas swiftly by air to England.

Again, the most important freight (not the most valuable *per se*) is mail. Hence we can look to the most adventurous stages of the future of flight with mail services.

New Air Routes ?

Other exceedingly interesting transit routes come into being with the possibility of ultra-fast, ultra-high-flying, long-range aircraft. It is instructive to study a globe and see (with the aid of a piece of string) that the shortest route from New York to Moscow is via the North Pole, that from England to India is over Germany and Turkey, that to fly most directly to Hong Kong from London you should pass north of Moscow, and other interesting examples. That these are things of concern to the designer must be apparent.

The "new-route" potential is not to be lightly discarded since it has a material bearing on another aspect of tomorrow's aircraft. That is the question of maintenance.

Maintenance is a subject almost entirely

DESIGNED TO OPERATE *at speeds in the neighbourhood of 500 m.p.h., the 100-ton Northrop Flying Wing YB–49 bomber is powered by eight General Electric jet engines. This type of aeroplane may provide information of use in the design of large air-liners.*

devoid of the normal glamour of aviation. But it is also probably one of the most important of all the factors for assessing an aeroplane. Quick examples will bring home this truth. First, it must be clearly borne in mind that an aeroplane is designed and built for flight, and that time on the ground is as wasteful economically as having a ship in dry dock or a car in a garage.

Today's accepted mean utilization, or time in the air, is approximately nine hours a day; but technicians are giving increasing attention to this aspect of aviation transportation. Clearly, any present aircraft, such as the Dakota, which can fly at 150 m.p.h. for an average of 10 hours a day throughout the year, will have a better result economically than would a 1,000-m.p.h. machine which could average only one hour's flying a day because of protracted maintenance requirements on the ground. It is, after all, no more than a modern version of the hare and the tortoise of fable.

From this aspect we can see the immense importance of the new engines. An official statement announced that the maintenance time of the de Havilland Goblin engine during 500 hours' run was only 13 man-hours. Royal Air Force figures of maintenance on a piston engine during 500 hours of flight are 1,286 man-hours.

Maintenance Times

Any further doubt as to the importance of good maintenance figures is dispelled by another set of revealing figures. In summary, a B.O.A.C. report states: "Hythe class flying-boats operating from a pre-war civil base have achieved on long Empire routes and despite their slow schedule and night stops a utilization of some 2,100 hours per annum per aircraft, coupled with a figure of 4·5 man-hours per flying hour on direct maintenance. On the other hand, York aircraft of similar size, operating from a widely dispersed wartime R.A.F. base at Hurn, have achieved only 1,350 hours utilization per annum, with a maintenance figure of 10 man-hours per flying hour."

In this probe into the veiled future, and not at all unconnected with the maintenance factor, perhaps the reader will take part in the following exercise.

ONE OF THE LARGEST LANDPLANES in the world, the Consolidated Vultee XC-99 can carry 400 troops and their equipment or 100,000 lb. of cargo at over 300 m.p.h.

MAINTENANCE TIME *spent on a jet engine is far smaller than that necessary for a comparable piston engine. The large nacelles of this Meteor house Rolls-Royce Avon gas turbines.*

The first object of this exercise is to dispel any idea that might have been gained from the immediately preceding paragraphs that the hare with excellent maintenance is not far superior to the tortoise of equally excellent maintenance. Let us consider the fascinating problem of future aircraft against future ships, on the basis of present information.

We will assume that the ace of ships is the Queen Elizabeth, and that it is unlikely that any great advance in speed will occur. The Queen Elizabeth carries a maximum of 2,300 passengers, and to run that ship requires a crew of 1,200. Note that there is an approximate ratio of two passengers carried to one crew—a factor that would be nonsensical for air-lines attempting to pay their way.

We will also assume that an aeroplane with 30 passengers and a crew of four will be able, in the predictable future, to fly the same route as that followed by the Queen Elizabeth (linking Southampton—New York) in one hour. We will guess that under good maintenance schedules the aeroplane can "turn round" (that is, unload and re-load for the return journey) in two hours. We know the Queen Elizabeth takes three days (72 hours) to turn round except in special circumstances.

Two aircraft of the type mentioned above can carry 1,980 passengers across the Atlantic in the same time as the Queen Elizabeth takes 2,300 passengers. This is not strictly true: the Queen Elizabeth each hour takes 2,300 passengers as a unit on their journey, which cannot be finished for any one of them before the four days of the crossing, but the air-liner delivers 30 passengers per aircraft the whole journey on each crossing of one hour.

Increased Maintenance Facilities

This assumes maintenance facilities on only one side, but by having maintenance bases on both sides, and doubling the fleet to only four aircraft, it will be seen that the pride of the seas is very seriously challenged indeed. After all, by having 8 or 16 aircraft in the air-liner fleet, and correspondingly reducing the flight time, the possibility takes on a shape of probability, since far more wonderful developments have taken place in the lives of most adults today. Remember that a 1941 aircraft, the de Havilland Mosquito, long ago flew the Atlantic in under six hours.

And now regard closely the statistics of the Brabazon, the original design of which dates back to pre-1939. Remember that not by any stretch of the imagination could a total crewage of 1,200 be required to operate an aircraft fleet of which the transportation characteristics could better those of the Queen Elizabeth; and then judge whether or not the queen of the seas does not stand in jeopardy, just as did the windjammer when threatened by the steam-paddle ship, and that in turn by the turbine-screw ship.

Nevertheless, it is extremely unlikely that air transport will ever replace surface transportation by sea. The centuries have rolled by and man has made many inventions, but the dhows that Cleopatra and Caesar saw on the Nile are there today.

On the contrary, one of the encouraging signs of inherent faith in the virility of civil aviation is the interest which the big shipping lines are taking in air transport in places as far apart as Malaya and China, West Africa and the West Indies. The true perspective of the picture is that air-lines are complementary to shipping lines, and in a world where even the most distant horizons draw nearer daily there is more than room for both factors in transportation. An almost exact parallel exists between road and rail transport.

Saving Weight

Yet another aspect of the air-liner of tomorrow exists in the technical phrase: weight control. This important subject we can only briefly touch on here. It means that the aircraft constructors are today so alive to the value of weight saving that their design and production staffs and technicians are always on the watch for means to reduce weight.

The importance of this point can be briefly brought home. Actuarially, it is computed that any one pound of superfluous structural weight in the aeroplane means a loss of revenue of about £150 in

the life average of the machine. To show what this can mean, if one type of passenger seat in a 30-passenger aeroplane weighs 1 lb. more than that in a competing type the constructor using the heavier seat must accept an earning loss of £4,500 worth of payload over the period of the craft's average life. This can be seen in startling figures when it is stated that one four-engined air-liner of the last decade finally weighed no fewer than 7,000 lb. more than its original weight estimate! Small wonder that its production was stopped although it was one of the most lovely aircraft ever seen in the skies. Small wonder, also, that the weight-control engineer must keep his eye on such things as new radio equipment to see not so much that it is efficient, but that it is built as light-weight as practicable. In 1939, a big bomber carried forty to fifty wireless valves; ten years later that figure had been multiplied by ten!

Cost of Insurance

Although it is perhaps not directly connected with aircraft, nor, indeed, even associated with them in the minds of most people, one of the factors to be weighed in civil aircraft is the very necessary cost of insurance. This is a major charge in operating air-liners; and it requires only a moment's thought to appreciate that, on this score, the smaller the air-liner, the cheaper it is to run.

It would be futile to deny that ships, cars, railway trains and aircraft do have accidents, and the odds are that if there is an aircraft accident it is likely to be far more costly to the insurance underwriters than in other forms of transport. One member of Lloyd's put the matter very succinctly: "Insurance of freight—yes; but insurance of hulls—no, because there is always the risk of 100 per cent loss on the hulls." How few people who daily see big aircraft coming into a major airport realize that in terms of insurance, the loss of a hull (that is, the complete aircraft) runs into something like £500,000 for a present-day air-liner, its crew, passengers and freight.

Whilst it will be appreciated, from the factors so far set out, that development of future aircraft is an exceedingly complicated technical business, at the same time it is a very costly process. The Chief Designer of Vickers-Armstrongs has given some illuminating figures on this score.

A new civil aeroplane (he said) cost £2 10s. to £3 per lb. of gross weight. Development costs added £30 to £35 per lb. of gross weight, and tooling for a production line in the factory another £10 per lb. Hence, to build a new machine of only 100,000 lb. all-up weight involved at least £4,000,000.

To give an actual example, the Consolidated Vultee Convair-Liner, a 40-seat air-liner, cost approximately £6,250,000 to develop to production standards.

Nevertheless, exceedingly interesting aircraft are now going through the development stages, some much more advanced than others, and will be seen in service during the next few years. We will, first,

confine ourselves to British aircraft, since they alone provide adequate food for thought. Secondly, we will ignore the helicopter, which is at present in a very primary stage of development. Far-sighted pioneers of the aircraft industry have no doubts whatever as to the ultimate success of this form of transportation. A 24-seat helicopter is projected for flight in the early 1950s.

In the following list, the name of the maker and the name of the aeroplane is followed by the maximum number of passengers that can be carried. (Obviously, the minimum is nil, and, according to range and luxury, the number will vary up to the maximum.)

Taken at random, the picture of tomorrow's British aircraft for the air-lines is: Handley Page-Miles Marathon (20); de Havilland D.H. 106 Comet (36), four-jet long-distance transport; Armstrong Whitworth Apollo (31), four propeller jets; Bristol Brabazon (224), eight engines, of various kinds, but all Bristol designs; Vickers Viscount (53), four propeller jets; Bristol Type 175 (62), four propeller jets or

BRABAZON AIR-LINER *outside the hangars at Filton, near Bristol, in which it was built. The Brabazon is the world's largest air-liner, designed to carry up to 224 passengers.*

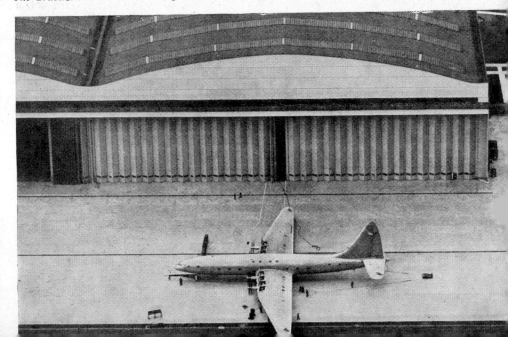

PENCIL-SLIM FUSELAGE *of the Consolidated Vultee jet-propelled XB–46 is* 106 *ft. in length. Two jet engines are mounted in each nacelle. The XB–46 can carry over ten tons.*

piston engines; Armstrong Whitworth tail-less, flying-wing mailplane, no details available; Handley Page Hermes V (63), four propeller-jets; Saunders-Roe S.R.45 or Princess, flying-boat (100), ten propeller jets; Airspeed Ambassador (50), two piston or two propeller jets; Blackburn and General Aircraft Universal Freighter (90, or equivalent in freight).

In this short cast, which makes no allowance for the possible products of other important firms and the possible adaptation of military transport aircraft, it will be seen that a full bill (in more senses than one) faces civil aviation in the next decade.

It is an impressive list, boldly covering all stages from the small four-engined Marathon with 14-passenger luxury accommodation to the mighty Bristol Brabazon with 224 passengers. Let us, therefore,

conclude with a translation of an inspiring passage from a noted French aviation expert who wrote in 1926:

"Thus, we must be truly convinced that in a future more or less near we shall see at last the dream of the birdman—a machine obedient to his wishes which will behave as in the Arabian Nights whereby on pushing a button he will ascend, descend, stop in the air and move in this or that direction at his will; a machine which, in a phrase, will do everything in the air and which he need not fear, by chance or failure, will crash to the earth leaving him gaspingly inanimate, paying with his life for the imprudence of having tried too much with still insufficient wings. Fly! Certainly, but fly happily as the whim takes him without risk—that is the goal. . . . Nobody can deny the utility and the interest and the nobility of such an aim."

INDEX

Names of air-liner and flying-boat types are grouped together under the headings AIR-LINERS, TYPES OF, and FLYING-BOATS, TYPES OF. Similarly, names of operating companies are grouped under AIR-LINES, and those of engine types under POWER PLANT. Page references in italics relate to illustrations.

318

ACKNOWLEDGEMENTS

The Publishers wish to express their thanks to the following for valuable assistance in connexion with the preparation of this book :

Aer Lingus; Aerofilms, Ltd.; The Aircraft Operating Co. of Africa (Pty.), Ltd.; Air France; Air India International; Air Ministry; Airspeed, Ltd.; Airwork, Ltd.; Alaska Airlines; American Airlines, Inc.; American Overseas Airlines, Inc.; Armstrong Siddeley Motors, Ltd.; Sir W. G. Armstrong Whitworth Aircraft, Ltd.; Australian National Airways Pty., Ltd.; Blackburn and General Aircraft, Ltd.; Boeing Airplane Co.; The Bristol Aeroplane Co., Ltd.; British European Airways Corporation; British Overseas Airways Corporation; Canadair Ltd.; China National Aviation Corporation; E. K. Cole, Ltd.; Consolidated Vultee Aircraft Corporation; Curtiss-Wright Corporation; The de Havilland Aircraft Co., Ltd.; Douglas Aircraft Co., Inc.; The Fairey Aviation Co., Ltd.; *Flight;* Flight Refuelling, Ltd.; Foote, Cone & Belding, Ltd.; The General Electric Co., Ltd.; Hunting Aerosurveys, Ltd.; His Majesty's Stationery Office (Crown copyright reserved in photographs on pages 113, 155, 156, 157, 272, 273, 278 and 279); Iberia Lineas Aereas Españolas; K.L.M. Royal Dutch Airlines; John Laing & Son, Ltd.; Jones & Nicholson, Ltd.; Lockheed Aircraft Corporation; Marconi's Wireless Telegraph Co., Ltd.; Glenn L. Martin, Co.; Ministry of Civil Aviation; New Zealand National Airways Corporation; Handley Page, Ltd.; Panair do Brasil, S.A.; Pan American World Airways System; Percival Aircraft, Ltd.; Port of New York Authority; Pratt & Whitney Aircraft; Pye, Ltd.; Radio Industry Council; A. V. Roe & Co., Ltd.; A. V. Roe Canada, Ltd.; Rolls-Royce, Ltd.; Sabena Belgian Airlines; Saunders-Roe, Ltd.; Scandinavian Airlines System; Short Brothers & Harland, Ltd.; Skyways, Ltd.; Society of British Aircraft Constructors, Ltd.; Societa Italiana Servize Aerei; The Sperry Gyroscope Co. Ltd.; Scandinavian Airlines System; Svenska Aeroplan A.B.; Trans-Canada Air Lines; Trans-World Airline; Vickers, Ltd.; Vickers-Armstrongs, Ltd.; West African Airways Corporation; Wright Aeronautical Corporation.

Printed in Great Britain by Keliher, Hudson & Kearns, Ltd., London. Copyright S. 350.S.